MW00573933

PRE-HISPANIC MAYA AGRICULTURE

PRE-HISPANIC MAYA AGRICULTURE

Edited by
Peter D. Harrison and B. L. Turner II

UNIVERSITY OF NEW MEXICO PRESS Albuquerque

Library of Congress Cataloging in Publication Data

Main entry under title:

Pre-Hispanic Maya agriculture.

Bibliography: p. 375
Includes index.
1. Mayas—Agriculture—Addresses, essays, lectures. 2. Indians of Mexico—Agriculture—Addresses, essays, lectures. 3. Indians of Central America—Agriculture—Addresses, essays, lectures. I. Harrison, Peter D., 1937– II. Turner, Billie Lee, 1945–
F1435.3.A6P69 338.1′0972 78-55703
ISBN 0-8263-0483-4

Manufactured in the United States of America
Library of Congress Catalog Card Number 78-55703
International Standard Book Number 0-8263-0483-4
First edition

For Cyrus L. Lundell,
a pioneer in early studies of
Maya agriculture
and
in memory of Dennis E. Puleston,
our friend and colleague

Contents

Preface

In 1975, Pierre Becquelin of the Musée de l'Homme invited me to organize a symposium on the subject of pre-Hispanic Maya agriculture to be held during the Forty-second International Congress of Americanists in Paris. In the course of recruiting participants and searching out the extent of available data, I found that far more scholars were involved in, or concerned with the subject than had been imagined.

The symposium, held in September 1976, generated a great deal of interest, although of necessity it could not represent all the available data and points of view. This volume has been compiled in order to allow more comprehensive coverage than was possible in Paris.

It should be pointed out that this volume does not supplant the papers of the ICA symposium in any way, but rather succeeds those papers. No paper contained herein is an exact duplicate of any paper presented in Paris, although a few of the Paris papers are incorporated in modified form because their basic data and approach were essential.

Therefore, the greatest debt of this volume is to Pierre Becquelin, who planted the first seed for the creation of these collected papers. There are many other debts: to T. Patrick Culbert, whose introduction to officials at the University of New Mexico Press led to publication; a most heavy debt to Elizabeth Hadas Heist, Chief Manuscript Editor at the press, whose unflagging encouragement and direct energies have led to phenomenally swift publication; to Jeremy A. Sabloff for his careful reading of the text, and very helpful suggestions for improvement, including pointing out some gaps in the coverage. Such flaws we have tried to amend. Similarly, we are grateful to James J. Parsons for his helpful reading with a particular eye to the geographical side of our subject.

I owe particular personal thanks to my coeditor, without whose efforts this work truly would not exist in its present form. The content of certain chapters is beyond my expertise, and in such cases B. L. Turner II had the editorial responsibility dumped in his lap. Beyond this, his editorial guidance is prevalent throughout the volume, not least in my own contributions.

Finally, I extend my gratitude to all the contributors, who cooperated so well in the meeting of deadlines, and received with such equanimity my sometimes bellicose memos.

Santa Fe, New Mexico
February 1978

Peter D. Harrison

1

PETER D. HARRISON
Middle American Research Institute

So the Seeds Shall Grow: Some Introductory Comments

And some fell on stony ground . . .
  and because it had no root, it withered away.
And other fell on good ground,
  and did yield fruit. . . .—Luke 8:6–8

THE THRESHOLD

In the last five years research in the Maya lowlands has revealed a considerable quantity of small but significant fragments of information on pre-Hispanic Maya agriculture. These data have been accompanied or rapidly followed by rather larger amounts of interpretation, theory, and ideas. Such a variety of data and ideas are appearing with such astounding frequency that it is often difficult for interested students of the Maya to keep pace with the developments. This volume attempts to cope with the rapid increase in knowledge and change in attitude toward ancient Maya economy.

It is appropriate to view this collection of papers as a figurative threshold. From our present position we can look backward and view the history of our arrival at the existing state of knowledge and approach. We can define the threshold itself, but within the limitations of rapid change. The most encompassing limitation, however, is the inability to prognosticate from the threshold to the future. A backward look from the threshold should be enough to show us that we cannot accurately predict data and their consequent interpretations. Despite this humbling lesson, we should not be inhibited from using the discoveries to date and our knowledge of current research to forecast some directions that will probably be followed in future concepts of ancient Maya agriculture and economy.

Past understanding of the pre-Hispanic Maya has been based rather too firmly on the assumption of a maize-oriented, swidden-dependent economy, and all that this assumption implies. New data and their interpretations show that this assumption was incorrect. Several papers in this volume allude to the history of realization of the error. In chapter 2, Turner deal thoroughly with the ideas and events that culminated in the reversal of thought. Other papers, concerned with specific aspects of the new agricultural view, also make reference to this change. These authors are looking backward from the threshold while examining the present situation.

While this lesson from the past illustrates the risks embodied in broad assumptions, it can also point to some new bases of thought. The most important of these is that premises should be flexible in their nature, especially premises about agriculture that have such a direct effect on so many other aspects of a discrete culture.

Although we should not and cannot attempt to predict the qualitative and quantitative nature of data yet to be recovered, the rich variety of material related to agriculture contained in the papers of this volume does permit some guesses, at least, about the qualitative nature of future expectations. With preconceptions about the pre-Hispanic Maya toppling to the left and right in almost every area of major importance, we are cautioned by several authors to "go slow" and to seek a firm data base in support of a new conception of Maya economy. These cautions are certainly valid and they represent a major stance of this volume. However, the temptation to peek over the threshold and utilize the newfound information to hazard a few guesses is overwhelming. Some indulgence in speculation and the formulation of theories based on the small evidence already at hand can make a contribution in its own right by pointing out directions of research for future fieldwork—directions that might otherwise be overlooked. After all, concrete evidence for certain types of agriculture—such as terraces and raised fields—was overlooked for many years. The former were observed and reported over forty years ago, but their significance was not noted, or was forgotten, until recently. Evidence for raised field agriculture in any of its various forms was not noticed until five years ago in the Maya area.

Some papers in this volume can serve as a guide to future fieldwork. These papers deal with such matters as the relative usefulness of different kinds of evidence. For example, how much can we trust the evidence from pollen cores, micro- and macrofossils, and chemical analyses? How much of the interpretation of this evidence relies upon preconceptions of the stability of tropical ecosystems? Alan Covich (chap. 7) provides an assessment of this problem. The evidence of pollen analysis and its relationship to population cycles is further explored by Don Rice (chap. 4). Similarly, in the search for concrete evidence of the various types of food support systems, papers by Hammond (chap. 3), Culbert, Magers, and Spencer (chap. 8), and Puleston (chap. 12) comment upon or make additions to the known varieties. To what extent can geographic or other ecologically related studies guide and aid archaeologists by examination and analysis of terrain? Papers by Turner (chap. 9), Siemens (chap. 6), and Wiseman (chap. 5) deal with this approach. Other new approaches are provided by Vlcek, Garza, and Kurjack (chap. 11), and by Matheny (chap. 10) in consideration of apparently unique situations of food dependence and water control. Chapter 11 gives a case of high population concentration in a situation where the local ecological niche appears incapable of providing the means of support. This example underlines the probable importance of trade. It seems likely that in certain rare instances populations need not be self-supporting on a local basis if some other feature of a complex economy can take the place of self-support. Chapter 10 discusses the roles of water control as a major factor in the northern lowlands and the likelihood that it served many different purposes, including agricultural ones. Finally, the setting of the central lowlands is placed in perspective by comparison with environmental exploitation in other tropical forest regions by Bronson (chap. 14).

Perhaps the most startling feature of these papers is the revelation of the sheer variety of means of food production now known in the Maya lowlands. The details of their distribution over time and space are not yet known. The existence of a large variety is known, and an even greater variety is suspected. In chapters 15 and 16 David Harris and Gordon Willey have assessed and summarized the new data presented in this volume.

A PRINCIPLE OF FOOD RESOURCE VARIABILITY

In the remainder of this paper I wish to expand upon a critically important point. This is the principle of variability in the distribution of food-producing systems in lowland Maya agriculture. Despite the calls for caution and the admitted need for further data, sufficient information (and theory) exist to establish as fact that more than one system of agriculture was employed by the ancient Maya, and that agricultural systems themselves are only one type of several food-resource systems. The systems of agriculture could be classified in a number of ways—on the basis of crop-fallow cycles, agronomic skills, labor input, and other such factors. Although we are not yet certain that all the possible systems were in use in the Maya lowlands, we can still distinguish, on an open-ended basis, those features and variables that now appear to have governed the distribution of various known systems and that influence the significance of any given system.

The quality of variability is the cornerstone of a new approach to ancient Maya economy and is illuminated by the papers in this volume. In order to grasp this quality it is pertinent to discuss at this point those features and variables that appear to have governed the exploitation of food sources.

Sources of food other than that which is cultivated have been discussed in the literature, and some are reviewed in the following chapters. I will not concern myself here with nonagricultural resources such as game and fish, but will restrict the consideration to agricultural and aboricultural systems. A distinction must be made between the *total food resource framework* (see chapter 17 below) that supported a given population at a fixed point in time, and individual *systems* of agriculture. It is assumed that more than one individual system could have been in use at the same time. For example, extensive swidden agriculture could have accompanied any system of intensive agriculture at all times. The following analysis of features and variables is concerned with individual systems, not with the total food resource framework for a fixed point in time and space. The frame of reference, therefore, is the relative significance of any discrete system of agriculture.

The significance of any discrete system of cultivation is governed by at least three factors: (1) its temporal distribution; (2) its spatial distribution; and (3) its contribution to the total food resource framework (including nonagricultural food resources). The utilization of each discrete system fluctuated with reference to these factors. In turn, these factors were influenced by at least three variables: (1) the food requirements of the population; (2) the environmental situation of the population; and (3) the organizational level of the population with respect to its ability to command labor.

Population requirements for food are perceived as a variable that would stimulate the adoption or abandonment of particular systems of agriculture. Presumably this variable fluctuates in relation to population size. The environmental situation of the population influences the number of possible discrete systems that potentially may be employed at any location. Furthermore, environmental conditions are variable; changes may occur because of climatic or human alterations, and such physical alterations may create or allow for changes in the systems of agriculture. Organizational level and ability to command labor can obviously fluctuate, and may influence the system of cultivation. Certain systems of agriculture may require high levels of social organization in order to be maintained over large areas for lengthy periods of time, although this observation needs much study. Several authors have noted that over time rather extensive areas of terraces or, perhaps, raised fields may be constructed by small groups of workers, often with low-order social organization. Finally, it should be noted that all of these variables interact.

A graphic model of these features and variables illustrates the avenues of influence (fig. 1.1). This model suggests that at no point in time and space will a single system constitute the total food resource framework, and that no one system is likely to contribute the same percentage to the total framework throughout time and space. Herein lies the principle of variability.

A nearly unlimited number of hypothetical situations can be constructed to illustrate the three features of an agricultural system. Using a selected number of discrete systems of agriculture, three such hypothetical situations are outlined below to illustrate the fluctuating nature of the features. In addition to the selected systems of agriculture, I am including in these examples the arboriculture of ramon, because the importance of this food-

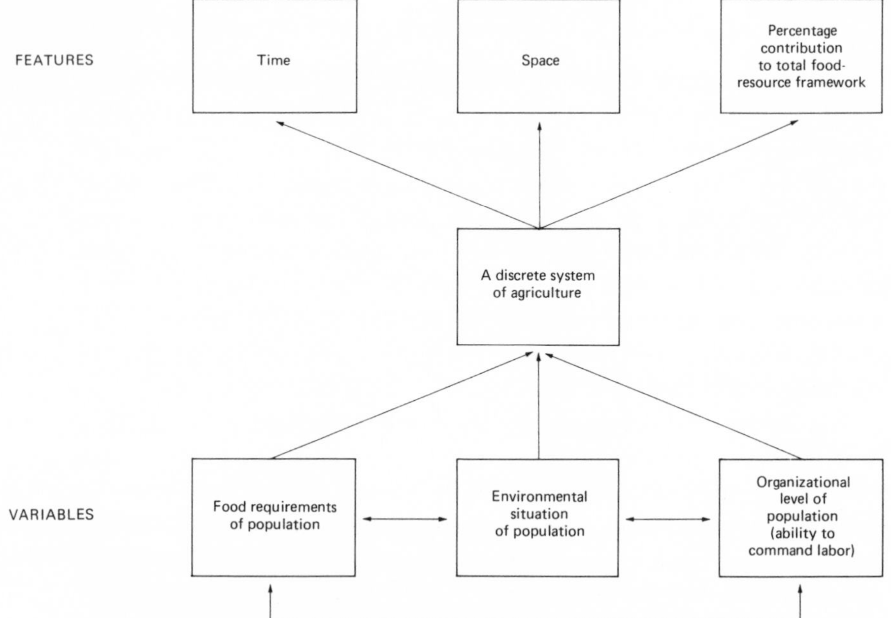

Figure 1.1. Avenues of influence of variables upon a discrete system of agriculture and some features of that system.

producing system has been previously suggested and is also argued in this volume (chap. 12).

Feature 1: Time. At any given location, over the full range of the prehistoric period, several or all of the following systems could have been utilized in accordance with the influencing variables: terraces; raised fields in *bajos* or in river drainages; ramon collection; kitchen gardens emphasizing root crops, in conjunction with outfield swidden agriculture. These systems may have been used either serially or simultaneously over time.

Feature 2: Space. At a given point in time, over the entire lowlands, fifty different populations could have been engaged in each of the above systems. Several or all of these populations might have been engaged in several or all of these different systems simultaneously.

Feature 3: Contribution. At one location, at a single point in time, the contribution that each of the above systems made to the total food-resource framework could have been: outfield swidden, 20 percent; raised fields, 35 percent; ramon collection, 15 percent; kitchen gardens, 15 percent; and other, nonagricultural sources, 15 percent. At the same location, but at a different point in time, the distribution could be: outfield swidden, 15 percent; raised fields, 0 percent; ramon collection, 60 percent; kitchen gardens, 10 percent; and other, nonagricultural sources, 15 percent. I have assumed a locality where the use of raised fields was feasible and exploited at one point in time, but not at the other; and where terrace agriculture either was not feasible or had not been exploited. Of course, the reverse situation could be postulated with equal ease. The changes in percentage contribution of each system to the total food-resource framework from one point in time to the other result from fluctuations in the three variables.

The purpose of citing these imaginary situations is to illustrate the immense variety of food production systems available to the pre-Hispanic Maya, and the variability of their utilization. Because of this variability it is unproductive to champion any one system on a broad basis. No single system of food production can be usefully characterized as the major supplier to the resource framework without delimiting the claim by specifying parameters of time and space.

The above discussion is based upon a situation in which site populations produced the majority of their own food supply in the vicinity of residence. It is possible to theorize a situation where this was not the case, but where the majority of food was introduced from outside. In such a case a new element, trade, would have to be considered as a food source. A model for this kind of special community, in a different culture area, has been outlined by Jane Jacobs (1969). Evidence from the site of Çatal Hüyük in northern Anatolia showed that a complex society had developed at a date earlier than at other sites to the south in the Fertile Crescent. Jacobs's explanation is a scarce-resource model, in which the resource (obsidian, in this case) was traded for food, an exchange that encouraged precocious cultural development at the site.

A possibly parallel case does occur in the northern lowlands. The peculiar situation of the site of Chunchucmil is reported herein by Vlcek, Garza, and Kurjack. Although the authors are cautious in their claims, one explanation of this situation could be that trade salt served as a scarce resource that led to the rise of a community too large to be supported by local agriculture. Recognition of an unusual economic situation, whatever its explanation, must lead us to wonder what other factors contributed to the total food resource framework that have yet to be recognized. Situations such as the above represent cultural-economic exceptions in my scheme of features and variables, and the existence of such exceptional situations must be allowed.

In the foregoing discussion, two simple but very important features of pre-Hispanic Maya agriculture have been explored. These are that a wide variety of systems was utilized, and that the significance of each individual system was variable, subject to fluctuating influences. These points formulate my assumed principle of variability.

Like the parabled seeds of St. Luke, we hope that the ideas and data in this volume will yield fruit, at least in part.

APPENDIX: DEFINITIONS

The fact that archaeologists are a little bit like fish out of water when they are dealing with agriculture is attested by the fact that many of the terms related to the subject are used with varying shades of meaning by different authors. Although, as an archaeologist, I am one of the fish out of water, the coeditor of this volume (Turner) is not, and we have collaborated to provide a series of definitions of relevant terms according to our use of them. We have furthermore made a concerted effort to ensure that whenever these terms are used in the papers of this volume, they conform to the following definitions. Some terms are more troublesome than others in their shades of ambiguity (for example, multi-cropping), and particular attention has been paid to the use of such terms. We have no intention of imposing these definitions on the community of concerned scholars at large, but have outlined them according to our usage and understanding in this volume.

In previous publications a number of authors have defined their use of some of the terms included here (Bronson 1975; Logan and Sanders 1976). Because of the subject of this volume, more agricultural terms are employed than have been previously defined in an archaeological context. Therefore, we found it necessary not to rely on the few extant definitions.

Agriculture. The manipulation, including planting and harvesting, of domesticated plants for food or commercial produce. This definition is purposely strict because this volume does not deal with animal husbandry and because precise distinctions must be made between "true" agriculture and other varieties of plant collecting, gathering, or manipulation.

Arboriculture. The manipulation, including preservation, domestication, or improvement, of a tree crop (especially fruits), including the plant itself or the crop. *Arboriculture* is a difficult term. All the papers in this book attempt to make a distinction between arboriculture as applied to wild or semidomesticated plants and as applied to domesticated plants.

Chinampa. A form of raised field, although not often recognized as such in the literature. Specifically, the chinampas of the Valley of Mexico are monolevel or bilevel platforms, in raised-field terminology.

Crop. This is a most troublesome term because of the variety of valid definitions, as follows:

(1) Any cultivated or collected grain, fruit, or root.

(2) A specific cultivar within a given field.

(3) The entire sequence of cultivation from planting to harvesting.

(4) To cultivate.

Cultigen. Strictly speaking a plant for which there are no known progenitors, but also a plant that cannot reproduce itself.

Cultivar. A domesticated crop.

Cultivate. To prepare land for the production of crops.

Cultivation. Same as *agriculture.* Cultivation and agriculture are entrenched in the literature as synonyms.

Harvest. Strictly defined as the collection of a cultivated crop(s), but also used in this text to refer to semidomesticated or wild food resources.

Horticulture. Gardening; the cultivation of fruits and vegetables.

Intensive and extensive agriculture. These terms are relative, but when not defined otherwise they refer to the frequency of cropping. In this volume, *intensive* equals a crop-fallow cycle of 1:0 or higher; *extensive* means systems in which the fallow period exceeds the cropping period (1:2 or lower). A 1:1 crop-fallow cycle may be referred to as semipermanent cultivation.

Recent works that deal with agricultural intensification tend to focus on various methods of measuring intensity without specifically defining the concept that is to be measured. Nevertheless, a uniform meaning of the concept is implicit in various works (Boserup 1965; Brookfield 1972; Brown and Podolefsky 1976; Turner, Hanham, and Portararo 1977). *Agricultural intensity,* in brief, refers to the amount of food obtained by cultivating a constant land area over a specified period of time. In this respect, agriculture may be intensified in two ways. The frequency of cultivation (planting to harvesting) over the period of time may be increased, or the amount of production per cultivation may be increased. Both intensification processes tend to take place simultaneously, although as high levels of agricultural intensity are obtained a tendency exists to shift to efforts that increase production per cultivation (Turner, Hanham, and Portararo 1977).

Given this definition, an increase in the amount or type of land under cultivation is not itself an increase in the intensity of agriculture because the land area does not remain constant. Furthermore, an increase in the amount of land under cultivation may actually lower production per unit area and time. The increase in cultivated land is referred to as agricultural expansion, not intensification (see Hammond, chap. 3 below). The subject of intensification will be discussed further in the final chapter of this volume.

Intercropping. The cultivation of more than one crop in a single field.

Irrigation (agricultural). The artificial control of soil moisture by the application of water.

Kitchen garden or dooryard garden. A plot or space, surrounding or adjacent to a dwelling, in which plants are cultivated. It should be noted that this definition is stricter than that supplied by Anderson (1952). It is also important to note that this term should be applied to plots in which specialty or experimental crops are grown. Large-scale production of staples, regardless of their proximity to dwellings, is not considered to be kitchen-garden cultivation, a form of agriculture that is usually highly intensive.

Multi-cropping. More than one cropping phase (planting to harvesting) per annum on the same field. Two crops (two cropping phases) per annum may be referred to as a double crop or double-cropping.

Multi-harvesting. The differential collection of a cultivated plant(s) from the same field over a specified period of time.

Raised field. Prepared land in which soil is transferred and elevated above the natural surface of the earth in order to improve cultivating conditions.

Ridged field. Formerly a term for all raised fields, originally used by Denevan (1970) and Parsons (1969). In the new classification a ridged field is a category of raised field that is either linear or curvilinear and that maintains a cambered cross section (Denevan and Turner 1974).

Silviculture. Literally, management of forest systems, not to be confused with *arboriculture.* Puleston, however, uses this term to refer to the culling or manipulation of one species of tree within a forest.

Slash-and-burn. A specific agricultural technique. Not used in this volume with reference to an agricultural system.

Swidden. An extensive system of cultivation that tends to maintain two to four or more years of fallow for every year of cultivation. This term is used in this volume in place of *milpa, slash-and-burn,* or *shifting cultivation.*

Root crops. Those plants that take the growth forms of bulbs, roots, tuberous roots, rhizomes, or corms.

Terrace (agricultural). Prepared land in which the surface slope has been modified by a lateral obstruction across a slope or drainage channel.

2

B. L. TURNER II
Department of Geography, University of Oklahoma

The Development and Demise of the Swidden Thesis of Maya Agriculture

THE THESIS AND THE EVIDENCE

John L. Stephens (1843:1:137), H. H. Bancroft (1883:719), and other nineteenth-century explorers were perhaps the first to suggest that the ancient Maya were swidden agriculturalists. By the mid twentieth century this view of pre-Hispanic agriculture in the Maya lowlands was entrenched in the literature, a formal thesis with significant theoretical ramifications (Steward 1949). In brief, the swidden thesis held that for several reasons Maya civilization was sustained by extensive slash-and-burn systems of cultivation.[1] This view of Maya subsistence has endured despite the paucity of evidence and has influenced numerous arguments concerning the growth and decline of the lowland Maya Classic civilization (Meggers 1954; Dumond 1961; Rathje 1973).

Archaeological evidence supporting the swidden thesis has been limited to several Maya frescos and codices. The frescos on the inner walls of Structure 16 at Tulum depict, among other things, a maize god, maize symbols, and a doubled or bent maize stalk.[2] Two intertwined serpents are also portrayed, one with an open mouth, probably blowing incense, above which are twin ears of maize. These symbols and designs have been interpreted as the serpent (symbol of rain) making an offering to the maize god (Lothrop 1924:57). Similarly, several Maya codices display gods planting maize with the use of dibble or digging sticks (Villacorta and Villacorta 1930:267, 278; C. Thomas 1882:671). Doubled maize, dibble sticks, and the rain-maize connection, key elements associated with contemporary milpa or swidden cultivation in the Maya lowlands, have been interpreted as supporting the swidden thesis.[3]

Analyzed pollen samples from the Laguna de Petenxil (Tsukada 1966) and Lago Izabal (Tsukada and Deevey 1967) have been offered as paleoecological evidence supporting the swidden thesis. The Petenxil analysis established three pollen zones corresponding to the Preclassic, Classic, and Postclassic phases of Maya chronology. *Zea* pollen (maize) and carbonized fragments of monocotyledonous plants (presumed to be grasses) were concentrated throughout the three zones, although *Zea* pollen had minor peaks in the Classic zones. These and other evidences of vegetational disturbance were suggestive of large-scale burning associated with swidden cultivation, especially during the Classic period (Tsukada 1966). Similar results and interpretations have come from pollen analyses of Lago Izabal and three lakes situated in the Maya highlands. Vegetational disturbance, *Zea* pollen, and carbonized fragments, all of which appear somewhat cyclical in the pollen rain, have been taken to indicate large-scale burning characteristic of swidden cultivation (Tsukada and Deevey 1967:326–27).

Interpretations aside, the archaeological and paleoecological data have described several aspects of the pre-Hispanic Maya and the Maya lowlands that are undoubtedly related to agriculture. Maize was important to the Maya and has been cultivated in the lowlands since Preclassic times if not earlier. The dibble stick was a tool used for cultivation. The Maya lowlands have incurred in the past considerable vegetational disturbance associated with burning.

The swidden thesis is one interpretation of this evidence. A better interpretation is that swidden cultivation varied both temporally and spatially in the pre-Hispanic lowlands, a view that is indisputable. The evidence by no means confirms the notion that the Maya never expanded beyond extensive modes of cultivation. Indeed, the evidence can be interpreted as suggesting that various intensive agricultural practices were utilized by the pre-Hispanic Maya.

The Tulum frescos and the codices imply little about the intensity of pre-Hispanic cultivation. Maize and rain symbols are as applicable to interpretations of various intensive forms of agriculture as they are to swidden cultivation. The use of the dibble, moreover, does not imply the practice of slash-and-burn agriculture. Numerous contemporary peoples use digging sticks in intensive cultivation, often in less socially and technically advanced contexts than that of the pre-Hispanic Maya (Brookfield and Brown 1963; Serpenti 1965; E. Waddell 1972; Netting 1968).

Furthermore, the type of digging stick used by the pre-Hispanic Maya appears to be a sophisticated tool, possibly of multiple agricultural functions. The codices depict the Maya dibble as a waist-high stick with an upper handle and with a point that was either narrow and sharp or, perhaps, chisel-shaped. This dibble type bears a strong resemblance to the *huriri,* a footspade of great antiquity that is used in Peru to turn and loosen the soil (Gade and Rios 1972:8). Such a possible function for the Maya dibble suggests a form of land preparation commonly associated with semipermanent or more intensive cultivation, not slash-and-burn.

The paleoecological data strongly indicate that burning and vegetational alterations were associated and were widespread throughout the Maya lowlands in pre-Hispanic times.[4] This evidence does not suggest, however, that such burning was necessarily associated with woody species or forest in a manner indicative of medium- or long-fallow swidden agriculture. Rather, the carbonized fragments of monocotyledonous plants reported by Matsuo Tsukada and Edward S. Deevey (1967) suggest that burning was practiced on grasses or the immediate successional flora of cultivated fields. Indeed, Tsukada and Deevey (1967) found that the carbonized fragments have a positive correlation with *Zea* (maize) and weed pollen but not with tree pollen. Barring the possibility of major climatic changes that transformed the tropical forests to savannas, the paleoecological evidence suggests an extremely short-fallow system of cultivation.[5]

Grasses are the initial successional flora during and immediately after cultivation in most parts of the Maya lowlands. After six months to a year, however, various shrubs and ferns dominate abandoned agricultural plots.[6] Scrub forests are established within several years of abandonment. If this successional pattern is projected into pre-Hispanic times, the evidence of carbonized fragments suggests that some form of annual or, at a minimum, semiannual cultivation was taking place in some areas. The interpretation of these data as supporting exclusively an extensive slash-and-burn system of agriculture is a testimonial to the past dominance of the swidden thesis.[7]

Comparative and negative evidence constitute the more common forms of support for the swidden thesis. Comparative evidence involves analogies between post-Hispanic and pre-Hispanic agriculture in the Maya lowlands. Early post-Hispanic accounts of Maya cultivation are provided by the works of Friar Diego de Landa, who described the northern Yucatecan Maya as cultivating with fire and digging sticks (Tozzer 1941:97). Interpretations of Landa's work and the prevalence of swidden cultivation since European occupation of the Maya lowlands have led to the conclusion that post-Hispanic and pre-Hispanic cultivation were similar (Lundell 1933b:164; Sanders 1962:89). Such comparisons might be valid if the factors that affect agriculture were static during the two time periods. Unfortunately one factor, population pressure, apparently differed considerably from one period to the other, making comparisons tenuous. Furthermore, Landa's references to small, demarcated plots, land (soil?) manipulation, and well-organized granaries might suggest an alternative interpretation to that of swidden cultivation (Gates 1937:38; Tozzer 1941:97).

The absence of substantial evidence indicating that the pre-Hispanic Maya employed some form of intensive or nonswidden agriculture has been, perhaps, the single most influential factor sustaining the swidden thesis in the past.[8] This position was often adopted and defended with minimal attention to the identification of agricultural evidence, especially in the central lowlands.[9] Furthermore, when evidence was available, such as the long-noted relic terraces in the foothills of the Maya Mountains that border the once densely settled central lowlands, it was ignored or set aside.

THE HIATUS

The swidden thesis was questioned in the early part of this century by Thomas Gann (1925:219–25) and by Oliver G. Ricketson (Ricketson and Ricketson 1937:12–13, 15–24). Their questions stemmed from the belief that lowland Maya sites represented centers of substantial concentrations of people and that such populations would have required intensive forms of agriculture for support. Cyrus Lundell (1933a:72–77) and P. W. Schufeldt (1950:225–26) provided evidence of nonswidden cultivation in the form of relic terracing in Belize and land demarcation throughout the various zones in the lowlands.[10] The antiswidden arguments were not well accepted, but they laid the foundation for the numerous reevaluations of the swidden thesis that followed.[11]

The swidden thesis was seriously challenged in the late fifties when scholarly interests turned to the critical issue of Maya agriculture in relation to population (Palerm and Wolf 1957:26–28), and settlement pattern research in the lowlands began in earnest with the survey of northeastern Peten by William R. Bullard (1960); the examination of the Belize River Valley by Gordon Willey et. al. (1965); and, of course, the extensive research conducted by the University of Pennsylvania at Tikal (Haviland 1965, 1969, 1970; W. Coe 1965). These studies produced estimates of pre-Hispanic Maya population densities that would strain, if not exceed, the capabilities of any known forms of swidden agriculture. Such results led to a variety of hypotheses for alternative food procurement systems that were available to and may have been utilized by the Maya. Bennet Bronson (1966) attacked the maize-swidden thesis, arguing that the lowlands could have supported large populations by emphasizing root-crop cultivation. Dennis Puleston (1968a) argued that the Tikal region may have relied on the breadnut, or ramon (*Brosimum alicastrum*), for subsistence, and B. Leroy Gordon (1969) suggested that multilevel orchard gardens may have been important. Frederick W. Lange (1971) speculated on a variety of subsistence alternatives, especially the use of marine resources, and Gene Wilken (1971) argued that conventional, intensive forms of agriculture could have been utilized by the lowland Maya. In synthesizing these arguments, David R. Harris (1972) rejected the maize-swidden thesis on the basis of comparative evidence from the tropics.

The swidden thesis remained persistent, however, despite its inconsistencies with the population and settlement data. Several swidden proponents attempted to rectify these discrepancies by questioning the large population estimates from the settlement studies (J. E. S. Thompson 1971; Sanders 1973:330–31). Other proponents leaned heavily on Ursula Cowgill's (1961, 1962) liberal assessment of the carrying capacity of 77 persons per square kilometer for swidden cultivation in Peten.[12] William Haviland (1965:23), for instance, suggested that a 500-square-kilometer zone around Tikal could have supported the population of the site given Cowgill's carrying capacity. As William Coe (1965:52) retorted, however, the 500-square-kilometer zone was densely settled at the time that Tikal had its greatest population. Furthermore, other carrying capacity assessments of the Maya lowlands produced substantially lower estimates than those provided by Cowgill (Reina 1967; Carter 1969:142; H. O. Wagner 1968:185).

CONTEMPORARY THEMES

Three factors have been instrumental in the most recent evaluations of pre-Hispanic lowland Maya subsistence. Ester Boserup's (1965) theory of the relationship between population pressure and agricultural growth has been a major influence on assessments of the topic, particularly in regard to the erroneous view that tropical environs set absolute limits on agricultural growth. The growth of Maya agriculture has recently been viewed as a response to pre-Hispanic population pressures, although the extent of these pressures and the growth of agriculture are both controversial topics (Sanders 1972, 1973; B. L. Turner 1974a). A second factor has been the demonstration that Maya sites were not isolated centers of populations engulfed by empty zones for swidden cultivation but were surrounded by rather large "suburban" or "rural" populations (Puleston 1974b; B. L. Turner 1976b). The third and most important factor has been the identification of several relics of agriculture indicating that the pre-Hispanic Maya pursued a variety of cultivation techniques generally associated with intensive cropping systems.

The identification of relic raised fields in the Candelaria River Basin by Alfred H. Siemens and Dennis Puleston (1972) was a major breakthrough in the agricultural controversy. This discovery (which has not received proper recognition) was followed by similar finds in northern Belize (Puleston 1977; Olson et al. 1975) and in Quintana Roo (B. L. Turner 1974a; Harrison 1974). Furthermore, extensive zones of relic terraces and field demarcation have been recorded in Campeche and Quintana Roo (B. L. Turner 1974a) and along the eastern coastal zone of the Yucatan Peninsula (Sabloff and Rathje 1975:78). More recently, evidence of possible irrigation at Edzna has been uncovered (Matheny 1976). Similar types of evidence have been tentatively identified in several other areas of the lowlands and are currently under investigation.

The recent flood of agricultural and related data indicates that the pre-Hispanic Maya were not limited to swidden cultivation as a subsistence base. Rather, agricultural systems in the lowlands undoubtedly varied through space and time in association with demographic, environmental, and, possibly, commercial factors. This view does not deny the significance of swidden cultivation to the development and continuance of the lowland Maya civilization. It does, however, emphasize that Maya agriculture was responsive to several stimuli and that these stimuli often led to intensive agriculture. The controversy today, as set forth in this volume, no longer centers on the validity of the swidden thesis but involves the spatial and temporal distributions of all types of cultivation utilized by the Maya and the level of agricultural intensity that was obtained and sustained during peak periods of pre-Hispanic occupation.

THE THESIS IN PERSPECTIVE

The establishment and acceptance of the swidden thesis in the first half of this century can be attributed to several interlocking factors: research interests in the Maya, terrain visibility problems in the lowlands, and overestimations of ecological influences on early civilizations. The early explorers and archaeologists in the Maya region devoted most of their energies to the enormous task of recording and examining sites with monumental architecture. Understandably drawn to the vestiges of the major Maya centers of intellectual and artistic activity, the early researchers paid minimal attention to the areas that lay beyond the limits of the centers. Relic agricultural and related features that modified the Maya landscape were small in comparison to the monumental stoneworks of the centers, and the density of the lowland forests often made it difficult to recognize the presence or the extent of the agricultural features. In lieu of strong research interests in, or evidence of, Maya agriculture, the swidden thesis apparently drew some measure of support from deterministic doctrines.

Views concerning environmental influences on cultural development were popularized largely by American geographers during the first several decades of the 1900s (e.g., Semple 1911). Their often extremist position, known as *environmental determinism,* attempted to establish the influence that particular physical environs exert on cultural activity and growth. Pervading these arguments was the view that tropical zones were not conducive to the maintenance of various elements that were deemed necessary for advanced civilization, such as intensive agriculture. In brief, the extremist position assumed that the tropical lowlands imposed limitations on the intensification of agriculture, *forcing* the Maya to adopt an extensive, swidden form of cultivation that could not be improved. Ellsworth Huntington (1917:160–64) offered such a position. More recently Betty J. Meggers (1954) attempted to resurrect the deterministic argument.

Several of the factors that gave rise to the swidden thesis also helped sustain it into the present decade. The paucity of research and interests in lowland Maya habitats and food production—in part a product of the dominance of the swidden thesis—continued through the 1950s and early 1960s. The initial agricultural evidence presented by Lundell (1933a:72–77), Schufeldt (1950:225–26), and others was basically ignored. Furthermore, most of the opposition to the swidden thesis after 1950 was relegated to speculation (Palerm and Wolf 1957; Lange 1971; Wilken 1971). Field data that could have countered the thesis were limited or based on sets of assumptions that many students found difficult to accept, such as Puleston's (1968) controversial ramon argument. Perhaps most important in allowing the swidden thesis to persist, however, were the recent interpretations of human-ecological relationships in the pre-Hispanic lowlands and of the Classic Maya collapse.[13]

Theories of a swidden-stimulated collapse have been promoted since the early 1920s (O. F. Cook 1921), although they probably have had their strongest support and appeal during the past two decades. These theories have combined assumptions about the limited nature of Maya food-production capabilities with assumption about the environmental quality of lowlands. Meggers's (1954) view of the quality and influential nature of the tropical forest represents a minority opinion that has been seriously criticized for a variety of reasons (W. Coe 1957; Hirshberg and Hirshberg 1957; Dumond 1961). Nevertheless, variations on her theme have persisted (e.g., Gyuk and Harrison 1975).

William T. Sanders, to whom modern human ecological work in the Maya region is indebted, has been a major proponent of a swidden-related collapse thesis. In his view (1973) the ancient

Maya did not possess the technical capabilities to pursue highly intensive agriculture for lengthy periods of time, and their attempts to shorten fallow periods in an environment that Sanders considers marginal for agriculture (especially as compared to the highland Mesoamerican environs) led to grass invasion and loss of soil fertility. Unable to cope with these problems, the Maya allowed the lowlands to deteriorate physically and the collapse was imminent. While Sanders's thesis correctly focuses on technological-environmental interactions, with technology given the major role, controversy centers on the interpretations given to the level of agrotechnology developed by the pre-Hispanic Maya and to the quality of the lowland habitat for cultivation. While Sanders has maintained a human ecological perspective in regard to the swidden thesis, others have succumbed to more deterministic views that give too much weight to ecological constraint in regard to Maya agriculture (e.g., Rathje 1973).

The popularity of swidden-related collapse theories and the persistence of the swidden thesis of Maya agriculture may be viewed as a response to the interests placed on human ecological research and on nomothetic explanations in the past decade. Unlike many explanations of the collapse, which tend to rely on factors that were unique to the Maya civilization, the ecological-swidden approach is adaptable to a variety of general explanations that fit the standards of positivistic science. Furthermore, these explanations are appealing because they tend to be simplistic, if not always satisfying, and because they are a suitable footnote to the population-food crisis that doomsday prophets predict for the modern world. As with all theory, however, explanations of the collapse must not only be valid statements (adhere to nomothetic syntax), but must be truthful statements as well. Herein lies the test for the swidden thesis in the next decade. To judge from the increasing new data concerning the forms and intensity of ancient Maya agriculture, it is a test that the thesis most likely will not withstand.[14]

NOTES

1. A large number of scholars have supported the swidden thesis, although many of them have abandoned or altered their positions. A partial list of references to the swidden thesis includes (in chronological order): O. F. Cook (1921:314); Gann and Thompson

(1931:65); Lundell (1933b:164, 1961:43); Steggerda (1941:89); Roys (1943:38); Morley (1946:71–72); Higbee (1948:459); Brainerd (1954:71, 1956:162); Altschuler (1958:195); Gallenkamp (1959:94); Bullard (1960:367, 1964:279); M. Coe (1961:80, 1966:138); Stevens (1964:299); Vogt (1964:386); Haviland (1965:23); J. E. S. Thompson (1965:357, 1966:24, 26); Willey and Bullard (1965:372); Willey et al. (1965:575); Sabloff and Willey (1967:315–16); Ruz Lhuillier (1970:56); Sabloff (1971:19); Rathje (1973:443); Webb (1973:387).

2. The doubling of maize (*Zea mays* L.) is a cultivation practice in which the maize cob is bent downward before the harvest to protect the maize grains from pest and environmental damage.

3. The term *milpa* literally means cornfield but is often used as a synonym for swidden cultivation, especially in Central America and Mexico.

4. Large-scale burning was conducted by the pre-Hispanic Maya for numerous purposes other than agriculture, especially in the preparation of mortar. An enormous amount of forest must have been felled to have provided sufficient fuel for the construction of the profusion of sites in the Maya lowlands.

5. The pre-Hispanic Maya induced considerable environmental change in the lowlands. Forest lands were denuded, soils were eroded, and drainage patterns were altered. Climatic change during the Maya occupation of the lowlands, whether induced by the Maya or resulting from natural causes (such as upper atmospheric changes), is a controversial topic in its research infancy. Huntington (1915, 1917) was one of the first to suggest that natural climatic changes had taken place in the Maya area. More recent studies suggest that the Maya lowlands may have incurred slight increases in annual precipitation since Preclassic times.

6. The following list includes some of the more common varieties of first-stage successional growth that invade swidden plots in southern Campeche, Mexico: *Viguiera dentata* (Cav.), *Pterididum aquilinum* var. *caudatum, Iresine celosia* L., *Elviara biflora* (L.), *Montanoa* sp. More detailed descriptions are available in Lundell (1934).

7. Future interpretations of pollen data from the Maya area may differ considerably from past interpretations because of the changing views on pre-Hispanic Maya agriculture.

8. For examples, see Vogt (1964:386) or Willey and Bullard (1965:372), although numerous others exist.

9. Hester's (1954) search for evidence of pre-Hispanic agriculture in northern Yucatan is an exception. Unfortunately, Hester found no direct evidence of past agriculture in the area.

10. Lundell was not the first to report on the terraces in the Maya Mountain region, but he was one of the first to offer them as evidence of intensive cultivation on the part of the lowland Maya.

11. Interestingly, Gann (1926:241–42) and Lundell (1933b:164, 1961:43) were inconsistent in their support of the antiswidden argument and apparently reversed their positions on the topic.

12. Cowgill never dismissed the possibility that Maya cultivation may have obtained more intensive levels than the short-fallow system she used to calculate the carrying capacity in the central Peten.

13. For a discussion of the swidden thesis as it relates to views of urbanism in the Maya lowlands, see Mathewson (1977).

14. I thank Jeremy A. Sabloff for several criticisms of this paper.

3

NORMAN HAMMOND
Department of Classics, Douglass College

The Myth of the Milpa: Agricultural Expansion in the Maya Lowlands

> The modern Maya method of raising maize is the same as it has been for the past three thousand years or more—a simple process of felling the forest, burning the dried trees and bush, of planting, and changing the location of the cornfields every few years. This is practically the system of agriculture practiced in the American wet tropics even today, and indeed is the only method available to a primitive people living in a heavily wooded, rocky, shallow-soiled country like that of the northern Yucatan Peninsula, where a plow cannot be used and where draft animals are not obtainable. This system is commonly known as *milpa* agriculture. . . . (Moreley 1946:141)

Since Sylvanus G. Morley wrote these words more than three decades ago, the focus of Maya archeology has expanded beyond the temples, tombs, and public buildings that, with epigraphy and calendrics, first absorbed most scholars. It now embraces rural settlement patterns, the relationships between settlement and resources, and the nature of those resources. Whereas we once looked merely at the pinnacles of achievement of Maya civilization, our view has dropped to comprehend the economic substructure upon which that dazzling edifice was raised.

The change began in earnest when Willey introduced systematic settlement archaeology into the Maya field (Willey et al. 1965). With the investigation of dispersed settlement far from the great ceremonial precincts and their surrounding zones of residence came an interest in daily life and the realities of obtaining one's daily bread. Morley himself (1946:156–57) had noted the presence in the modern Maya diet of beans, squashes, root crops, and fruit, and the economic potential of breadnut, or ramon (*Brosimum alicastrum*). Others pursued each of these further as possible major constituents of the prehistoric diet (Bronson 1966; Puleston 1968a), in some cases overarguing the case for their chosen comestible like Portia advocating mercy.

Even so, the use of agricultural methods other than milpa swiddening and aboriculture, passive or active, was not consciously considered until quite recently. Although the existence of raised-field complexes in other regions of the pre-Columbian Americas had been emphasized (Denevan 1970; Parsons and Denevan 1967), they remained unnoticed in the Maya area until the work of Siemens and Puleston (1972). New areas of such fields are still being discovered even in relatively well explored parts of the Maya lowlands; the debate about their precise function, economic contribution, and chronological position continues unabated, in this volume *inter alia.* Similarly, the use of terracing to create artificial fields in marginal econiches, although noted by J. Eric S. Thompson (1931) and by A. C. S. Wright et al. (1959), was not brought into the forefront of Mayanists' attention until the work of B. L. Turner II (1974a). Our awareness of the range of agricultural options open to the ancient Maya has greatly increased since the time when Eric Thompson (1954:234) could say, quite accurately on the basis of information then available, "Maize was . . . the economic basis of Maya civilization" and envision no other means than the milpa for acquiring it. We recognize now that other foodstuffs, and other ways of growing them and maize as well, were important, and that the Maya economy was far more complex than archaeologists had imagined.

In this paper I outline some of the ways in which agricultural production could have been expanded in the Maya lowlands. I draw a fine distinction between *expansion* and *intensification* in genuflection to the editors of this volume and the uniform terminology that they wisely impose upon their contributors. *Intensification* I use in their sense of the frequency with which a particular plot of land is cultivated, measured by the crop-fallow cycle or the percentage of the time that the land is in crop. In an earlier paper (Hammond 1976a) I used this term as I now use *expansion,* to describe agricultural activities that absorbed a larger proportion of the total labor-time available in a society. With the word used in that way, an increase in acreage under cultivation, involving both an absolute increase in man-hours worked and, in many cases, a higher proportion of the total work-hours available, would be a form of intensification. Here, however, such an increase is treated as a form of expansion. I suggest that certain forms of expansion may, in conditions of adequate but not excessive ("critical") population density, actually be preferable in terms of labor economy to the milpa system, which we have assumed to be the ideal under conditions of low population pressure, and that such conscious decisions may have been taken at least as far back as the later Early Formative, ca. 1400 B.C. (calibrated ^{14}C years).

Expansion of agricultural production may be spatial, temporal, specific, or more than one of these. Spatial expansion may be lateral, vertical, or both.

Lateral expansion. At its simplest, lateral expansion is merely an extension of the area of land under cultivation at any one time. Under the present and historically attested regime known as milpa, extensive swiddening on a crop-fallow ratio of 1:3 or greater, this would be carried out by clearing more high bush (climax or long-term regenerate forest) each year, or by beginning the recycling of shorter-term second-growth *wamil* areas at an earlier date (producing temporal compression, a form of increased activity midway between expansion and intensification).

In the first instance the degree of expansion would be limited by (1) the proximity of other communities practicing swiddening, and perhaps expanding simultaneously, and (2) the maximum socially acceptable journey-to-work time, estimated by Michael Chisholm (1968) to be up to five kilometers, although Ruben Reina (1967) demonstrates that greater distances are traveled in the modern special case of communities bordering Lake Peten-Itza, where motor-driven canoes are used. In any case, the creation of too great a distance to work would result in the growth of subsidiary communities that would then act as a limitation because of their proximity, as in condition 1. Lateral expansion as such—that is, input of an increased proportion of the total labor-time available into a larger surface area cultivated by the same methods and with the same yield per unit area—is thus constrained both statically and dynamically. Demand for an absolute increase in output may be governed not only by population increase (in which case the labor-time available also increases, after several years' lag) but also by rising expectations in an evolving society with increasing social differentiation, such as that of the Formative and Classic Maya. In either case constraints operate; as more land is required, less is available.

A second type of lateral expansion is the utilization of previously uncultivated soil sets. It is a truism, the ramifications of which have not been sufficiently appreciated in Maya studies, that the most productive soils for a given economic situation will be exploited first, and that exploitation of successively less productive soils will follow as necessary thereafter. Given the complex soil pattern of even so topographically uniform a landscape as northern Belize, consisting of low limestone ridges with a maximum elevation of 25 meters (Wright et al. 1959), certain patches of land are today preferred for what may be a marginal advantage, degree of acidity; if necessary, however, the less attractive soils will be exploited. Another example of this preference may be seen in southern Belize, around the Classic Maya site of Lubaantun, where present cultivation extends in a band along the eastern slope of the hills, between 25 and 100 meters in elevation. This land is not only as fertile as more elevated slopes, but it is also nearer to the riverside settlements and so minimizes journey-to-work time (Hammond 1975: fig. 40).

Vertical expansion. In the course of lateral expansion across the landscape, cultivation may be extended into higher or lower econiches than those initially exploited or than those utilized when demand is low. In the Maya lowlands this means the use of steep hill soils or those in seasonally or permanently waterlogged valley bottoms. Hill soils are avoided normally not only because of their thinness and susceptibility to erosion, but because of their greater distance from settlements and water, and thus the increased journey-to-work time that their exploitation entails. When steep hill soils must be used, various devices may be employed to restrict erosion, to trap the eroded soil, and to create areas of more level land. These devices, known generically as "terracing," have been most recently described for the Maya lowlands by B. L. Turner (1974a; 1976b; chap. 9 below).

Terracing often occurs on land higher and steeper than the slopes normally used for swiddening. It involves the construction of stone walls, often of some bulk, by a work force presumably cooperative, in the sense that each terrace would have been built by more men than would subsequently have been needed to cultivate the land it created. Whether cooperation was voluntary or coerced by secular or numinous sanctions cannot be inferred from the immediate archaeological evidence.

Similar corporate activity may be detected in the extension of cultivation into waterlogged bottomlands, where *bajo,* or marginal river-valley swamp, is converted into drained land by the construction of raised (ridged) fields. These have been the subject of much recent study and discussion, notably on the Candelaria River in the western lowlands (Siemens and Puleston 1972; J. E. S. Thompson 1974), in southern Quintana Roo (Harrison 1977), around Tikal (Harrison 1977; Dahlin 1976a), and in northern Belize (Hammond 1974b:188–89, 1975; Puleston 1977). They consist of drainage canals, dug in parallel or grid formation a few meters apart, the upcast from which is piled between canals to create an area of terrain raised above the water table; the similarity to chinampas is close.

Periodic cleaning of the canals and the casting up of muck onto the raised fields increases their elevation and counters erosion; the upcast organic detritus (vegetable matter, fish feces, defunct water creatures, and so forth) from the bottom ooze renews fertility. The canals themselves provide easy access to the fields for cultivation and the removal of produce by canoe, and also act as fish refuges; they may even be intentionally operated as fish hatcheries (J. E. S. Thompson 1974). Bruce Dahlin (personal communication) has pointed out the symbiotic relationship that would exist if, as he suggests, cacao was being grown on the fields, with the midges that pollinate cacao breeding in the canals, their eggs forming a source of fish food, and the resultant fish feces a mulch for the cacao trees.

Whether cacao was cropped in this artificial econiche is a matter of debate, but the conditions would be conducive to it in raised fields in general (Wright et al. 1959; Thorold 1972), and in particular in the studied case of the Rio Hondo and Rio Nuevo raised field complexes around such sites as Nohmul and San Estevan in northern Belize (Hammond 1974b; Dahlin 1976a). Puleston (1977) is of the opinion that maize rather than cacao was cropped, citing the presence of maize pollen and the absence of cacao pollen in cores taken from the beds of interfield canals. Although maize may have been one of the crops, we might note that the fields are immediately adjacent (less than 50 meters in some cases) to the limestone ridge terrain currently used for maize swiddening, and that pollen could easily have been transported this distance by wind or rainfall runoff. The absence of cacao pollen is similarly not a conclusive argument, since "cacao does not shed pollen and its survival in canal silts is extremely unlikely" (Thorold: personal communication). In other words, even if cacao was grown on the raised fields, it would leave no palynological evidence, so one cannot argue *ex silentio* for its noncultivation; the point is therefore moot according to the botanical evidence. Other evidence, however, may be taken into account. The limestone ridges are not (in northern Belize at least) the most suitable terrain for cacao, which needs constant water at the roots, and the region's reputation as a cacao-producing area at the time of the conquest (Roys 1931:52) cannot easily be equated with inland cultivation. The planned investigation of one of the best-preserved raised-field complexes within the purlieus of the major site of Nohmul, lying just off the ridge and with the canals still open and water-filled even in the dry season, should provide us with more evidence, though not necessarily more certainty, in the dispute.

Vertical expansion thus raises a number of questions—about construction logistics and about the motives for expansion and cooperative construction—that have important implications for the degree of organization of Maya society at the time when the terrace and raised-field facilities were constructed. I shall return to this subject below.

Temporal expansion. This mode, which is more closely related than lateral or vertical expansion to the definition of *intensification* used in this book, involves an increase in the number of person-hours devoted to each unit area of cultivated land. In lateral expansion the absolute number of hours will rise, as will the proportion of the total work-time available in the community; in the temporal mode of expansion they are focused on a constant rather than an enlarging area of land. This focusing can take two forms—simultaneous and extended temporal expansion.

Simultaneous expansion involves the labor of more people at the same time, carrying out any task more quickly or allowing it, as with weeding, to be carried out more often. It is one way of raising yield per unit area by removing crop competitors more efficiently. *Extended temporal expansion* is the cultivation of the same area for longer—fitting in an extra crop or using the plot for an extra year. The increase in weed growth with successive years in swiddening probably means that extended temporal expansion will mean increasing simultaneous labor input also, so the two forms are to some extent interdependent.

Temporal expansion may or may not covary with a decreased fallow period, but the total area of land required by a community of any given size will clearly decrease with the degree of temporal expansion. Since land closest to the settlement would be worked first, the decrease in area would also result in decreased journey-to-work time, and an effective increase in the working day. The increased labor input may be more cost effective than extensive swiddening even without the stimulus of pressure on resources, provided that the critical mass of labor necessary to operate such a system is available and controlled.

A variant form of temporal expansion is multi-cropping in a single year. Here the additional person-hours might have been devoted to only a slight increase in the amount of weeding, since fewer weeds would have had time to develop between crops. Moreover, the crop return per person-hour invested would rise because a higher proportion of the time was being devoted directly to cultivation rather than to ancillary occupations such as clearing land. On the other hand the direct process of cultivation might be considered to include mulching plus the time needed to collect and transport mulch material. The observation by several workers (e.g., Culbert, Magers, and Spencer: chap. 8 below) of multi-cropping in southern Peten, Guatemala, on soils not notably more fertile than those of much of the rest of the Maya lowlands, suggests that even with usual swiddening methods, let alone the more highly organized creation of artificial econiches involved in terracing and raised fields, we may have substantially underestimated carrying capacity by overlooking this form of temporal expansion.

Specific expansion. This involves an increase in the number, variety, and productivity of crops exploited. While it remains largely unchallenged that maize, beans, and root crops such as camote and yuca (cassava) bulked largest in Maya agriculture and diet, a case for the exploitation of tree crops, especially ramon, has been made by Puleston (1968a), who has also shown that chultunes can be used for the storage of ramon nuts. Although I accept Puleston's data on the nutritional value and yield of ramon trees, I feel that the reputation of ramon nuts as a famine food among the Postclassic and historic Maya indicates that it was not a preferred food for humans. The stands of ramon trees around Maya ruins first remarked by Lundell (1937) are more likely to be the result of selective culling—that is, of not cutting down a potentially useful tree—than of intentional arboriculture. Nevertheless, when the overall nutrition of the Classic Maya began to deteriorate (Saul 1972) while the number, size, and density of settlements increased, and when competition ensued, erupting into warfare (Hammond 1974a; Webster 1976), then the ramon, despised but not ignored, may have provided an invaluable supplement to stretch the Maya diet and extend the collapse into a long drawn-out agony rather than a quick cultural death.

The ethnobotanic knowledge of the historic Maya (Roys 1931) indicates that the pre-Hispanic Maya could use a large number of uncultivated plants and trees for subsistence. Expanded resource procurement could thus presumably occur simply by increasing the number of person-hours spent in collecting; the only limits would be the maximum economic distance, the presence of others' territories, and the rate of reproduction of the species utilized. Such expansion would be archaeologically impossible to detect in the usual Maya lowland contexts, since no special equipment would be necessary for collection, processing, or consumption besides that already utilized for cultivated plants; a wooden mortar and stone metate and mano would suffice for all. The difference in carrying capacity generated by minimal, optimal, and maximal exploitation of such resources might well exceed differences caused by many more formal and archaeologically detectable modes of expansion or intensification.

Even in formal cultivation plots, whether swidden clearings or constructed terraces and raised fields, more than one species can be grown simultaneously. Many species can be cultivated at once within a complex schedule based on the varying maturation rates of different crops.

The symbiosis of maize and beans, the latter twining up the stalks of the former, is a natural (Flannery 1973:291) as well as an agricultural commonplace, as is the growth of squash species on the ground surface between the corn plants. Root crops can be grown below ground in a field occupied by another crop without a commensurate increase in horizontal area, and useful trees such as the cohune palm or copal and ritually important ones such as the yaxche are even now left standing in swidden plots. Some root crops, such as cassava, continue to be cultivated after corn production in the same field has ceased. The variety of plants that can be productively juxtaposed within a small space has been well illustrated by Robert Netting (1977) from African and Mesoamerican ethnographic evidence. Netting has also emphasized the subsistence importance of dooryard gardens, where the fertility of the soil is enhanced by mulching with household refuse and the feces of both human and animal inhabitants.

In studying the Classic Maya settlement around the Lubaantun ceremonial center I estimated the area of a *plazuela* house-compound at twenty-five hundred square meters, ample to support the trees required by the household and still leave space for intensively fertilized garden plots (Hammond 1975:91–93). For ventilation, light, drainage, and defense, the *plazuelas* occupied the tops of knolls, so, because of the thin soil and degree of eroison, the sites were not desirable for swidden. The perimeter wall of the basal platform of the house compound not only created a level surface for habitation, but also acted as a terrace and silt trap to retain soil on the top of the knoll. Thus a marginal econiche was rendered useful in several ways. The artificial environment of the *plazuela* platform should perhaps be regarded as a special case of intensive cultivation, with emphasis on nonstaple crops.

Not only can the quantity of crops grown be increased, but also their quality. A. V. Kirkby (1973: fig. 48*a, b*) has shown how mean corncob length has increased through time from 5000 B.C. to the present in highland Mexico, and how yield per hectare has simultaneously increased at an even greater rate (perhaps because cob diameter and thus seed-bearing surface increases as well as length). Whether this increase in size was a conscious development, the result of deliberate seed selection, or the result of a random but beneficial process, we cannot know. At present there is no evidence from the Maya lowlands to parallel that from Mexico, although the preservation of carbonized plant material at the Early Formative through Late Classic site of Cuello in Belize gives some cause for hope. From data such as Kirkby's, increases in unit-area productivity under different temporal regimes can be calculated to give a band of carrying capacities attainable at different periods, based solely on cultivars that survive archaeologically. Root crops present a problem; not only do they survive less well than seeds, even in well-preserved deposits, but they are less likely to be recognized in excavation and more susceptible to damage by wet- or dry-sieve recovery methods. Furthermore plants reproducing vegetatively may reproduce at a different rate from those cultivated by cloning.

Although I have described each of these possible modes of agricultural expansion—spatial, temporal, and specific—separately, it is clear that they could operate in concert and with mutually reinforcing effect. Both spatial and specific expansion demand a greater absolute and probably relative investment of time for the construction of terrace walls, digging of canals, clearing of larger areas for swidden, cropping the same area more often, weeding it over a longer period, and planting more species in the same plot. Time is available as a direct function of population level and density, given a constant age and sex composition. The more people present within a specified area at a given moment, the more work-time is potentially available. Since more people equals greater consumption, a prudent community will satisfy demand with the least possible expenditure of energy in order not to increase demand by the effort involved in satisfying it.

The present swidden regime exactly fulfills this necessity, producing maximum return for minimum effort, in the given context of low population density. The land utilized is that best suited to swidden—sloping, well-drained limestone soils—given a level of demand that permits a long-fallow cycle. Steep hill soils and *bajo* are not utilized because the present population is neither dense nor organized enough to construct and maintain the artificial econiches that would be needed. That these soils *could* be used productively seems unquestionable.

Archaeologists have tended to extrapolate back from the ethnographic and historic milpa regime into the Classic period, although they are well aware of the demographic and cultural differences between the Classic and the present situation. Studies of agricultural intensification have been implicitly based on the notion that terracing, the use of raised fields, multi-cropping, and other ways of getting more food out of the same area of land were innovations that supplemented an existing swidden system by utilizing hitherto marginal terrain or increasing the efficiency of the swidden cycle itself.

What we have not considered to date is the possibility that the artificial environments of silt-trap terraces and perennially productive raised fields may have been created deliberately, under no compulsion of population pressure, as a conscious maximization of resources. By making a small area close to the settlement extremely productive, it would be possible to avoid long journey-to-work times; the extra effort involved in the construction of the artificial econiche would be largely or entirely offset by the time thus saved. This effort might only be feasible with a certain degree of cooperative labor, however—one obtainable only from a population more densely clustered and more socially organized than the Postclassic and historic inhabitants of the central and southern Maya lowlands. Given this critical mass of population size, density, and organization, none of which need have been close to the maximal levels of the Classic period, it may have been a sounder investment of labor to create and maintain a highly productive and easily protected econiche close to the settlement than to engage in extensive swiddening at some distance, with the onerous clearing of new or second growth each year. The institution of swiddening could then be seen as a response to increasing population pressure, with new and less labor-efficient means of production becoming necessary as demand increased, but as the labor supply increased also.

The initial pattern of penetration of the central and southern Maya lowlands seems likely to have been riverine, exploiting the greater variety of resources in and adjacent to the stream, its banks, and marginal swamps. In this situation the raised-field econiche in the swamp margins could have been created early in the Formative. In the Early Formative (2500–1300 B.C., calibrated ^{14}C dates) both architecture and trade goods (including metates from 150 kilometers away and jade from 400) attest a society of some degree of organization and sophistication at the Cuello site in northern Belize. A radiocarbon date of 1110 ± 230 b.c., calibrating to 1400 B.C., for a post from the bank of a raised-field canal in the region indicates that such an artificial environment was already in use by the end of the Early Formative (Puleston 1977). The mollusc evidence from Cuello indicates intensive exploitation of swamp-dwelling species through the Early Formative, but an absence of species characteristic of cleared and burnt-over land. The latter appear in the Middle Formative, suggesting the introduction of swiddening (L. Feldman, personal communication). It would therefore accord with the present evidence, sparse though it is, to suggest an initial phase of intensive exploitation of riverine and swamp resources, including the construction and cultivation of raised fields for subsistence crops, followed, as population increased, by the exploitation of the limestone ridge for swiddening. The decline of swamp Mollusca in the Middle Formative may be due to the draining of their habitat for raised fields; a more precise tabulation of their occurrence in occupation and midden deposits through the long Early Formative may help to document the beginning of drainage activity.

There is as yet no evidence of the use of terracing in the Formative. This form of artificial environment, occurring not in the river valleys but on hillsides, may have been introduced after swiddening as the result of still-increasing demand. (This speculation is independent from that suggesting the use of raised fields as an early, deliberately chosen means of agricultural production.) What seems certain, in these hypotheses and others, is that the myth of the milpa is moribund; we may not, and do not, any longer think of swiddening on the ethnographic and historical model as the sole support of Classic Maya society and civilization.

4

DON S. RICE
Department of Social Sciences, The Florida State Museum

Population Growth and Subsistence Alternatives in a Tropical Lacustrine Environment

The increasing disillusionment with the assumption that swidden-grown maize was the staple crop of Late Classic Maya populations in the central Maya lowlands has led several investigators to propose hypotheses on cropping alternatives, notably the use of root crops (Bronson 1966) or ramon (Puleston 1968a), and the intensification of the swidden system (Sanders 1972). Previous studies have discussed one or another of these subsistence options while attempting to construct processual models for the origin of Maya civilization (D. E. Puleston and O. S. Puleston 1971; O. S. Puleston and D. E. Puleston 1974) or for the nature of the Maya "collapse" (Sanders 1973). Such options have not been reviewed with respect to the dynamics of a single community in its own particular environmental context. To assess adequately the probability and potential of agricultural alternatives, they must be framed within an evolutionary system, as integrated yet flexible crop complexes or strategies that may exhibit both spatial and temporal variability.

Recent settlement analyses centered on the basins of Lakes Yaxha and Sacnab, Peten, have provided the chance to investigate the ramifications of population growth within an ecologically heterogeneous region that was probably sociopolitically as well as geographically defined (Rice 1976). In this essay I shall attempt to establish and compare maximum hypothetical population densities with potential subsistence productivity within such a region. The value of the exercise is the opportunity to evaluate subsistence options and constraints within a localized segment of Maya society through time, and to isolate periods of stress or change that conceivably influenced the configuration of that society. The possible subsistence choices examined here will, I hope, elaborate processes important not only to the evolution of Maya society but to tropical land use in general.[1]

THE YAXHA–SACNAB PROJECT

Environment

The Department of Peten is characterized geologically by a series of east-west folds and ridges of Miocene and Eocene limestone that form a low and uneven surface varying between 100 meters and 300 meters in elevation above sea level. Like the Yucatan Peninsula, the northern Peten is a continuation of a karst limestone plateau marked by sinks, poljes, and ridges, by caverns and underground streams, and by a scarcity of surface water (Stevens 1964). The broken topography of the southern Peten and the Maya Mountains of southern Belize is tied to the Antillean orogenic belt, a region of geological thrusting and mountain building that sweeps east from the Guatemala highlands into the lowlands (Ower 1928). These folded east-west ranges of Antillean origin formed, with the hilly karsted region to the north, a line of depressions or troughs on an east-west fault fracture roughly coinciding with 17° north latitude that have filled with water and become the central Peten lake system (fig. 4.1).

The central Peten lakes may be generally described as shallow basins of interior drainage. The principal lakes, from west to east, include Sacpuy (or Seipuy), Peten-Itza, Petenxil (or Petenchel), Quexil (also seen as Eckixil and Exiquil), Salpeten (variously called Sucpeten or Petensuc), Macanche, Yaxha, and Sacnab. Lake Perdida follows the same east-west axis, but falls west of the actual fault-line depression. Within the almost-100-kilometer-long axis of the chain, small streams may discharge into the large bodies of water, but there is no surface outflow to the sea.

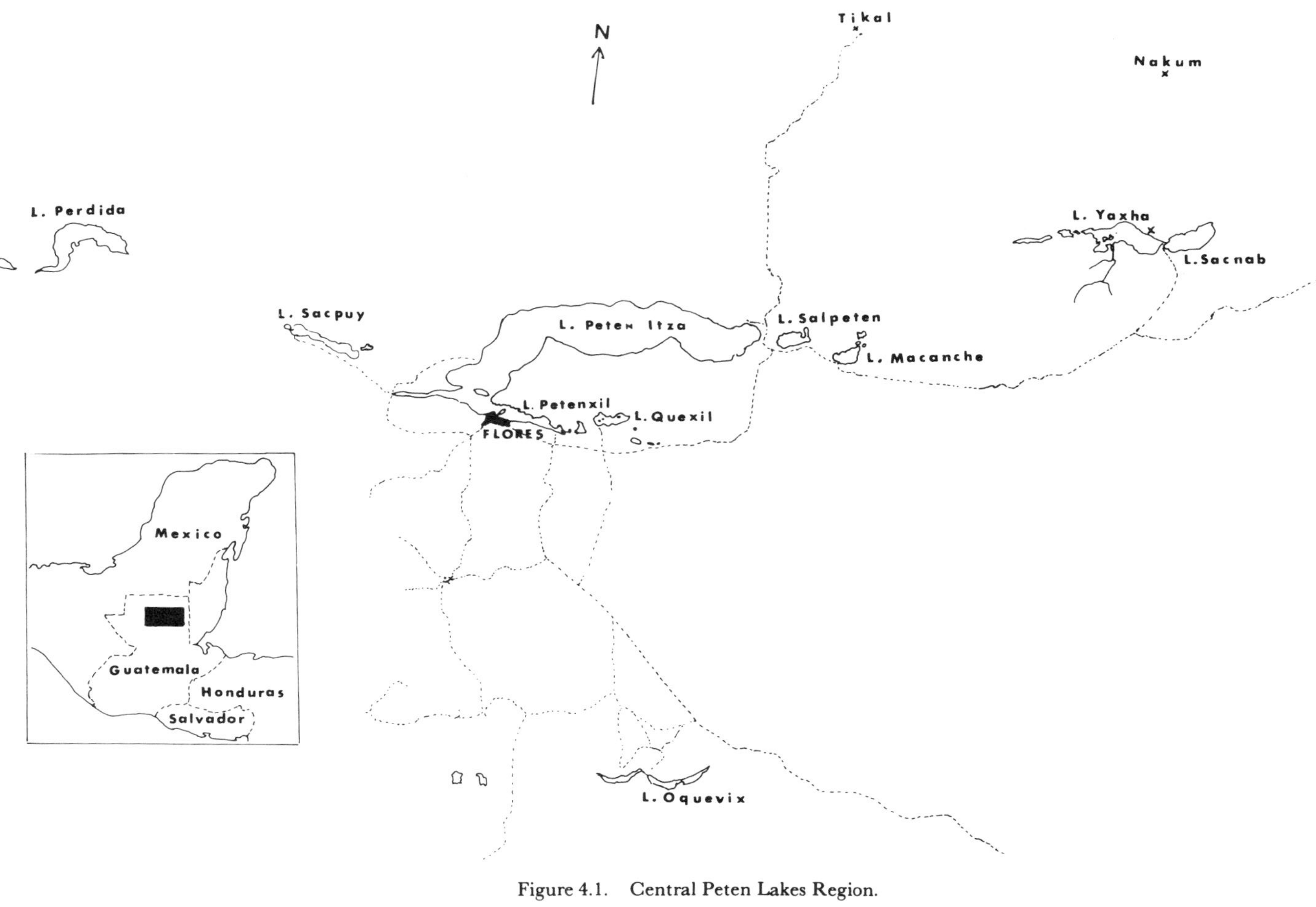

Figure 4.1. Central Peten Lakes Region.

The karsted and wrench-faulted rocks of the central Peten, together with considerable relief, have produced a number of different soil types. Although the dominant rocks are dolomitic limestone, sufficient variability in parent material, altitude, drainage, and vegetation cover exists to produce soil suites with varying fertility, friability, and erodability (Simmons, Tarano, and Pinto 1959).

Of the thirteen soil series that have been identified in the Maya Central Zone, more than half are directly accessible from one or another of the lakes. These soils include the highly fertile calcimorphic rendzinas of the Macanche and Uaxactun series; the thinner, but equally fertile, black calcareous lithosols of the Chachalte and Yaxha series; and the leached reddish-brown lateritic soils of the Chachaclun series. In the areas of permanent or intermittent flooding, the hydromorphic soils of the Sacpuy, Yaloch, and Eckixil series have developed (Simmons, Tarano, and Pinto 1959; Stevens 1964). The significance of the existing soil variation cannot be overstated, as soils have a great influence on the natural vegetation, the water resources, the rate and character of natural and man-made perturbations, and the food-production capabilities of aboriginal and contemporary populations. Such ecological variation would be expected to give rise to many different settlement and subsistence configurations in time and space.

Research Program

In 1973–74 archaeological surveys were undertaken in the vicinity of Lakes Yaxha and Sacnab as part of a historical ecology project directed by Edward S. Deevey and conducted under the auspices of the Florida State Museum and the National Science Foundation. This multidisciplinary effort resulted from a recognized need for intensive environmental analyses coordinated with archaeological surveys within areas of both major Classic and Postclassic occupation. The stated goals of the project were "to search the sedimentary record for evidence of Maya land use; to learn enough of the special limnology, botany, and archaeology to evaluate the record of airborne and waterborne substances; and to evaluate the basin-wide budgets of water, carbon, and major cations and anions at the present time and as they were modified by Maya exploitation of the environment . . ." (Deevey 1973). Lakes Yaxha and Sacnab were chosen as a research target becasue the Yaxha Basin is the location of the architectural remains of two Maya organizational centers: the Classic site of Yaxha on the northern shore (Hellmuth 1972), and the Postclassic site of Topoxte, which occupies the several islands in the lake (Bullard 1970). In addition, Bullard had reported the existence of house ruins and a minor center in the Yaxha-Sacnab vicinity during his northeast Peten surveys (1960). The limnological, hydrological, and biological studies of the historical ecology project in the area were coordinated with an archaeological settlement survey of the Yaxha-Sacnab basins, the explicit objective of which was to provide data on the characteristics and location of Maya occupation around the lakes that could be correlated with ecological information and incorporated into ecosystem models.

An underlying contention of this study was that it should be possible, using time- and space-controlled settlement analyses, to estimate the growth of archaeologically identified populations within a specific region and to infer from archaeological data the plausible agricultural systems for support of the population. It was also assumed that the present vegetation is not so different from that of Maya times as to preclude recognition of prehistoric microenvironments of varying potential, requiring varying tactics for utilization. The field study itself consisted of three phases: the mapping of settlement remains within the basins; a test-pitting program to control the temporal factor in interpreting the settlement pattern data; and an analysis of modern vegetation within the research area.

The three operations all took place within a geographical entity defined as the "Yaxha-Sacnab region," which is assumed to delimit the immediate resource area available to a population, and upon which a discussion of environmental variability and carrying capacity can be based. Hammond's (1974a) lead in applying Thiessen polygon construction to the Late Classic sites of the Maya Lowlands was followed in outlining a Yaxha-Sacnab region. The polygon for Yaxha was constructed from nearest neighbor vectors to the sites of Tikal, Nakum, Naranjo, Tikinchakan, Ucanal, and

San Clemente, and it is most probable that the 239 square kilometers encompassed do include the "sustaining" or residential area aligned with the civic center of Yaxha. Within this unit, which contains the total range of microenvironmental zones (as might be defined by soils, vegetation, hydrography, or topography) available to the populations around the lakes, it is possible to attempt reconstruction of the demographic characteristics and natural productivity of the settlement system.

The actual archaeological surveys took place within ten transects radiating out north or south from the shores of the two lakes. These transects, each 500 meters × 2 kilometers, represent a stratified random sample that includes percentages of known microtopographic variation relative to the total heterogeneity evident in the region. They incorporate approximately 25 percent of the area within the 200-meter contours used by the natural scientists to define the lake basins. The ruins of Classic Yaxha were skirted by one transect, and an eleventh survey strip was placed on one of the islands of Topoxte. Mapping of settlement remains was achieved by a variant of the pace-and-map technique developed at Tikal (Fry 1969:44). Once each transect map was complete, a random 25 ± 2 percent of the mound loci in each survey strip were sampled by test pitting, with the individual mound as the sampling unit. The test pits were located so as to sample mound construction, on the assumption that the structures would be datable from the cultural materials found within them.

A quantitative vegetation survey was initiated for the purpose of obtaining a gross measure of relative potential productivity within the region (Rice 1977a). Vegetation observations, primarily species counts and recording of growth characteristics, were made within thirty 10 × 100-meter transects strategically distributed among the archaeological survey strips. A vegetation map of the region was prepared on the basis of correlation between field-survey ground truth and interpreted aerial photographs (fig. 4.2). Four major vegetation units were distinguished: tall upland forest, 41.8 percent; tall forest of moist slopes, 28.1 percent; swamp forest, 18.6 percent; and swamp thicket, 11.5 percent. As might be expected, the four units are closely related to topographic variation, the first two associations being upland zones that do not experience inundation but vary in drainage and fertility, and the latter two being lowland types that are flooded for at least part of the year.

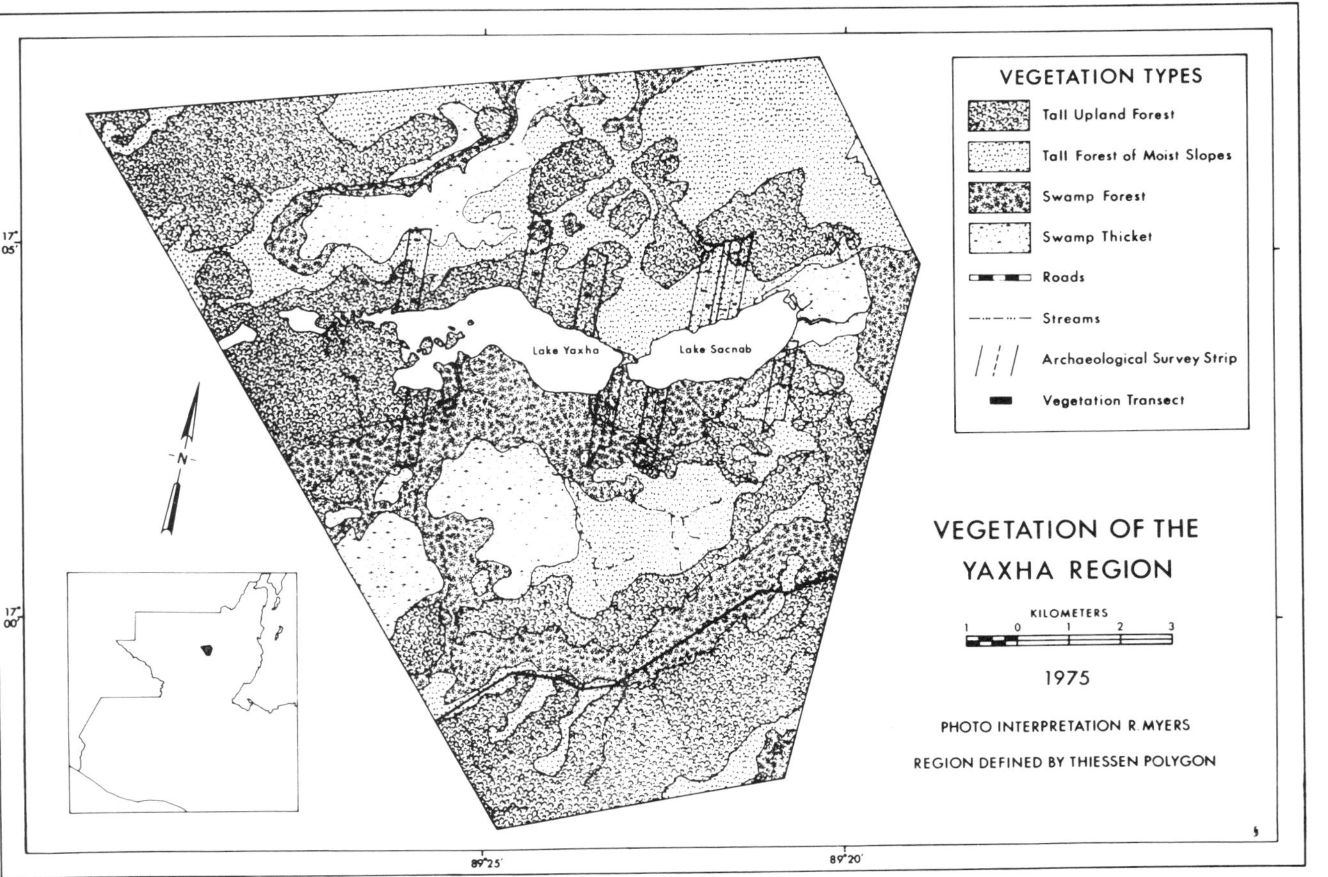

Figure 4.2. Vegetation map of the Lake Yaxha Region.

Population Estimates

The Yaxha-Sacnab project relied on mound counts and test-pit-derived chronologies as the foundation for population estimation. The excavated sample of mound loci provided percentages of mounds occupied per vegetation zone for each period of Maya occupation that could be extrapolated to the total mound population recovered during the surveys. These estimates, in turn, allowed the computed population densities to be extrapolated to the region as a whole. Sherburne F. Cook (1972:3) has suggested that field procedures must produce estimates of four essential variables: the quantity of the element being considered; the duration of the complex being studied; the turnover rate or life expectancy of the unit; and the magnitude of association between population and that particular element at any given time. I have presented a fuller discussion of the subject elsewhere (Rice 1976), but I should briefly describe the methods I used to deal with these four variables in relation to the crucial element in my investigation—the residential structure.

Determination of the quantity and density of residential structures for any sample area requires consideration of two sources of ambiguity: the problem of hidden house mounds and uncertainty as to the function of a given structure. A few hidden structures have been recovered at Tikal (Puleston 1973:165–68), and in two instances in the Yaxha-Sacnab area (Rice 1976:261); at both sites they appear to have been constructed prior to the Late Classic. Without systematic means of accounting for them, but believing their proportion to the total to be small, we have ignored their distortion of density estimates. Haviland estimated that 16 percent of all mounds at Tikal were nonresidential (1970:193). Although this proportion probably varied through time and space, it is used here as a constant factor to eliminate structures not intended for habitation.

The periods of occupation for residential structures were defined through test excavation and based on the duration of artifact complexes. For time markers, I relied on the familiar general groupings of Middle Preclassic (1000–250 B.C.), Late Preclassic (250 B.C.–A.D. 250), Early Classic (A.D. 250–550), Late Classic (A.D. 550–880), and Terminal Classic (post-A.D. 880).

Discussing the turnover rate or life expectancy of residential structures within any given ceramic phase, Haviland has suggested that at least during the Early and Late Classic periods more than 93 percent of the structures were contemporaneous, and he has presented evidence in support of a high degree of continuous residence (1969:429, 1970:191). Even assuming continuous occupation of structures, it is obvious that population does not increase immediately by some increment of structures as one archaeological phase ends and another begins. A workable approach might be to assume contemporaneity of all structures occupied during a particular phase for the closing date of that phase. This gives a population figure by which the phase might be characterized, and a time-population curve constructed from end-of-phase estimates rather than from midpoints assumes growth (or decline) over each phase as a whole.

Estimates for the actual number of inhabitants associated with each occupied structure have ranged from 5 to 8.3, based on ethnographic and/or ethnohistoric population records of Maya house and household size (Haviland 1970, 1972). Utilizing a constant of dwelling floor space per individual developed by Raoul Naroll from cross-cultural surveys (1962), Puleston (1973:183) recently arrived at an average of 5.4 inhabitants per structure for Tikal house structures. This figure was adopted for computing the Yaxha-Sacnab population size.

Given the above data, it is possible to generate preliminary population estimates for the Yaxha-Sacnab survey transects (see table 4.1). A total of 586 structures were mapped within the survey samples, and the percentage of structures occupied during each period, as determined by analyses of test excavation data, are as follows:

Middle Preclassic	*Late Preclassic*	*Early Classic*	*Late Classic*	*Terminal Classic*
9.4%	22.8%	38.3%	79.2%	8.1%

Population figures are produced according to the formula:

(number of mounds) x (percentage of occupation) x (residence factor) x (number of occupants)

A demographic curve based on the combined survey strip estimates can be established by plotting the maximum population for each phase at the time corresponding to the close of that phase (fig. 4.3). Although the intervals are rather coarse and the

Table 4.1. Population Estimates for Yaxha-Sacnab Transects

	Middle Preclassic	*Late Preclassic*	*Early Classic*	*Late Classic*	*Terminal Classic*
Mounds	55.1	133.6	224.4	464.1	47.5
Residences	46.3	112.2	188.5	389.8	39.9
Population	249.9	605.9	1,017.9	2,104.9	215.5

dynamics of growth from one point to the next may be highly variable, the graph shows log-linear, or exponential, population growth through time until the end of the Classic period. The rate of growth, given by the slope of the line, was constant at approximately 0.17 percent per year until the Late Classic. The existence of a "collapse" following the Late Classic is clearly shown by the data, a decline that brings measurable occupation back within the Middle Preclassic range. The implication is that through time there was an increasing population—and, presumably, subsistence demand.

Such a curve is nothing more than the growth curve for recovered structures, and multiplication by a correction factor and a constant population per structure adds no new information. A more useful population figure in discussion of environmental utilization is the average population density per square kilometer, per time period:

Middle Preclassic	*Late Preclassic*	*Early Classic*	*Late Classic*	*Terminal Classic*
24.9	60.6	101.8	210.5	21.6

In assuming these population figures for the entire region, as is necessary in order to discuss the utilization of that region, a possible bias should be recognized. The survey design was preoccupied with that geographical area defined as the drainage basins, the major contributor of the pollen rain. Because the sampling universe was centered on the lakes, lying at the core of the Thiessen polygon, the population data may be inflated by a lacustrine focus for settlement during those periods when such a residence choice could be accommodated by available land. Bullard's map of his survey route in the Northeast Peten (1960:356) shows that ruin groups occur throughout the Yaxha-Sacnab region, and the existence of such remains in upland and moist-slope vegetation zones both north and south of the sampling universe has been confirmed. There has not been any systematic

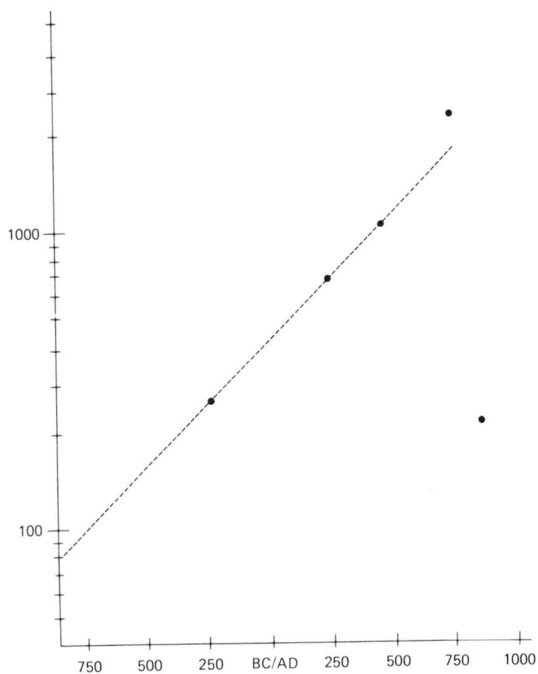

Figure 4.3. Semilog population curve.

mapping of these more peripheral formations, however, and chronological information is lacking from the perimeters of the region.

Preferred topography for residence location is not arranged concentrically around the lakes, but rather in a ribbonlike mosaic throughout the region, a patchwork for which sampling close to the lakes was the only basis for population projection. Variation in settlement density is assumed to be no more discontinuous than the vegetation categories, and the survey transects reflect the percentage vegetation composition for the region, as shown in table 4.2.

While *bajos* are underrepresented in the sample and uplands overrepresented, the differences are small and probably constitute

Table 4.2. Vegetation Composition, Yaxha-Sacnab Region

Vegetation Type	*Percent of Region*	*Percent of Transects*
Tall upland	41.8	44.1
Moist slope	28.1	28.3
Swamp forest	18.6	22.6
Swamp thicket	11.5	5.0

a small fraction of the uncertainty in any extrapolation from a small area to a large one. Hence no special weighting procedure seems necessary, and population densities for the Yaxha-Sacnab region are inferred from the sample. If a bias is created by the possibility of a lacustrine focus for settlement, it is probably confined to the earliest period of occupation. With growth, space would be at more of a premium, settlement more evenly dispersed through the region, and assumed densities more legitimate. In this regard, regional estimates represent maxima for the area through time, suitable for the discussion of different subsistence strategies and the Yaxha-Sacnab region vis-à-vis other sites.

LAND AVAILABILITY AND LAND REQUIREMENTS

Population densities for any given period can be expressed as an average number of persons per square kilometer, as given above, or in terms of units of arable land. The latter—termed *economic densities* in animal ecology (Allee et al. 1949)—would seem appropriate here because we are attempting to suggest how people might relate to environmental heterogeneity, not just to a total region. While vegetation as it exists today is not necessarily an accurate indicator of productivity or land use in aboriginal times, the four community types mapped at Yaxha-Sacnab demonstrably represent increasing degrees of drainage difficulty from upland or steep slope to wet *bajo* as well as variation in inherent fertility. If we assume that drainage and concomitant characteristics were important to Maya agriculture, but we do not define any land category as unusable, we can express four measures of economic density in terms of population per successive increments of available land in the region (minus standing water): tall upland forest (TU); tall upland forest and forest of moist slopes (TU & MS); tall upland forest, moist slope forest, and swamp forest (TU, MS, & SF); and tall upland forest, moist slope forest, swamp forest, and swamp thicket (TU, MS, SF, & ST), the last embracing the entire region. Reciprocals of these density figures express the actual amount of land available, in hectares, per individual of the population, per time period, and per defined increment unit (see table 4.3).

Taking the Middle Preclassic period to explain the implications

Table 4.3. Economic Densities for the Yaxha-Sacnab Region

	TU	*TU & MS*	*TU, MS, & SF*	*TU, MS, SF, & ST*
Middle Preclassic				
Density per square kilometers	57.2	34.2	27.0	23.9
Hectares available per person	1.75	2.92	3.70	4.18
Late Preclassic				
Density per square kilometers	139.1	83.2	65.7	58.1
Hectares available per person	.72	1.20	1.52	1.72
Early Classic				
Density per square kilometer	229.8	137.4	108.6	96.1
Hectares available per person	.44	.73	.92	1.04
Late Classic				
Density per square kilometer	486.0	290.6	229.6	203.1
Hectares available per person	.21	.34	.44	.49

of these figures, if the maximum population (as estimated for the close of the period) were to rely only on the upland forest vegetation areas as a base for agriculture, 1.75 hectares would be available per person for cropping. If the adjacent moist slopes were also cultivated, the population density decreasing, each individual would have 2.92 hectares for support. The addition of seasonally dry and then wet *bajos* increases land availability per person to 3.7 hectares and 4.18 hectares respectively.

Having proposed a table of economic densities for the Yaxha-Sacnab region through time, we can proceed to establish the support potentials of various staple crops and levels of agricultural intensification (see table 4.4). Sanders (1973:342) has computed general crop yields for maize, root crops, and ramon, and the land required per person to ensure a minimum necessary annual caloric intake for four classes of cropping: forest fallow (1:6 rotation ratio), bush fallow (1:3 rotation ratio), grass fallow (1:1 rotation ratio), and permanent cultivation (no rotation). The land requirement figures must be adjusted if surplus production is needed to make up loss margin, tribute, and/or trade. Sanders allows a surplus requirement of one-third of the yield per hectare of agricultural land, and per-capita land estimates are adjusted accordingly. The proportion of total production necessary for tax or tribute depends on the growth and degree of centralized authority. Sanders's percentage is not to be considered invariant; rather it is a useful approximation for the purpose of illustrating the need to support evolving sociopolitical and economic structure.

Table 4.4. Land Requirement per Person (in Hectares)*

Stable Crop	Forest Fallow	Bush Fallow	Grass Fallow	Permanent Cultivation
Maize				
Basic subsistence	1.3	1.0	0.65	
Plus surplus	1.92	1.52	.97	
Root Crops				
Basic subsistence	0.53	0.40	0.27	
Plus surplus	.79	.60	.41	
Ramon				
Basic subsistence				0.17
Plus surplus				.26

*(adapted from Sanders 1973:342–43)

SUBSISTENCE OPTIONS THROUGH TIME

Comparison of land availability and land requirements under different cropping categories makes it possible to evaluate the feasibility of subsistence options. Such a comparison is presented in tables 4.5–4.8, which give, for four time periods, the ratios of economic densities to the amounts of land required per person for each cultivar and cropping strategy. Estimates have been established for conditions of both no-surplus and surplus production. If the quotient of any cell is less than 1.00, the particular subsistence mode involved is not sufficiently productive to support the projected population density under the land stricture imposed. Cells showing quotients of 1.00 or more, on the other hand, indicate combinations which remain practicable at the end of the phase. Likewise, the various ratios permit discussion of the degree of feasibility for any option, or set of options. These determinations are based on magnitudes of population, land types, and productivity, however, and findings must be tempered by consideration of the compatibility of land, crop, and management characteristics.

Middle Preclassic

It is apparent that if subsistence activities in the Middle Preclassic (table 4.5) were confined to areas that today support tall upland vegetation, sufficient land would be available to support

Table 4.5. Feasibility Ratios for the Middle Preclassic Period

Land Required per Person (in hectares)

Land Categories	*Subsistence Only*							*Assuming Surplus*						
	Maize			*Root Crops*			*Ramon*	*Maize*			*Root Crops*			*Ramon*
	1:6	*1:3*	*1:1*	*1:6*	*1:3*	*1:1*	*Permanent*	*1:6*	*1:3*	*1:1*	*1:6*	*1:3*	*1:1*	*Permanent*
TU	1:35	1.75	2.69	3.30	4.38	6.48	10.29	.91	1.15	1.80	2.22	2.92	4.27	6.73
TU & MS	2.25	2.92	4.49	5.51	7.30	10.81	17.18	1.52	1.92	3.01	3.70	4.87	7.12	11.23
TU, MS, & SF	2.78	3.70	5.69	6.98	9.25	13.70	21.70	1.93	2.43	3.81	4.68	6.16	9.02	14.23
TU, MS, SF, & ST	3.22	4.18	6.43	7.89	10.45	15.48	24.59	2.18	2.75	4.31	5.29	6.97	10.20	16.08

the population size calculated for the period. Even surplus production on the order of 33 percent could be accommodated by all combinations except perhaps a forest fallow cycle of swidden agriculture based on maize and confined to tall upland forest. While no firm evidence supports any of the staple crop alternatives over another, my inclination is to accept maize because of the conspicuous presence of *Zea* and of disturbance species common to successional vegetation in cleared areas in pollen profiles from Lakes Quexil (Brooks et al. 1973; Vaughan 1976), Petenxil (Cowgill and Hutchinson 1966), and Yaxha and Sacnab (Deevey 1976), at levels corresponding to this phase. In addition, Middle Preclassic mounds are confined to the tall upland zones, and their dispersal on the upland soils around the lakes suggests consideration of the requirements of some type of swidden agriculture. At least three distinct sociopolitical zones had formed by the end of the Middle Preclassic, including that of the center of Yaxha, each exhibiting architectural attributes indicative of civic or ceremonial function (Rice 1977b). It appears that even during this earliest period of occupation specialized activities existed that required support from surplus.

Late Preclassic

The Late Preclassic (table 4.6) was a period of continued settlement growth and expansion. By the end of the phase the first indications of possible subsistence stress in the region appear. Pollen profiles constructed from lacustrine cores show both *Zea* and disturbance indicators increasing in the Late Preclassic, but through time it would have been more and more difficult for the population of Yaxha-Sacnab to support itself on maize-based agriculture. Under a growing burden of surplus production, maize could have been cultivated on both upland and moist slope soils at a 1:1 rotation, or on these and seasonally dry swamp-forest soils at a rotation of 1:3. For maize grown without taxation, it would still have been necessary to shorten the fallow period or expand land considerations, or both. In contrast, root crops and ramon remain gainful alternatives regardless of production demands. Stress on

Table 4.6. Feasibility Ratios for the Late Preclassic Period

Land Categories	*Land Required per Person (in hectares)*													
	Subsistence Only							*Assuming Surplus*						
	Maize			*Root Crops*			*Ramon*	*Maize*			*Root Crops*			*Ramon*
	1:6	*1:3*	*1:1*	*1:6*	*1:3*	*1:1*	*Permanent*	*1:6*	*1:3*	*1:1*	*1:6*	*1:3*	*1:1*	*Permanent*
TU	.55	.72	1.11	1.36	1.80	2.67	4.24	.38	.47	.74	.91	1.20	1.75	2.77
TU & MS	.92	1.20	1.85	2.26	3.00	4.44	7.06	.63	.79	1.24	1.52	2.00	2.93	4.62
TU, MS, & SF	1.17	1.52	2.34	2.87	3.80	5.63	8.94	.79	1.00	1.57	1.92	2.53	3.70	5.80
TU, MS, SF, & ST	1.32	1.72	2.65	3.25	4.30	6.37	10.12	.89	1.13	1.77	2.18	2.87	4.20	6.61

preferred terrain, or a shift in subsistence emphasis, or both, is further suggested by the first appearance of residential structures on the moist-slope zones at some time during the phase.

If a short-cycle situation were approached in maize production at Yaxha-Sacnab, the results could have been degradation of the nutrient levels of the soils, reduction of soil water-holding capacity, and the destruction of soil structure to the point where erosion would occur. Intensification, when combined with soil depletion, leads to a reduction of arable land and a decreased caloric yield per capita. The result would undoubtedly be increased dependence on more productive, or nonswidden, food sources and marginal soils. Management practices for the conservation of soil and soil nutrients, such as agricultural terraces like those found in conjunction with Classic Maya settlement in the Rio Bec region (B. L. Turner 1974a), might have been instituted on tall upland and moist-slope zones. Farming could also have been extended to swamp soils, which discourage modern agriculture because of their inherent drainage difficulties and high acidity, through the construction and cultivation of raised fields similar to those reported from the *bajos* of Quintano Roo, Mexico (Harrison 1977).

Unfortunately, no data recovered to date in the Yaxha-Sacnab region suggest the existence of agricultural architecture. That is, we have no more reason to assume intensive agricultural techniques than we have to hypothesize shifts in staple crops or their supplements. It is only possible to demonstrate that, because of population growth and limited land resources of varying quality, subsistence decisions would have been forced to include these alternatives. While swidden was still a viable cropping strategy in the Late Preclassic, we can infer a shortage of certain classes of land and the necessity either to reduce the fallow cycle or to deemphasize maize as a staple crop.

Early Classic

During the Early Classic period (table 4.7), the civic center of Yaxha emerged as truly dominant in the basins, although a number of minor or "satellite" centers in the basins continued to expand. Social differentiation also became more obvious with the

Table 4.7. Feasibility Ratios for the Early Classic Period

Land Categories	Land Required per Person (in hectares)													
	Subsistence Only							*Assuming Surplus*						
	Maize			*Root Crops*			*Ramon*	*Maize*			*Root Crops*			*Ramon*
	1:6	*1:3*	*1:1*	*1:6*	*1:3*	*1:1*	*Permanent*	*1:6*	*1:3*	*1:1*	*1:6*	*1:3*	*1:1*	*Permanent*
TU	.34	.44	.67	.83	1.10	1.63	2.59	.23	.29	.45	.56	.73	1.07	1.69
TU & MS	.56	.73	1.12	1.38	1.83	2.70	4.29	.38	.48	.75	.92	1.22	1.78	2.80
TU, MS, & SF	.71	.92	1.42	1.71	2.30	3.91	5.41	.48	.61	.95	1.16	1.53	2.24	3.54
TU, MS, SF, & ST	.80	1.00	1.60	1.96	2.60	3.85	6.12	.54	.68	1.07	1.32	1.73	2.54	4.00

appearance of "palace" structures and complex residential configurations. The architectural, sculptural, and artifactual manifestations of centralized authority and a complex society suggest that surplus production was essential. Under this stricture, maize can no longer be considered to have been a serious subsistence alternative. Yields would have been sufficient for population support only if all *bajo* soils were rendered cultivable. Cowgill (1961) reports that present populations in Peten employ portions of *bajos* for maize production, but with reduced yields. Further, *bajo* utilization in Peten is limited to the dry season and requires high labor expenditures. Even without need for a significant surplus, maize production would still be restricted to a 1:1 rotation and/or require the employment of *bajos.*

Swidden agriculture based on root crops has the capability to sustain the projected population densities, but by the Early Classic problems with this resource may have occurred. Full fallow production would require planting of swamp-type zones, and a 1:3 cycle could only be accomplished with the incorporation of moist slope or *bajo* soils. Discussions of root-crop cultivation (e.g., Cowgill 1971) have noted the need for well-drained soils; this requirement would tend to eliminate the *bajo* soils and some moist-slope soils from consideration. In addition, root crops have been criticized for being protein deficient. Populations at Yaxha-Sacnab might accrue some benefits by the presence of the lakes because they are the source of an expanded resource base. Amphibians, aquatic reptiles, fish, and shellfish would supplement vegetable proteins and captured terrestrial fauna attracted to cropped lands (Linares 1976). Population growth and the resulting disturbance of habitats must have taken a toll on exploitable game, however, perhaps negating the advantages of the lacustrine setting. Protein deficiencies might have been alleviated to some degree by trade from the Caribbean Coast (Lange 1971). For example, E. S. Wing (1975) has identified remains of many marine vertebrates from the site of Lubaantun; remains of sharks and parrot fish are reported from the site of Tikal (Wing 1974). Marine foodstuffs, though, are unlikely to have been consumed outside of elite households.

While major reliance on short-cycle root cultivation is conceivable, root rotting in less than well-drained soils and the low protein content of known root crops suggest that other alternatives would have been more productive. Among these, dependence on maize seems least likely. Without any evidence of agroengineering in the Yaxha-Sacnab region, it seems likely that by the Early Classic period, if not earlier, cultivation of a staple crop such as ramon in a kitchen garden context was necessary to insure caloric support for the population and the sociopolitical structure.

Late Classic

Whatever subsistence stresses may have been encountered in the Late Preclassic and Early Classic periods, they were apparently faced successfully, for population increased at a more rapid rate during the Late Classic (table 4.8). By the end of the Late Classic period, no conditions existed under which maize could have been the staple crop. If a surplus is assumed, swidden agriculture based on root crops would have been limited to a 1:1 rotation and would of necessity have been grown in part on *bajo* soils—soils that are deemed particularly unsuitable for root crops unless drained. By this time, ramon was almost certainly the important staple in an orchard or kitchen-garden cropping system; indeed, by the end of the Late Classic period the production of all foodstuffs, including, to some degree, ramon, was probably strained.

The tall upland vegetation area is insufficient to provide for all of the ramon production that would have been necessary for support of the Late Classic population. Moist slopes would also have been needed. Ramon is not well adapted for colonization of poorly drained soils (Puleston 1968; Ewel and Myers 1974), from which we may infer that ramon yields to the Maya might have been below maximum on much terrain of comparatively gentle slope. In the Yaxha-Sacnab vegetation samples, the incidence of ramon on moist slopes was diminished; ramon was found growing in only one vegetation transect in seasonal swamp forest, with indices of abundance and growth greatly reduced when compared to ramon in other stands. Sanders (1973:341) has also suggested that nut-bearing trees are highly variable in their yield from year to year, and any deviation from maximum production would demand supplementation through cultivation of some other crop in kitchen gardens or on bajo soils.

Table 4.8. Feasibility Ratios for the Late Classic Period

Land Categories	*Land Required per person (in hectares)*													
	Subsistence Only							*Assuming Surplus*						
	Maize			*Root Crops*			*Ramon*	*Maize*			*Root Crops*			*Ramon*
	1:6	*1:3*	*1:1*	*1:6*	*1:3*	*1:1*	*Permanent*	*1:6*	*1:3*	*1:1*	*1:6*	*1:3*	*1:1*	*Permanent*
TU	.16	.21	.32	.39	.53	.78	1.24	.11	.14	.22	.27	.35	.51	.80
TU & MS	.26	.34	.52	.64	.85	1.25	2.00	.18	.22	.35	.43	.57	.83	1.30
TU, MS, & SF	.34	.44	.68	.83	1.10	1.63	2.59	.23	.29	.45	.56	.73	1.07	1.69
TU, MS, SF, & ST	.38	.49	.75	.92	1.23	1.81	2.88	.26	.32	.51	.62	.82	1.20	1.88

MAYA IMPACT ON THE YAXHA-SACNAB ENVIRONMENT

Whether maize and/or root swidden agriculture was supplanted by ramon arboriculture, or swidden agricultural techniques were pursued into the Late Classic, population growth was accompanied by intensification of the subsistence system and the disappearance of larger vegetation from much of the landscape. The continued decline in arboreal pollen during the periods of Maya occupation in cores from Lakes Petenxil, Quexil, Yaxha, and Sacnab shows this trend clearly. At the high densities of cultivation necessary to support Late Classic populations, nonswidden food sources, such as kitchen gardens, also had some impact. It is almost impossible for any integrated garden complex to recreate the structure of the natural forest and its role within the ecosystem. The fact that produce is acquired by human populations suggests that gardens are a nutrient drain on the soil, however slight. With increasing population and decreasing space, periodic garden shifts would no longer be accommodated and only concerted efforts at organic fertilizing could compensate for harvesting of produce and prevent nutrient depletion. Moreover, the increased area taken up by structures and paved plazas would alter the natural flow of surface waters, and the water-retaining quality of the residential regions would be lost. The presence of construction thus increases runoff and erosion, which in turn would affect either fields or gardens.

The disruptive influence that the intensification of cropping has on the natural environment, and, in turn, on the productivity of crops and cropping techniques, manifests itself in a number of different ways. The most serious such effects detected thus far in preliminary analyses of the paleolimnological data from Yaxha-Sacnab is the massive erosion of sediments into the lakes (Deevey 1976). While other indicators suggest environmental disturbance during the Middle Preclassic, the first strong pulses of sedimentation come from the Late Preclassic. The subsequent history of the lakes is marked by a conspicuous increase in the sedimentation rate, clearly related to landscape management and construction within the basins during the Classic Maya occupation of the region. Evidence of large-scale erosion has also been reported for the nonlacustrine area of Tikal (Olson 1969). The close of the Late Classic period at Yaxha-Sacnab is marked by sharply decreased inorganic deposition, increased organic sedimentation, and evidence of Postclassic reforestation.

Because of the topography of the lakes region, erosion affects both terrestrial and lacustrine microenvironments. Where drainage is into *bajos* or low areas marginal to lakes and streams, the silt-laden runoff may contribute to the reclamation of such lands; if the sedimentation is substantial, these areas may increase in agricultural potential. Such a process may have made *bajo* utilization more feasible. Along the southern shores of the lakes, periodic water-level fluctuations expose sediments enriched by deposition in the shallows. Raised fields, not unlike those mapped in the Rio Candelaria (Siemens and Puleston 1972) and Rio Hondo (Puleston 1977) riverine environments, are an agricultural possibility on these swamplike perimeters. Wilken (1971:438) quotes E. G. Squire (1858:556) in describing a similar lacustrine pattern of ditched fields for the Lacandon. We have searched for it, but no present evidence of such agroengineering on the lakes has been noted.

Continued sedimentation and deposition would also have contributed to the degradation of faunal habitats and, together with consumption by humans, precipitated the decline of animal populations. Although data for estimating the availability of faunal resources are sparse, the recovery rate of individual mollusc shells from archaeological contexts (given as the number of shells recovered per occupation per mound) suggests reduced mollusc populations through time: 24.95 for the Middle Preclassic; 10.7 for the Late Preclassic; 3.69 for the Early Classic; 2.99 for the Late Classic; and 28.26 for the Postclassic. The assumpiton that the growth of human settlement had an effect on the dynamics of the mollusc populations is reinforced by the apparent recovery of the latter after the Late Classic period and prior to Late Postclassic occupation of the basins. A similar effect might be expected for fish and other aquatic fauna, since heavy siltation reduces the natural productivity of open waters, and thus their food supply.

As a result of such environmental perturbations, the capability for support of human populations would have been greatly reduced from potential levels, and it is possible that environmental degradation is correlated with the massive depopulation that occurred at the close of the Late Classic period. Productivity figures for a variety of crops and cropping techniques suggest that subsistence alternatives in the Yaxha-Sacnab region became more and more restricted with increasing population growth. If to nutrient and soil loss we add climatic variation, or crop loss through human intervention, the situation becomes more precarious.

SUMMARY AND CONCLUSIONS

Data from archaeological surveys in the vicinity of Lakes Yaxha and Sacnab, Peten, Guatemala, have been presented as a basis for investigating Classic Maya subsistence alternatives within a prescribed geographic region. Archaeologically estimated population figures were utilized to project presumptive economic densities for various staple crops under different cropping strategies. Results demonstrate that subsistence options in the Yaxha-Sacnab region became restricted through time. A great deal of flexibility in resource utilization existed during the Middle Preclassic period, although archaeological and ecological data suggest that certain choices were pursued over others. By the end of the Late Classic period, however, the settlement system was more rigid and major reliance on swidden cultivation was no longer feasible. Indications are that population growth and concomitant food production had a deleterious effect on the local environment and, in turn, on the support capability of the region.

The evolutionary perspective presented focuses on population pressure as a prime mover for agrarian change. Undoubtedly, fortuitous opportunities for reduction of risk or increase in yields (with a minimum of labor investment) can also alter the trajectory of a subsistence system. It was deemed more useful, however, to frame speculation in terms of Boserup's (1965) density-dependent model of agricultural intensification. The resulting discussion assumes the nature of change, but makes explicit the magnitudes of independent and dependent variables in order to hypothesize periods of potential stress and available options for reducing stress. For example, the Late Preclassic appears to have been a phase of economic transition. According to the model, the inadequacies of a maize-based swidden strategy should first have become apparent in this period. Field data indicate that residence location departs for the first time from apparently preferred tall upland to moist slope zones, and inorganic sedimentation into the lakes begins. In an unrelated study, Webster (1977) has suggested that by the Late Preclassic period the process of population growth and dispersal in Peten would have progressed to a stage where land shortages might be felt, with important ramifications for subsequent sociopolitical developments.

Such evaluations are based on single-crop production and variability therein, but the tendency to diversify or stratify cultivars has probably occurred to some degree during all periods. Intercropping and other techniques could compensate for the marginality of some options or counteract the impact of minor degradation or increases in surplus demand, thus in the short run maintaining the status quo. It is difficult to account for such supplementation, however, and legitimate to rely on staple crop productivity as the major component and maximum producer in an agricultural complex. On this level it is possible to trace change and even demonstrate the value and effect of integrated cropping through time. The point is that, although the accuracy or fineness of the projected alternatives may vary with the quality and intricacy of the component estimates, we have used interacting cultural, demographic, and ecological variables, and verified the need for complex models of Maya land use.

Recognizing the covariance of settlement and subsistence characteristics with economic densities, we can predict that rates of agrarian and societal evolution will differ from place to place according to variability in local environment and population dynamics. Herein lies the value of a site-regional level of analysis for studies of Maya culture and tropical agriculture. Once internal population and resource parameters have been established, interregional comparisons of economic densities can be attempted. Such comparisons may provide valuable insights into differential site development and size, interregional sociopolitical hierarchies and alliances, trade, and regional susceptibility to cultural and/or environmental perturbations. These insights then form a basis for modeling future land use, predicting capacity for and response to population loading and agricultural manipulation of a heterogeneous lowland environment.

In conclusion, the variability existing in Peten, as determined by topography, soils, and water sources, appears to have been a major determinant of settlement location and the evolution of Maya sites. It will exercise similar influence on future development. If changes in subsistence systems are density dependent, the responses to stress are in large part governed by locally available resources. Modes of intensification may have varied from site to site, and lowland zone to lowland zone, just as population characteristics would vary. For periods of probable stress, such as the Late Classic, our grasp of Lowland Maya cultural dynamics will depend upon our understanding of site-regional variations in productivity and demography, and of modes of integration of local patterns into broader pan-Maya adaptation.

NOTES

1. I acknowledge the support of National Science Foundation Grant BMS 72-01859 and the assistance of Dr. Edward S. Deevey (Florida State Museum), Project Director for that grant, in making possible the investigations upon which this paper is based. Special thanks are also extended to my wife, Dr. Prudence Rice (University of Florida), for her role in the collection and preparation of the data during this study. A more complete report on the Yaxha-Sacnab Historical Ecology Project is contained in my doctoral dissertation (Rice 1976).

5

FREDERICK M. WISEMAN
Department of Geography and Anthropology, Louisiana State University

Agricultural and Historical Ecology of the Maya Lowlands[1]

As archaeological research expands beyond the traditional cultural-historical perspective, new tools and fields of thought are being brought to bear upon the problems of the preliterate past. Archaeologists must now have an acquaintance with pedology, geomorphology, and palynology, modern ecological theory, paleoenvironmental research, and prehistoric demography to describe extinct socioecological systems. Understanding the relationship between prehistoric society and environment is complex because of the passage of time and the number of fragmentary variables to be considered. I shall discuss, as a natural historian, an enigmatic prehistoric relationship between the civilized Maya and the Central American forest during the first millennium A.D.

Although we may indeed know the dynastic rulers of the Maya lowlands of twelve hundred years ago, we cannot yet visualize all of the landscape over which they presided. Were there fields of maize stretching to the horizon, or vast ordered orchards, or a patchwork of many kinds of farmlands, each nestled into its own edaphic niche? Were the *bajos* shallow lakes, bearing commerce in canoes laden with crops and manufactured goods, or vast artificial fields of maize and cacao, or swamps to be avoided except to harvest wood for fuel?

This paper employs an interdisciplinary approach in an attempt to render a cohesive portrayal of the pre-Hispanic landscape in the central lake region of Peten. The contemporary environmental niches of the region are described, and various hypothesized subsistence systems are analyzed within the bounds of these niches in order to describe optimal habitats. Finally, the hypothetical constructs are compared to the actual paleoecologic and paleodemographic data through the use of simulation models.

THE VEGETATIONAL SETTING FOR MAYA AGRICULTURE

Reconstruction of past landscapes necessitates a thorough understanding of both modern landscapes (the analogue) and the fossil evidence that is the vestige of the extinct system under study (Ogden 1969). In this section, I will describe the natural setting of modern lowland Maya agriculture with data that are requisite for constructing more realistic models of past man-land systems. This is necessary because numerous scholars have described the lowland tropics as a region in which little variability of habitats exists (Rathje 1971; Sanders 1973). Such a view has resulted in a conceptual dichotomy between highland Mesoamerica or the southwestern United States, which are both characterized in the literature by a suite of habitats with differing exploitable potentials (MacNeish 1964), and the "resource redundant" tropical American lowlands (Rathje 1971). To test the validity of this dichotomy, I established a network of vegetation sampling sites in the "core" area of central Peten, and an independent set of sample sites in the Sonoran Desert zone, an area fitting the "high habitat variability" model.

The data set used in Peten vegetation analysis comprised approximately thirty stands that I selected in 1973 and 1975 (fig. 5.1). The sample stands were chosen subjectively, without bias (Mueller-Dombois and Ellenberg 1974; Poore 1962), owing to the limited time available and the proposed use of nonparametric statistics in entiation (characterization of the vegetation type from sample data). Although I did not initially recognize it, sampling was along a gradient that was objectively determined in later analysis. Prospective sample sites were chosen to meet three requirements: (1) a site must include most of the species that belong to the community it represents; (2) the habitat and cover

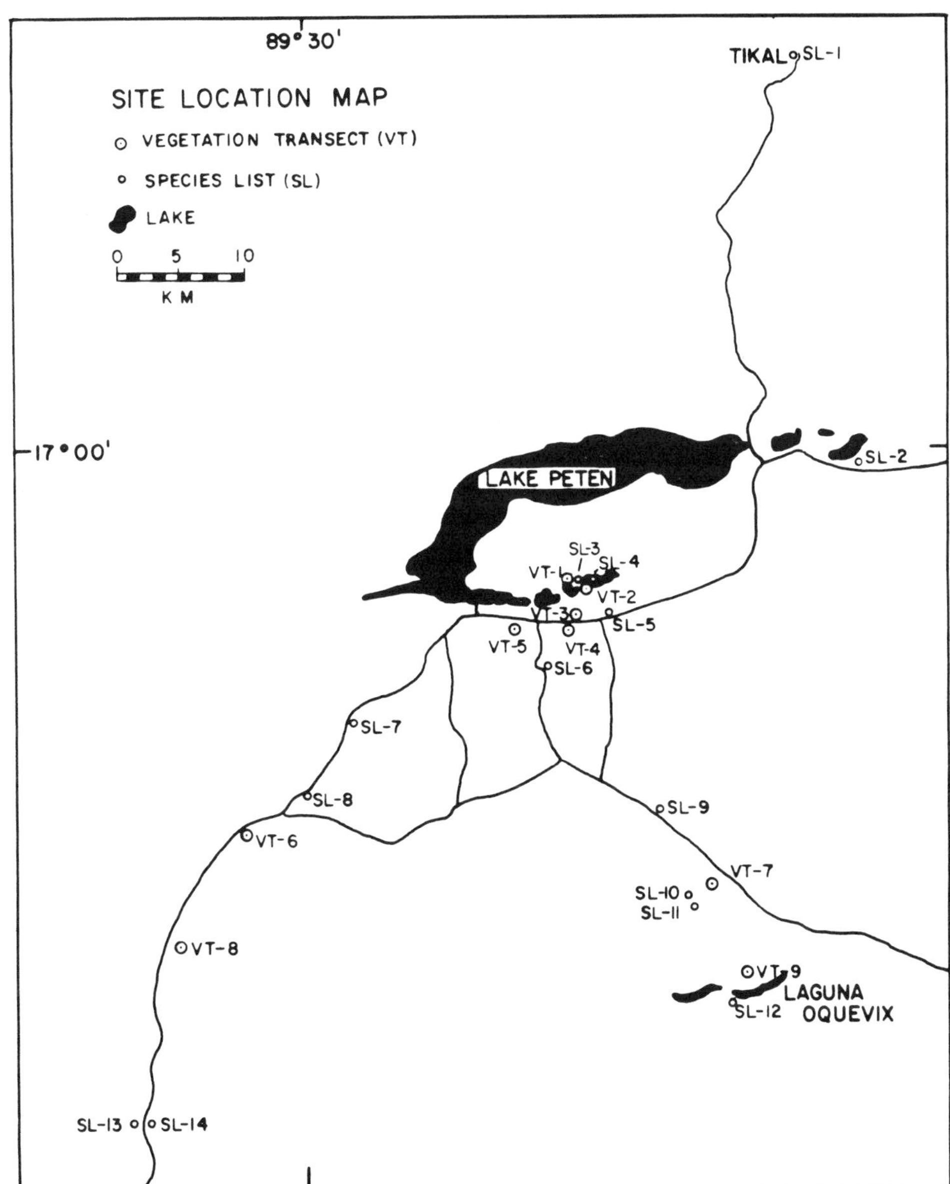

Figure 5.1. Site location map, Peten.

must be fairly homogeneous; and (3) the zones traversed must be under no great stress from human activity.

Stands that met the criteria were sampled both qualitatively and quantitatively. A species-abundance list was taken at each site, using the Daubenmire cover scale (Daubenmire 1959, 1968). At many sites, this list was checked quantitatively.

Quantitative sampling took three distinct forms. In predominantly herbaceous communities—grassland and savanna—a two-decimeter × five decimeter plot frame (Daubenmire 1972) was placed at one-meter intervals along the arms of a cross oriented to the cardinal directions. The results yielded 40 cover estimates that were averaged into a site mean. Shrub and tree cover was estimated by the line-intercept method (Cain and Castro 1959). One-tenth-hectare plots (Cain and Castro 1959) were used in many cases to derive quantitative data on tree cover, abundance, and size.

Numerical Classification

To derive an objective classification, numerical seriation methods were used. Sites with the requisite number of species were chosen for similarity index analysis. The index used is Sorenson's (Mueller-Dombois and Ellenberg 1974),

$$I_s = \frac{2C}{A + B} \times 100,$$

where A = total number of known taxa in site A, B = total number of known taxa in site B, and C = number of taxa common to A and B. This index yielded a matrix of similarity coefficients for 22 sample stands that contain a requisite number of taxa. I selected stands that showed maximum dissimilarity among them in the matrix (fig. 5.1: sites SL-1 and VT-9) and expressed all other sites as deviations from these. Agreement among the derived gradients was strong, indicating an objective ordering of sites by their component taxa. This ordination (a single "mean" gradient) proceeds from swamp forest to grassland, exhibiting a grouping of sites along the gradient into plant communities (see table 5.1).

Vegetation Types

Pachira aquatica-Terminalia swamp

Where the Peten forest abuts water's edge, a distinctive vegetation type, dominated by *Pachira aquatica,* can be found. Arising from slim, buttressed roots, *Pachira* forms an open canopy 6 meters high at lakeside, rising to over 16 meters in the swamp's interior. The subdominant *Terminalia* (or *Buchenavia*) occupies a habitat slightly less moist than *Pachira.* Various species of figs (*Ficus* spp.) are common in the lacustrine swamp. The sparse understory includes young *Pachira,* ferns, *Pistia stratioides,* isolated clumps of *Typha dominguensis,* and *Hymenocallis* cf. *americana.* The epiphytic component is large, composed of an assortment of scaly lichens, many epiphytic ferns, *Tillandsias* of various types, *Catopsis* cf. *aloides,* a *Cereus,* and clambering Araceae.

Mesic Forest

The mesic Peten forest has been described elsewhere (Lundell 1937) in such detail that I can add little here because of the sterile

Table 5.1. Classification of Sample Stands Derived from Similarity Indices*

Site No.	*Site Name*	*Vegetation Type*
VT-2	Finca Eckixil	*Pachira aquatica–Terminalia* swamp
SL-1	Tikal	Mesic forest
VT-1	Petenxil	
SL-3	Petenxil-Eckixil	
SL-6	Porucita	Monsoon forest
VT-5A	Santa Elena	
SL-7	La Libertad	
SL-2	Macanche	Corozo forest
SL-5	Paxcaman	
VT-8	Bosque el Caobal	Aguada forest
SL-11	Excocon	
VT-4	Santa Marta–S	Ecinal
VT-3	Santa Marta–N	
SL-10	Excocon	
SL-13	Sibun	Thorn scrub
SL-14	Sibun	
VT-6	El Guanal	Sahalal
VT-7	Santa Ana Vieta	Nanzal
VT-9	Pacay	Grassland

*SL-4 (Eckixil Isle), SL-12 (Oquevix), and VT-5C, D, E do not fit this gradient.

condition of many component taxa, and because of the limited nature of the study. Sites SL-1, VT-1, and SL-3 were grouped as mesic forest (table 5.1). Strictly speaking, these forests are not rain forests in Richards's sense (1952), since they are neither as high nor as stratified as true rain forest, but they are essentially evergreen.

No arboreal species are dominant in sites VT-1 and SL-3, but a suite of about 12 species seem to be codominant. These include *Brosimum alicastrum*, *Ficus* spp., *Coccoloba belizensis*, *Lysiloma bahamensis*, *Cedrela mexicana*, *Sweitenia macrophylla*, *Simaruba glauca*, *Bursera simaruba*, *Pseudobombax ellipticum*, *Ceiba pentandra*, *Manilkara achras*, and *Chrysophyllum* sp. They vary in their degree of codominance from locality to locality.

Monsoon Forest

The monsoon forests are arboreal; few shrubs, epiphytes, or lianas are found there. Only along brightly lit openings do we find leguminous shrubs in any quantity. Lianas (large vines) grow in areas that receive much light and give an impression of being common, but in undisturbed portions of the forest, only an occasional *Smilax*, *Monstera*, or *Philodendron* will be seen, with other unknown lianas. The epiphytes are mainly members of the Bromeliaceae; orchids, cacti and ferns are rare. Diverse trees support the epiphytes, from the towering *Ceiba pentandra*, through intermediate-sized trees such as *Cassia grandis*, *Brosimum* sp., *Cecropia peltata*, *Coccoloba belizensis*, *Spondias* sp., *Guazuma ulmifolia*, and *Tabebuia* sp., to the hemiepiphytic *Ficus* and *Clusia*.

Since the monsoon forest is found on well-drained sites, such as the karstic knolls south of Lake Peten, or in clay-filled valleys, water stress probably is an important determinant of its distribution. It is similar in structure and composition to the deciduous tropical forest found in Yucatan (Lundell 1934) and the Pacific slope of Mexico (Rzedowski and McVaugh 1966), zones that receive as few as 500 millimeters of annual rainfall and have a lengthy dry season.

Corozo Forest

Occasionally on gentle slopes with deep soils, a palm-dominated association can be found. The dominant perennial is the corozo,

Orbignya cohune, a tall "feather palm" sometimes reaching 17 meters in height. The palm groves, called *corozal* in Belize, may be anthropogenic in origin, since the tree is sometimes spared in clearing new milpas. Also occurring with *Orbignya* may be *Scheelia lundellii,* which looks vegetatively similar to *Orbignya* but is easily differentiated by inflorescence characters. Portions of the *corozales* lack other dominant tree species, but shrubby perennials are common. Valley bottoms contain a more broad-leafed vegetation type, similar in composition to the mesic forest found elsewhere in the Peten. In addition to the taxa mentioned above, *Bursera simaruba, Brosimum alicastrum, Ficus* spp., *Chrysophyllum* sp., and *Spondias* sp. are found on well-drained sites.

Aguada Forest

Situated within the grassy plains south of Lake Peten are numerous small *aguadas,* depressions of varying sizes that are capable of holding water for part of the year. During the dry season of 1975, most savanna-region *aguadas* dried to mud-cracked sediments or contained a rapidly diminishing puddle of cattle-muddied water. Usually the clay sediment forms an impervious "cup," allowing no water to flow out, although some *aguadas* seem to have underground discharge.

Surrounding the *aguada* is an arboreal vegetation vastly different from the broad, grass-covered plains. This vegetation type, which I call *aguada forest,* is high forest (trees from 5 to 20 meters) consisting of a jumbled, closed canopy and numerous emergents. It is most closely related to monsoon forest and encinal, sharing most plant species with these two types.

Encinal (Oak Woodland)

The tropical oak woodland is similar in aspect to temperate Sierra Madrean and Californian oak woodlands. It is dominated by the *encino, Quercus oleoides* var. *australis,* an 18-meter-high tree with widespread crown and small entire or three-toothed coriaceous leaves.

An understory of typically savanna trees may be evident. *Byrsonima crassifolia* forms a sparse undercanopy in open situations, but not within the shade of the encinos. The coyol palm, *Acrocomia mexicana,* is a minor constituent of the encinal, but it is nowhere common. *Acacia spadicigera,* a common understory tree, also grows as a disturbance indicator in the drier parts of the encinal. Other minor encinal dwellers are *Miconia* and several other Melastomaceae, *Bromelia karatas, Eugenia,* and many unknown species. The herb component is dominated by grasses and sedges, with a tiny *Mimosa* being common. Vines and lianas are virtually absent in the encinal, except for an occasional *Rhynchosia, Ipomoea,* or *Philodendron.* Oaks grow on alluvial clay soils, and quickly give way to a dry, partly deciduous forest on slopes or a mesic high forest along some streamways. Where edaphic changes are not abrupt, however, the encinal grades imperceptibly into mixed forest with a slow enrichment by new species. The encinal may also occur as isolated pockets within savannas occupying slightly undulating terrain.

Thorn scrub

A rarely encountered vegetation type is the Peten thorn scrub, a low, xeric woodland with an infusion of leaf and stem succulents, not unlike Sinaloan thorn forest (Shreve 1937). This vegetation formation, between two and five meters high, is mostly deciduous during the dry season. It occupies well-drained karstic outcrops in the Peten savanna country. A dominant tree is the bull-horn acacia (*Acacia spadicigera*). Subdominant Leguminosae are *Acacia angustissima,* a two-meter-high *Mimosa* (*M.* cf. *albida*), and other unknowns. The silktree, *Cochlospermum vitifolium,* is found as scattered individuals on the rubble-covered slopes, highly conspicuous because of its yellow flowers.

A semiepiphytic *Clusia* appears on rocks and road cuts in the thorn scrub, as do *Agave* sp. and the semisucculent *Plumeria acutifolia.* Herb cover is sparse, but a bright red *Salvia* is common, as is the semiwoody *Rhynchosia pyramidalis.*

Sahalal

The first savanna formation encountered along the gradient is the sahalal, a jumbled, weedy orchardlike formation. The dominant tree is the saha, *Curatella americana,* a tree three to six and one-half meters tall with large, sandpaperlike leaves on twisted, upright branches. The saha supports a few epiphytes, such as *Tillandsia* spp., a tiny orchid, and many lichens. Growing in the open shade under each saha is a jumbled mass of shrubbery of the melastome family.

The grasslands surrounding the *Curatella*-Melastomaceae are characterized by numerous forbs, of which *Salvia* and *Brickellia* were recognized. *Andropogon* spp. are less common than in more grass-dominated sites. *Byrsonima crassifolia,* usually found growing with the *Curatella* in tropical savannas (P. L. Wagner 1964), occurs only as a rare straggler in sahalals in the Peten. It forms its own association, indicating divergent habitat preference.

Nanzal

The most abundant arborescent savanna in the Peten is the nanzal, an open community dominated by *Byrsonima crassifolia* (nanze) and various grasses. The nanzal appears as an arm of a larger grassland, a transition to marginal forest, or, more rarely, as a glade in marginal forest or encinal. The subdominant family is the Melastomaceae represented by *Miconia argentea,* another species of *Miconia,* and *Conostegia* sp., which may nestle under *Byrsonima* or grow in solitary clumps.

The herb component is dominated by grass, mostly dried in February, under 50 centimeters in height. Herbs are rare in the nanzal, except for *Mimosa pudica* and *Rhynchosia* sp., which nonetheless have very low coverage values. The borders of the nanzal are well defined. Toward open grassland, the nanzes terminate in a ragged line, and toward the forest are rapidly supplemented by marginal forest elements.

Grassland (Campo)

Thousands of hectares south of Lake Peten are devoid of trees, forming small prairies. These grasslands occupy broad, level or slightly rolling plains bounded by low, limestone, forest-covered hills, sinuous forested streamways, and *aguadas.* The soils are acidic clays, with a dark brownish-red surface layer, that grades into a yellow-brown to brick-red horizon. Sparse organic material may mask the red tint of the classic oxidized savanna soils. The most common recognizable genus in the grassland is *Andropogon,* represented by several species including the taller *A.* cf. *condensatus* and the coarse-leaved *A. bicornis. Salvia,* possibly *S. coccinea,* is the most common forb, followed by *Brickellia* cf. *oliganthes, Erigeron* sp., and several other members of the Compositae, Leguminosae, and Acanthaceae families.

The border of the grassland is sharp, grading into marginal scrub forest, *aguada* forest or encinal. Forbs, especially the Compositae, Leguminosae, and Melastomaceae, favor this transition zone, obtaining significant light and increased fertility of forest soils. Fires often sweep the grasslands, retarded only by roads or marginal scrub that act as firebreaks.

HABITAT VARIABILITY: MAYA LOWLANDS VS. THE SONORAN REGION

The foregoing description of lowland vegetation covers only part of the range of potential habitats, since riparian, *bajo,* and probably other vegetation types have not been included in the study. The variability of lowland habitats has been demonstrated, but the degree of variance may be visualized by a simple comparison with a biome similar to the Tehuacan Valley (MacNeish 1964) or the Shoshonean region (D. H. Thomas 1973). The independent data set is a series of sample stands chosen in a manner similar to those in the Peten in the State of Sonora, Mexico, a region of ecological heterogeneity (Shreve and Wiggins 1964).

The similarity index matrices for the two regions were compared by testing for independence and normality of the 242 points within each matrix, then calculating a mean similarity index for each that, in essence, gives an average amount of plant taxa shared by sites in the region (Mueller-Dombois and Ellenberg 1974). The mean values (the Peten matrix is 36.7 ± 18.1, the Sonora, 32 ± 24.6) indicate that there is no statistically significant difference between the two matrices. The implications of this test are that the lowland "resource redundant" model may have to be rejected and replaced with a more realistic diversity model. The diversity model demands critical reevaluation of the current speculation on the origin of Mesoamerican agriculture and civilization.

A spatial array of vegetation types in the central Peten area has been delimited by remote sensing imagery (fig. 5.2). Vegetation types were determined by treating the sample stands as ground-truth sites, and then treating areas with similar reflectance values on the image bands as vegetation similar in composition to that of the sample stand (Turner and Wiseman in press). These data are essential for constructing realistic models of past Maya subsistence in that they set ecological bounds around possible economic options such as hunting or agriculture.

LIMITS TO AGRICULTURAL PRODUCTIVITY

Although many publications describing prehistoric Maya agriculture mention environmental limitations (Wilken 1971; D. E. Puleston and O. S. Puleston 1971; Turner 1974a), the specific biological and edaphic mechanisms that affect agricultural productivity have been ignored. To tropical cultivators, such factors often mean the difference between bounty and famine. The considerable literature on modern tropical pests, soils, and crops should be studied by those desiring to reconstruct prehistoric Maya subsistence.

The first factor limiting crop productivity in tropical America, the organisms that compete with man for his crops, is a constant, low-level destructive agent with occasional population surges. Although tropical forests support the most diverse population of herbivorous insects and plant diseases of any terrestrial vegetation type, the potential damage to crops by these pests has been little studied. Since pests are adapted to many different niches, a high potential exists for damage to cultivars from local or exotic species "preadapted" to a given cultivated host. Tropical woody plants have come into equilibrium with such pests through long association, but defense systems for imported seed crops, as planted today, are severely limited (Janzen 1970).

To protect itself from pests, a plant has two general defensive strategies. It may manufacture substances and structures harmful to larger herbivores, insects, and parasites (*internal defense*), or it may allow outside factors to reduce pest populations (*external defense*). One form of internal defense is the manufacture by the plant of a series of secondary compounds, such as oxalic acid

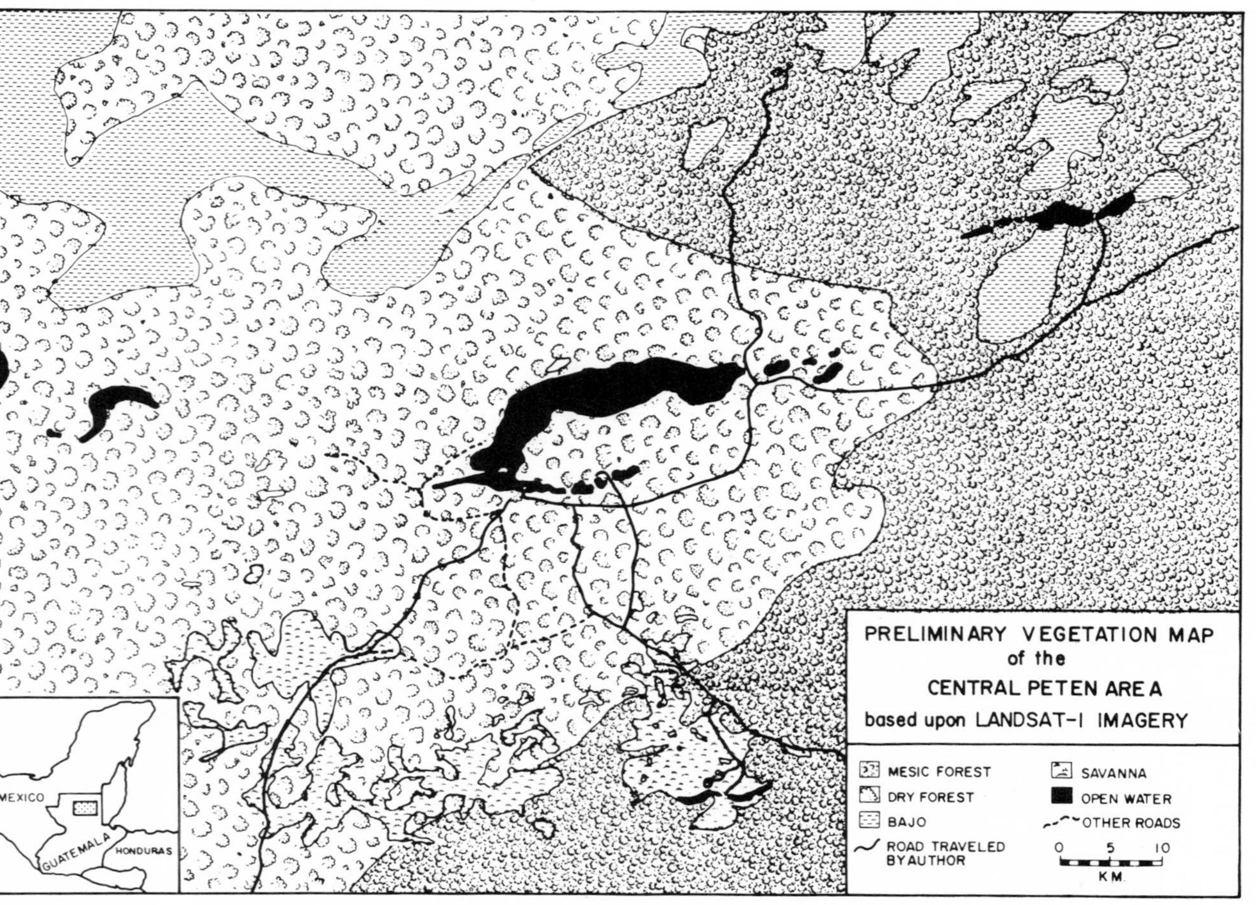

Figure 5.2. Vegetation of the central Peten.

crystals, latex, and strychnine, that are toxic to herbivores, and their dispersal through its tissues. Another internal defense is the generation of thorns, spikes, and spines—a protection against larger herbivores, a minor component of the forest biome. The third is the use of a symbiotic animal to repel herbivores, as is done by the biting ants inhabiting the bull-horn acacia (*Acacia* spp.).

External plant defenses consist of cyclic climatic variation, distance between individuals of a species, and predation upon herbivore populations (Janzen 1970). Rain forests and tropical evergreen formations have the least climatic variation of all vegetation types, so winterkill and drought kill of pests are much reduced. Only in northern Peten, toward the more arid Yucatan Peninsula, is there a dry season extensive enough to influence herbivore populations greatly. The lack of limiting climatic cycles allows herbivores to adapt faster to culturally caused variations in their food supply, which results in heavier densities of parasites, herbivores, and diseases at critical times. The artificial establishment of regular cycles in pest populations may restrict another external defense, that of predators. Carnivorous animals are specifically adapted to the habits and life cycles of their prey. For example, temperate-zone predators adapt to winterkill of their prey by either seeking alternate food sources (vertebrate predators), or surviving lean times as eggs or pupae, but their tropical counterparts have no such adaptation to cyclic variations. Since predator populations must stay at a level low enough to survive low prey frequency, they cannot check the population explosions that ensue when pests adapt to crop cycles. The net result is an inadequate biological check on herbivores or disease, a potential danger to continuous mono-cropping.

Natural internal and external defenses are limited or nonixistent for most seed crops, such as maize or beans. The best defense available for such cultivars is diffuse distribution of individuals throughout the plant community, a tactic clearly impossible with cereal cultivation, since harvest of seed from widespread individual plants is unproductive. The modern *milpero* uses this general principle by separating his plots in space and time so that localized outbreaks of pests such as corn borers or leaf-cutting ants will not become a pestilence (Cowgill 1962). Low human population density allows the *milpero* to choose secondary forest for clearing. Advanced secondary forests have lost those pests adapted to such early successional plants as grasses and forbs. Under human population pressure, however, fields may have short or no fallow cycles. Such fields would be highly susceptible to damage from the clearing of areas retaining early successional pests and from pest inoculum from adjacent croplands. Any type of intensive cultivation using seed crops, then, would have been prone to damage from rapidly expanding insect and disease populations that were difficult to handle with the technology available to the ancient Maya.

The next factor limiting pre-Hispanic agriculture is the loss of plant nutrients through solution transport. The combination of high diurnal temperatures, heavy rainfall, and calcareous parent material characteristic of the Maya lowlands allows intense leaching of soil to occur in many areas, which forms a relatively impoverished upper soil. In old forest, leaf litter and dead vegetation return stored nutrients to the upper soil horizons, where they may be released for building new plant tissue by decomposers in the soil.

In modern milpa agriculture, cutting, burning, and weeding release the stored minerals to the soil as ash or mulch, highly susceptible to solution transport. For a short time, the milpa is saturated with organics and minerals, until heavy rains, unrestricted by canopy or leaf litter, carry them away through percolation and runoff. During this fertile period, shallow-rooted seed-crop plants such as maize, beans, and squash may be grown effectively. Decreasing fertility then necessitates a fallow period to increase the necessary nutrients through reaccumulation by successional plants. Such loss is a major reason that a short period of cropping followed by a long fallow period must have been used by the ancient Maya, as well as their modern descendants, when raising seed crops in unmodified upland plots. Tropical seed crop cultivation will eventually fail if it does not provide from above ground the necessary nutrients, as either fertilizer or ash.

The alternative to fallowing is the use of fertilizer, which would necessitate composting, storage, and distribution of organic wastes. Because it allows loss through incomplete retrieval, leaching, and runoff, fertilizer exploitation would be generally unsuitable for stabilizing large tracts even without insect problems and erosion. However, this concentration of nutrients would be of value in establishing localized, highly fertile plots that could contribute valuable crops.

Another factor hindering effective utilization of the forest for agriculture is erosion. Modern milpa and intensive systems of agriculture are extremely destructive of natural vegetation cover and leaf litter. Since tropical forests have little humus, destruction of available cover results in the loss of several mechanisms for water retention. A cleared milpa yields more runoff than an equal-sized plot of forest. This water flows erratically as sheetwash and rills; its erosive potential may render the area useless for agriculture through gullying and removal of topsoil. Since soil is the result of climatic and biological alteration of the substrate for thousands of years, it cannot be quickly renewed. Topsoil loss would have had disastrous and long-term effects upon Maya civilization.

Other limiting factors, working on a smaller scale than those previously discussed, are root competition, shading, drought, and mechanical damage due to wind and hail. Those models that stress tree and shrub crops must deal with the effect of plants that cover much space with roots and photosynthetic surfaces. Trees with shallow root systems compete with herbaceous crops, stunting those that need copious amounts of water and nutrients. For this reason, plants such as *Manihot esculenta, Xanthosoma violaceum,* or *Vanilla planifolia* may be used effectively, since they make smaller inroads on the nutrient balance than do seed crops. Root competition from secondary weeds, such as the herbaceous members of the grass, sunflower, legume, and amaranth families, rapidly limits crop plants similar in niche, while scarcely affecting woody crops. Simple manual weeding or companion planting alleviates the problem but requires a great outlay of time. Substitution of useful crops in the weed niche will not only reduce weed infestation but also lower soil temperature, allowing survival of much-needed soil organisms.

Large trees or shrubs also affect crops by shading the ground beneath them. Many seed crops are intolerant of shade and suffer at light intensities under 3,000 footcandles. Others seem to flourish in shade and exist at less than 1,000 footcandles for a 12-hour day (Graf 1957). Examples of this type are the large-leafed root crops and vanilla. An equilibrium between overstory and understory crops needs to be established to derive maximum productivity from a mixed system.

Physical damage to crops by wind and hail is fairly uncommon in Peten and cannot be counteracted by agricultural technique.

Windbreaks may help, but meteorological catastrophe may have been a deciding factor in those parts of the Maya lowlands subject to hurricanes and violent thunderstorms. The effects of the monsoon's variable nature have been discussed by others (Morley 1946; Thompson 1954) and will be mentioned only in passing. Drought will affect those crops that are most dependent upon sufficient precipitation, such as the larger, leafy seed crops—maize, squash, and beans. Tree and root crops have a reserve to draw upon in times of water deficit, but all will fail in periods of protracted drought (National Academy of Sciences 1975). The agriculturalist had little recourse but to irrigation—and to his gods.

AGRICULTURE AND RELATED SYSTEMS

Swidden Agriculture

The slash-and-burn agricultural system practiced by the modern Maya has been much discussed (Morley 1946; Thompson 1954; Cowgill 1962; M. D. Coe 1966; Reina 1967; Culbert 1974). I shall present a quantified summary of the inputs and products of the Maya agricultural system derived mainly from data collected by Cowgill (1962) and Reina (1967) in the Lake Peten region. Data from northern Yucatan (Morley 1946) and other portions of the lowland tropics will only be used where the Lake Peten data are not sufficient, so as to keep the reconstructions applicable.

The *milpero*'s family averages 5.78 persons, which may include sons-in-law and aged relatives in addition to his nuclear family (Cowgill 1962). Either his son or his son-in-law may help him in the milpa throughout its cycle, aided when necessary by the rest of the household, usually during weeding and harvest (Reina 1967). The amount of land cared for by the *milpero* and his helper(s) averages 5.28 hectares (Cowgill 1962), which may be divided into several plots in slightly different habitats (Reina 1967). The use of multiple plots increases agricultural stability by means of pest quarantine effects and insulation from yearly climatic variation. If one field is affected adversely, there is a chance that the other fields will provide the family with sufficient food for the year. Labor input into the system has yet to be quantified in the Peten, so figures for nearby Yucatan will be used (Morley 1946, adjusted to Peten seasonality; Reina 1967). Locating a milpa site usually takes but a single day and may be done at any time of the year. Cutting the forest is the longest chore associated with milpa agriculture, taking 75 days, usually in late fall and spring. Burning, lasting but one day, occurs in April or May, in anticipation of the summer rains, and is immediately followed by planting the crops with the aid of a dibble stick, which takes about 14 days. Weeding the fields during the summer rains, using 14 days' time, is followed by harvest of the maize crop in late fall or early winter, which takes 36 days' labor. The result is approximately 150 days of activity for the *milpero* and his helper, leaving over 200 days not devoted to milpa activity each year.

The productivity of many indigenous American cultivars is shown in table 5.2. The data (especially considering the discrepancy between Cowgill's and Reina's maize productivity figures) may be little more than crude estimates of reality, but as far as I know, they are all we have. Cowgill (1971) lists the nutritional makeup of several indigenous cultivars. She includes the interesting statement that 285 kilograms (636 pounds) of maize or 658 kilograms (1,450 pounds) of manioc will support a human being for one year; obviously, these figures imply additional nutritional intake. These data are of prime importance to agricultural reconstructions since they determine the number of people that may be supported by a given plot of land, given the system of cropping.

After harvest, two options are available. The plot may be left fallow, or it may be planted for a second year, but rarely a third. The mean fallow time for one year of cropping is two and one-half years, and for two years' cropping, five years (Cowgill 1962). I believe that a conservative estimate of stable, long-term agriculutre would be four or more years of fallow for every year of cultivation. A milpa under cultivation normally produces tremendous amounts of *Zea* pollen, little of which, however, gets far from the milpa due to the rapid fall velocity of the large *Zea* grains (Raynor, Ogden, and Hayes 1972).

Dooryard Gardens

The modern dooryard garden, as seen in Flores and San Benito, Peten, is a small, fenced enclosure. Plants raised in the gardens are ornamental flowers, cash and subsistence crops ranging from

Table 5.2. Important indigenous tropical cultigens, their productivity, and ecological requirements

Crop		Yield per hectare	Edaphic habitat	Month planted	Harvest	Light intensity (footcandles)
Ramon	*Brosimum alicastrum*	1,122	Upland		Dry season	4,000–8,000
Cassava	*Manihot esculenta*	2,600	Moist, drained		Jan.–Mar.	1,000–3,000
Camote	*Ipomoea batatas*	22,469	Drained	May	Dec.	3,000–8,000
Macal	*Dioscorea alata*[a]	30,005[b]	Drained	June	Any time	1,000–3,000
Malanga	*Xanthosoma violaceum*	40,909	Moist, drained			500–3,000
Yam bean	*Pachyrrhizus erosus*					
Frijol	*Phaseolis vulgaris*	24,013		June–Aug.	Nov.	4,000–8,000
Piña	*Ananas cosmosus*	7,718[b]		June	Any time	1,000–8,000
Chile	*Capsicum annuum*			Mar.	June	4,000–8,000
Ayote	*Cucurbita pepo*	9,557[b]		Feb.–May	Oct.	
Zikil kum	*Cucurbita moschata*	8,005[b]		May	Aug.	
Maize 1 yr	*Zea mays*	1,600	Moist, drained	Apr.–May	Nov.–Jan.	4,000–8,000
Maize 2 yr	*Zea mays*	1,134	Moist, drained	Apr.–May	Nov.–Jan.	
Maize 3 yr	*Zea mays*	468	Moist, drained	Apr.–May	Nov.–Jan.	
Yaxkin	*Zea mays*		Dry slopes	Sept.–Nov.		
San José	*Zea mays*		*Bajos*	Feb.		
White	*Zea mays*	289	Upland			
Yellow	*Zea mays*		Drier areas			
Black	*Zea mays*		Moister areas			
Soursop	*Annona* sp.		Moist, well-drained		Any time	
Vanilla	*Vanilla fragrans*		Moist, well-drained			500–3,000
Papaya	*Carica papaya*		Moist, drained			4,000–8,000
Aguacate	*Persea americana*		Moist, drained			4,000–8,000
Cacao	*Theobroma cacao*		Moist, drained			4,000–8,000
Palmera	*Yucca elephantipes*		Dry, drained			4,000–8,000

a. *D. alata* figures are used, since data for the indigenous *D. trifida* (Coursey 1967) are unavailable.

b. Fruits or tubers per hectares, all others in kg/hectare. Data from Lundell (1937), Graf (1957), Cowgill (1961), Reina (1967), D. E. Puleston and O. S. Puleston (1971), and National Academy of Sciences (1975).

medicinal herbs such as *apozote* (*Chenopodium ambrosioides*), to crops such as chile (*Capsicum annuum*), semiarborescent plants (*Yucca elephantipes*), and fruit and shade trees (*Cocos nucifera*). Much household activity is carried out in the shade of the dooryard garden, and refuse is often used for mulching and fertilizer. Chickens and dogs seem to be allowed within the confines of the garden in February, probably since there are no delicate young plants that could be molested.

Dooryard gardens have also been observed in the savanna region of Peten, and the crops raised within them did not seem to suffer because of the dense, weathered clay soil. Perhaps the intensive care that garden plots receive negates, to a certain degree, the supposed poor edaphic conditions of red savanna soils.

Fuel Procurement

Virtually ignored in studies of contemporary Maya subsistence is the issue of energy sources. The modern Maya essentially rely upon hardwoods for fuel; firewood consumption is rapid. In one instance, I recorded a utilization rate of 0.1 cord of wood per day at San Benito, Peten. If this consumption rate is representative for two households, as would seem to be the case, then each family uses 10 to 20 cords of firewood per year, or about 3 cords per capita per year. This figure implies a considerable selective pressure on dense wood species, especially those with 2.5-to-12.5-centimeter boles, the preferred cuts. Since two-year-old milpas (*acahuales*) do not generally contain hardwoods of this size, it is doubtful that a short-fallow cycle could supply a sufficient wood harvest (Wiseman 1974).

An average firewood log diameter of seven and one-half centimeters, combined with the length of usable wood from each tree (about three meters), allows the calculation that nearly 120 trees are required to obtain a cord of firewood. In favorable situations, five cords of cut logs per hectare of forest may be obtained. Allowing five years as a minimum forest regeneration time, a sustained yield rate from the Peten forests would be around one cord per hectare per year. In an equilibrium model, three hectares of sustained-yield land could supply the energy requirements of each person. If an expansionist model were used, in which regeneration is not assumed, three-fifths of a hectare could support a person's fuel requirements.

Although these estimates are crude, the implications are that if the prehistoric Maya used grass or bush fallow systems (Sanders 1973), extensive terrace systems, or ridged field systems, the energy resource base may have been depleted. Since the prehistoric Maya had a population density many times greater than that of their modern descendants, the energy demands upon the tropical forest probably necessitated a well-programmed fuel production and allotment system. This could have been accomplished in several ways: by means of wood-lot plantations, milpas with a wood harvest during fallow times, or isolated wood-crop plants grown within other agricultural systems.

Hunting

The larger animal population of the Maya lowlands is quite diverse (table 5.3), and contemporary farmers hunt. Succulent, weedy growth and crop plants attract herbivores and their predators that find little sustenance in the climax forest. Hunting in the milpa decreases invasions by larger herbivores through harvest and learned fear. Unfortunately, game harvest data are unavailable at present, but it would seem logical that an increase in milpa and *acahual* (secondary vegetation) would increase populations of edge-loving fauna, providing hunters, both ancient and modern, with more protein per land unit.

The pre-Hispanic Maya lacked modern hunting equipment, but probably compensated for this by meticulous woodsmanship, game-drive techniques, and traps, as attested by several codices (Franco 1969). Hunting may be practiced at any time of the year in almost any habitat in the Maya lowlands, a situation that has not changed since Classic times.

PRE-HISPANIC MAYA SUBSISTENCE

The pre-Hispanic systems are difficult to understand, since observational data are lacking and secondary evidence is drawn from ethnographic analogy, interpretation of relict earthworks,

Table 5.3. Game Animals and Birds Inhabiting the Maya Lowlands (after E. R. Hall and K. R. Kelson 1959).

Order	*Common Name*	*Scientific Name*
Marsupial	Opossum	*Diadelphis marsupialis*
	Four-eyed opossum	*Philander opossum*
Primate	Howler monkey	*Alouatta villosa*
	Spider monkey	*Ateles geofroyi*
Edentate	Tamandua	*Tamandua tetradactyla*
	Armadillo	*Dasypus novemcinctus*
Lagomorph	Forest rabbit	*Sylvilagus brasiliensis*
Rodent	Yucatan squirrel	*Sciurus yucataensis*
	Yucatan squirrel	*Sciurus deppeii*
	Mexican porcupine	*Coendon mexicanus*
	Spotted cavy	*Agouti paca*
Carnivore	Gray fox	*Urocyon cinereo argenteus*
	Cacomistle	*Bassariscus sumichrasti*
	Raccoon	*Procyon lotor*
	Coati	*Nasua narica*
	Kinkajou	*Potos flauus*
	Jaguar	*Felix onca*
	Mountain lion	*Felix concolor*
	Ocelot	*Felis pardalis*
	Margay	*Felis wiedii*
	Jaguarundi	*Felix yagouraroundi*
Pinniped	Manatee	*Trichechus manatus*
Perissodactyl	Tapir	*Tapirus baindii*
	Collared peccary	*Tayassu tajacu*
	White-lipped peccary	*Tayassu pecari*
Artiodactyl	White-tailed deer	*Odocoileus virginianus*
	Brocket	*Mazama americana*
	Birds	
Cracidae	Plain chachalaca	*Ortalis vetula*
	Crested guan	*Penelope purpurascens*
	Great curassow	*Crax rubra*
Mealeagrinidae	Ocellated turkey	*Agriocharis ocellata*
Psitacidae	Scarlet macaw	*Ara macao*

house-mound density, palynology, and speculation. I have selected from published and unpublished data those subsistence methods (in addition to the modern) that I believe were likely to have been used by the ancient Maya. It must be remembered, however, that the systems described in this paper are not all of the possible options. Subsistence systems can be divided into two main groups, intensive and extensive systems. *Extensive* systems use much land, but less labor input. Examples are hunting, gathering, and milpa farming, techniques used by the modern Maya.

Intensive agricultural systems may be considered as either biointensive or geointensive. A *biointensive* system relies upon increased efficiency of energy flow through a modified vegetation composition and structure to increase usable productivity. Less attention is given to the physical environment of the cultivars than to the biotic. Examples of biointensive systems are ramon cultivation (Puleston 1969) and artificial rain forest (Wiseman 1973), few of which leave visible remains.

Geointensive systems alter the geomorphology of the agricultural plot to increase available moisture or to improve physical soil characteristics. Examples are irrigation and raised-field networks. Since they leave obvious remains, researchers have stressed geointensive agricultural methods in reconstructions of Maya subsistence. Such intensive methods are hypothesized due to the disparity between past high population density and present low agricultural productivity.

Intensive Milpa

The intensive milpa, a highly productive swidden system, is a biointensive model of Maya agriculture that has found acceptance among some archaeologists (Lange 1971; Sanders 1973). It employs techniques that allow multi-cropping with reduced fallow periods. Precipitation regimes restrict the use of this system to zones where few rainless months occur, such as around Poptun, Guatemala (Culbert, Spencer, and Magers 1976). Crop rotation and intercropping have been hypothesized as fallow-period-reducing mechanisms. Perennial species, such as manioc, planted with annuals produce cash or subsistence crops during the fallow period, materially increasing the overall productivity of the milpa. Since increased diversity and coverage insulate against pest and sheetwash problems, intensive milpa is a more stable system than the modern slash-and-burn system. Indeed, the use of these techniques and the high percentage of time that the land is in cultivation suggest that the term *milpa* (suggesting a swidden) is a misnomer. Intensive milpas are, in essence, intensive forms of cultivation, not to be confused with long-fallow slash-and-burn systems.

Artificial Rain Forest

The most ecologically efficient hypothesized biointensive agricultural system is essentially a proxy for the "quasi rain forest" that occupies much of the Maya lowlands (Lundell 1937). The artificial rain forest model is an array of tree crops, vine crops, root crops, and standard seed crops combined in such a way as to preserve the primeval energy (and nutrient) cycles of the parent forest (Wiseman 1973).

The system could have resulted from selective clearing as practiced by the modern Maya. Cowgill (1962), Reina (1967), and Lundell (1937) point out that the modern Peten *milpero* does not clear-cut the forest, but spares certain culturally useful species while eliminating those plants not considered valuable to him or to the society at large. Indeed, large, useful trees are considered communal property, and their harvest is accompanied by a local tax (Reina 1967). This gives a selective advantage to useful plants, increasing their relative numbers in the milpa. Favored species gain light, space, and nutrients as a result of reduced root and shade competition from other large productive species and their replacement by small herbaceous cultivars. Simple care in burning protects such trees and shrubs from smoke damage. When the field is fallowed, the nonselected plants sprout again from still-living root systems and seed from surrounding forest, but suffer from competition with more established useful plants and secondary growth. If pre-Hispanic population pressure caused the fallow period to be shortened to less than the maturation period of most forest plants (about 6–10 years), the nonuseful plants would have been cut again before reaching maturity and young useful plants spared. Over time, useless forest species would be repeatedly slain before reproducing and replaced by young secondary and useful species. The eventual result may have been regional extinction of nonuseful plants with a maturation period longer than the fallow period. Spared species would assume dominance and only the short-lived useless plants would remain. These would be lifeforms such as herbs, grasses, composites, and chenopods, plants similar in niche to the cultivars, producing a pollen rain similar to that of modern milpas (Wiseman 1974).

Plants that may have been used in an "artificial rain forest" include the following species:

Trees
- Sapodilla (*Achras zapota*)
- Sapote (*Casimiroa edulis*)
- Chirimoya (*Annona cherimola*)
- Oopchi (*A. reticulata*)
- Zaramuya (*A. squamosa*)
- Ramon (*Brosimum alicastrum*)
- Aguacate (*Persea americana*)
- Sabal (*Sabal* sp.)
- Coyol (*Acrocomia mexicana*)
- Cacao (*Theobroma cacao*)
- Mamey (*Calocarpum mammosum*)
- "Cherry" (*Pseudolmedia spuria*)
- Corozo (*Orbignya cohune*)
- Pom (*Protium copal*)
- Caoba (*Swietenia macrophylla*)
- Chacah (*Bursera simaruba*)
- Ayal (*Crescentia cujete*)

Vines
- Pitahaya (*Cereus* sp.)
- Vanilla (*Vanilla fragrans* or *planifolia*)

Herbs
- Maize (*Zea mays*)
- Bean (*Phaseolis* sp.)
- Tomato (*Lycopersicum esculentum*)
- Squash (*Cucurbita* spp.)
- Chile (*Capsicum annuum*)

Root perennials
- Yam (*Dioscorea trifida*)
- Sweet potato (*Ipomoea batatas*)
- Malanga (*Xanthosoma violaceum*)
- Cassava (*Manihot esculenta*)
- Yam bean (*Pachyrrhizus tuberosus*)

The establishment of an artificially selected woody plant component brings up the question of agricultural efficiency below the canopy. Would seed and root crops have been successful as an understory in view of the restricted amount and changed composition of light penetrating the layers of preserved forest? Light intensity at the rain-forest canopy is 10,500 footcandles, but only 100 footcandles on the densely shaded forest floor (data from Barro Colorado Island, Panama, [Allee 1962]). Small herbaceous crops do not have to raise their photosynthetic surfaces to canopy layers, but use their more modest metabolic expenditure for smaller aboveground structure and, more important, for manufacture of fruits, seeds, and underground starch bodies. Simple maize agriculture, which needs 4,000–8,000 footcandles per 12-hour day as practiced in open situations, would not have been successful with partial tree cover (1,000–3,000 footcandles). Selection for shade-tolerant varieties was essential, as well as extensive use of shade-tolerant root crops such as manioc (*Manihot esculenta*) and malanga (*Xanthosoma violaceum*) that produce starch bodies at 1,000 footcandles and make fewer demands upon the local nutrients than seed crops such as cereals and beans (Graf 1957). Of course, the density of larger woody plants would have had to come into equilibrium with the lower-story cultivation; a closed canopy would not be compatible with cultivation of an understory.

Once the artificial overstory was established, the understory cultivars would gain many advantages. First, leaf litter and unused fruit would fall from the overstory and recycle some nutrients to the soil. Decomposers would be less disturbed by tillage, so decay and release of nutrients to the cultivars would occur more quickly, while other soil organisms would improve the physical character of the soil. This process would have the effect of low-level tillage and fertilization that would yield more reliable harvests and reduce the fallow time. The combination of canopy cover, leaf litter, herb layer, and soil organisms would increase the water retention capacity of the soil. Slowing rainfall runoff has three favorable consequences: (1) elimination of destructive raindrop impact and solution erosion, preserving the little humus present on slopes up to 15° (Greenland 1975); (2) preservation of nutrients in the local soil by inhibiting nutrient solution in surface runoff; (3) slowing of the leaching process.

The woody trees, shrubs, and vines, already in equilibrium with forest pests, utilize internal defenses that make them steady, dependable sources for food and materials. Insects would still be a problem for stabilizing understory species, which generally lack internal defense systems. Alternation of maize, or other seed crops with manioc or yam (*Dioscorea trifida*) cultivation in the understory would decrease chances for attack by the same pest, since their lifeforms and edible parts have different constitutions, environments, and parasites. Crop rotation in the annual component of the artificial rain forest would limit incursions of species-specific pests to minor outbreaks. The problem of weed infestation could be solved by hand weeding or substitution of useful species in the "weedy" niche. This could be accomplished by companion planting of, for example, manioc and cucurbits (Cowgill 1971). The cucurbits, shading out the intolerant weeds, would increase the manioc's yield of edible tissue, resulting in maximum productivity. Root competition between tree and herbaceous crops is the main problem I can see for such a system. If tree crop species are characterized by extensive, shallow root networks, the advantage that the herbaceous crops gain by litter and shade may be offset by depletion of local nutrients. Root crops and the semiepiphytic *Vanilla fragrans* may produce under such conditions, since they use fewer nutrients than seed crops. There may have to be a zone around each tree that either is weed covered or supports slow-growing root crops. These areas may be used for storage or apiaries. However, since competition is *between crops,* rather than between crop and weed or pest, the net gain in usable productivity makes this model attractive from an environmental as well as an agricultural viewpoint.

A greatly simplified version of the artificial rain forest is illustrated in figure 5.3. *Brosimum alicastrum,* the ramon tree, occupies 28 percent of the simulated plot, approximating its density on large Maya sites in Peten (Puleston 1969). For our purposes, the 28 percent of the plot surface will be used by the tree alone, since root competition and shading decrease productivity of the herb component within this zone (Wiseman 1973). The trees may be cropped continuously, providing an average minimum of 1,122 kilograms per hectare per year (2,470 pounds) of fruit (data from D. E. Puleston and O. S. Puleston 1971). The remaining 72 percent of the plot, receiving full or partial sunlight, may potentially produce (using Cowgill's 1961 figures) 1,871 kilograms of manioc, or 1,151 kilograms of maize, or 17,289 kilograms of beans, or 4,773 kilograms of sweet potatoes, or 5,239 kilograms of squash per hectare of "artificial rain forest."

It is probable that the artificial rain forest required some fallow time, or that the system was not totally efficient. Therefore I will assume one year of rest for each year of understory cropping (the ramon produces each year). Fallowing also insulates the plot from pest invasion (Janzen 1970). Today a family of 5.78 persons can tend a milpa of 5.28 hectares (Cowgill 1962). Since an artificial rain forest plot would require hand weeding, mulching, and more care in general than a modern cornfield, I assume approximately 3.0 hectares is the area a family could have managed with efficiency if the homesite were near the plot.

In a maximum stability model, instead of planting the whole plot with one herbaceous cultivar, a combination of manioc, maize, sweet potato, squash, and beans would be planted to increase diversity, effectively stopping pest invasions and runoff (Wiseman 1973). The crops could be sown in groups or companion planted. Using figure 5.3 as a standard, approximately 32 percent of the plot had fairly full sun, as required by the shade-intolerant *Zea, Cucurbita,* and *Phaseolus,* and 40 percent occupied the semi-shade and root-competition zone allowed by the more tolerant *Manihot, Xanthosoma, Vanilla,* and *Ipomoea.*

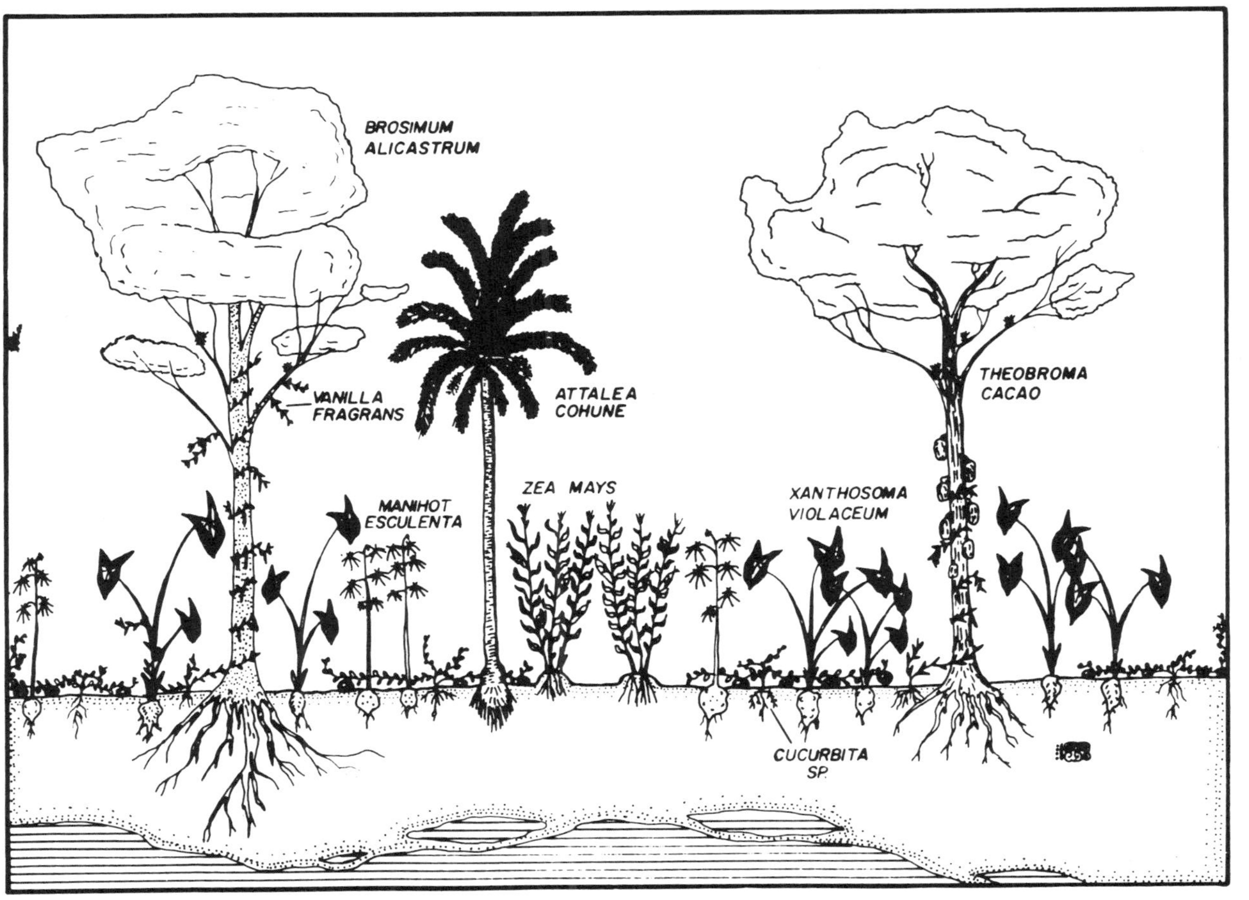

Figure 5.3. The artificial rain forest: crops and spatial array.

Aboriculture

The ramon tree (*Brosimum alicastrum*) has been proposed as a species used in a monocultural orchard system, as it is capable of sustaining high yield (Puleston 1971). A high correlation of ramon trees and archaeological sites has been noted by Lundell (1937) and Puleston (1969). This curious distribution may be evidence of ramon orchards that surrounded the sites when they were active, but edaphic factors such as better drainage, increased available phosphorous (Cowgill 1962), or different soil type may also account for this correlation. Ramon is not the only species exhibiting this curious distribution; Lundell (1937) lists guayo, aguacate, mamey, and other fruit trees as occupying archaeological sites, suggesting a more complex orchard system than ramon monoculture. The annual yield of ramon nuts is 1,245 kilograms (2,740 lbs) per hectare. Unfortunately, there are no data on the quantity of ramon needed to support an individual per year. Therefore, the potential carrying capacity of ramon orchards must at this time go uncalculated. Puleston (1971) indicates that ramon nuts are storable in chultunes (underground chambers) and that they may have served admirably as a reserve in times of necessity, insulating the ancient Maya somewhat against yearly climatic variation. The presence of secondary compounds in the ramon probably reduces its susceptibility to disease, making it a potential stable food source for the ancient Maya.

Terracing

B. L. Turner (1974a) gives an excellent summary of the evidence for upland geointensive methods in the Maya lowlands, as does Wilken (1971). Implicit in such intensive models is the use of fertilizer to allow these terraced zones to be highly productive. Without mulching or fertilizing, the terraces would be little more efficient than the abundant flatlands in the central Peten. The main use of terraces is centripetal in nature, as is the drained field; that is, it increases the amount of land available for agriculture in a way that avoids limiting factors such as erosion and chemical weathering. Terraces are good evidence for almost total land use, since all arable lowland would be under cultivation before the expense of terrace construction was undertaken. Since there is no evidence, either archaeological or ethnographic, to indicate such use, I do not treat productivity of terraced slopes differently from that of the flatlands. Silt trap terraces may be considered localized high-productivity sites, but they are more than offset by the xeric nature of the rest of the slope (which would best be planted with drought-hardy cash crops such as *Bursera, Agave,* or *Yucca*). In the quantitative reconstruction to follow, slopes will therefore be included as part of the general upland zones, to be treated with techniques only slightly differing from those used on flat or rolling terrain.

Raised Fields

The most difficult system to describe (or to determine potential yields for) is the raised field (or chinampa) system (Wilken 1971; Siemens and Puleston 1972). This geointensive system is best suited to swamps and river floodplains, which constitute approximately 21 percent of the central Peten. Although much has appeared in print concerning its supposed efficiency, there are few data amenable to a simulation scheme, for either amount of work necessary to construct drained field systems, or their potential productivity. The figures of support capacity of highland Mexican chinampas (Palerm and Wolf 1957) are almost certainly too high to be applicable to a Maya agricultural situation, owing to the sporadic nature of *bajo* inundation.

Some evidence suggests that corn borers significantly reduce maize yields in *bajos* that have not been modified by raised fields or other such techniques (Reina 1967). The influence of corn borers in *bajos* may be due to the host plants. What is not known is whether raised-field systems sufficiently altered the *bajos* to reduce the host plant population and, hence, the pest population. Nevertheless, pest incursions in raised-field *bajo* systems must be dealt with in agricultural assessments, particularly since 60 percent of some regions of northern Peten are *bajos* (Bullard 1960; Lundell 1937). In addition, vegetal patterns suggestive of raised fields have been observed to the west of Tikal (Dahlin 1976b). The presence of raised fields in Belize and Campeche, and apparently in the vast *bajos* of Quintana Roo, provides circumstantial evidence that raised field cultivation may have been utilized in the central lake region of Peten.

AGRICULTURAL SIMULATION

Both the quantitative and qualitative data presented above are bits and pieces of an organic system that has functioned in various forms since man arrived in the Maya lowlands, probably over 4,000 years ago (Cowgill and Hutchinson 1966; Hammond 1976b; Puleston 1976). These data may be linked in such a way as to simulate that system. While this method is fraught with problems, it points out those aspects of each system for which data are lacking. The researcher, in addition, by rigidly structuring his data, may obtain a new and perhaps different view of the organism under study.

The major problem with simulation is that it reflects the researcher's bias in its initial stages more than a hypothesis and test approach. The second problem is that, since it is a model, it may not reflect reality at all, but rather some chance patterning or correlation. The third problem in a simulation is the number of assumptions that must be made in lieu of actual data when they are lacking.

The program, adapted to a CDC6400 computer, simulates as closely as possible the actual relations of one subsystem to another. Program MAYAPOL handles variables of pollen emission, farm personnel, time (man-day) input, and productivity of crop plants in such a way that variables of one type may be expressed in terms of other variables. In this way, any variable may be manipulated to see how other variables of the system change in response. Resultant estimates may then be tested against archaeological and paleoecological data.

The program has several subroutines that must be described in a general way. The program MAYAPOL itself is merely a quantified system of labor and time, transforming one data set into another via ethnographic data transfer functions derived from Cowgill (1961), Reina (1967), and Emerson and Kempton (1935). The estimated pollen production output from the main program is put into subroutine A, essentially a semilog regression of pollen deposition against distance from source area. Data are derived from Raynor, Ogden, and Hayes (1972). However the spatial distribution of the pollen-producing plots is of prime importance, since a large field at a distance will produce the same pollen deposition at a given locus as a small plot up close. To avoid this problem, I have constructed a simulation polygon that is no more than a randomly generated landscape that approximates that of the modern Peten. Its dimensions are 10 kilometers a side (100 sq km), in the center of which is a hypothetical lake 0.4 kilometer in diameter. LANDSAT 1 imagery (fig. 5.2) indicates that approximately 10 percent of the land surface of the Peten is covered by tropical savanna (grasslands), 20 percent by *bajo* (swamps), and 70 percent by upland forest (fig. 5.2). These zones are expressed in the polygon as randomly placed one-kilometer-blocks of that vegetation type added until the requisite coverage is obtained (fig. 5.4). Agricultural fields of any type can be placed at random within the polygon.

Each randomly placed field within the polygon is a given distance from the lake, and therefore has a given potential downwind pollen input. Only those fields which are upwind of the lake will contribute pollen; those to the side will not. This factor is handled by randomly generated wind vectors expressed as 10 lines extending from the core site. All fields intercepted along each line are recorded as to their distance, converted to pollen influx via the regression formula, and totaled for that vector. This procedure is intended to simulate pollen from each field blowing along the line to the depositional basin. The 10 wind vector–pollen influx sums are averaged, and this value is used as the estimate of pollen influx for that agricultural system dispersed randomly within the simulation polygon.

The results of the MAYAPOL program as described above are within one yearly cycle and may be considered as an optimum model. In reality, other factors prevent expression of such an optimum efficiency. Therefore, the program is run for a one-hundred-year period with randomly selected years having adverse effects upon the productivity. Reina (1967) indicates that pests (corn borers), climate (insufficient rainfall), and miscellaneous cultural causes adversely affect the maize crop. The type, magni-

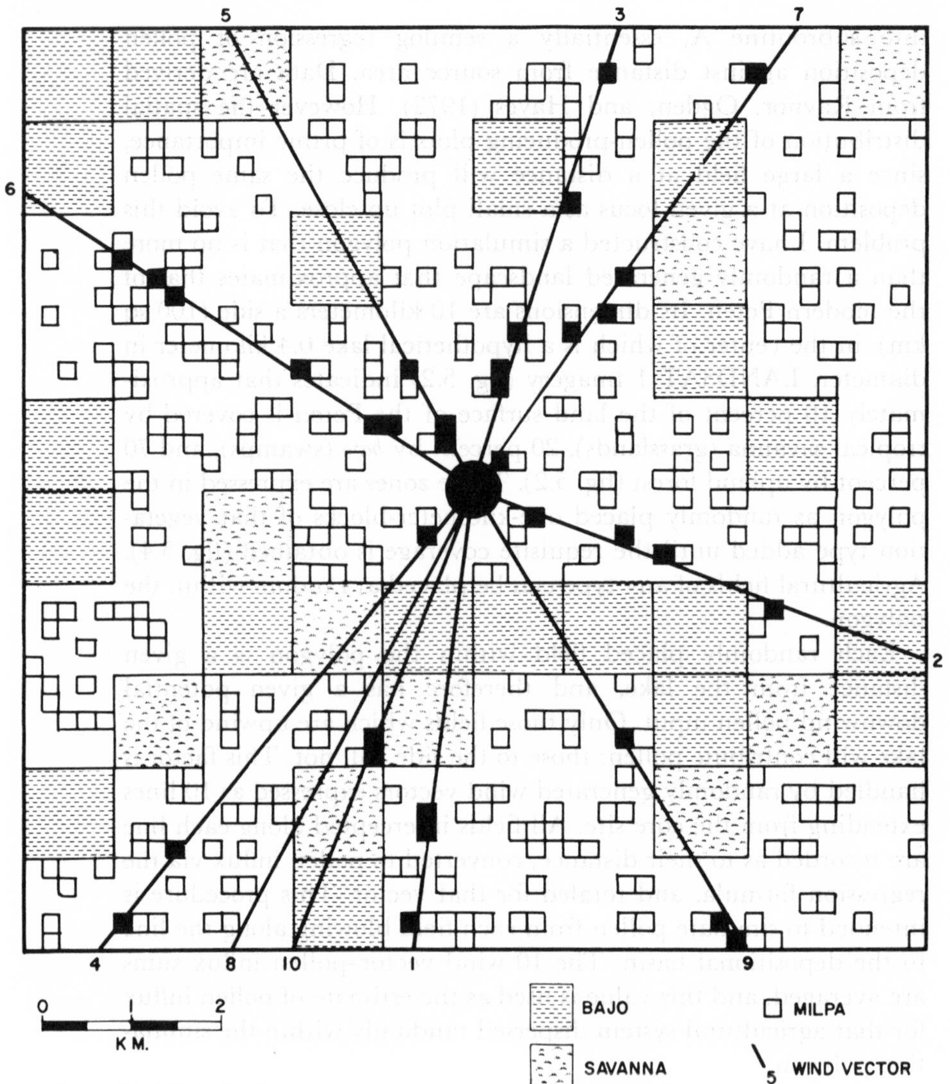

Figure 5.4. Simulation polygon used for calculating pollen influx values.

Table 5.4. Summary of treatments during a 100-year run of program MAYAPOL

Assumptions: **Climate decreases yield 7% in 20 randomly chosen years (1 in 5).**
Climate decreases yield 15% in 5 randomly chosen years (1 in 20).
Climate decreases yield 50% in 1 randomly chosen year (1 in 100).
Corn borers decrease yield 10% in 18 randomly chosen years (1 in 6).
Corn borers decrease yield 15% in 5 randomly chosen years (1 in 20).
Corn borers decrease yield 25% in 1 randomly chosen year (1 in 100).
Miscellaneous causes decrease yield 10% in 5 randomly chosen years (1 in 20).

Year	*Decrease in yield*	*Decrease in Pollen Prod.*	*Year*	*Decrease in yield*	*Decrease in Pollen Prod.*
2	7% C	7%	53	7% C	7%
4	10% B		58	10% B	
5	15% C + 10% M	15%	59	15% C	15%
6	7% C	7%	62	10% B	
8	15% C	15%	63	7% C	7%
11	10% B		68	7% C	7%
13	10% B		69	15% C	15%
14	7% C	7%	71	10% B	
17	7% C	7%	73	10% B	
19	7% C	7%	75	10% B	
20	7% C + 10% B	7%	78	10% B 3 7% C	7%
23	10% B		81	7% C	7%
24	7% C + 10% B	7%	82	7% C	7%
27	15% B		84	7% C	7%
31	10% B		85	10% M	
35	15% B		86	10% B	
37	15% B		88	7% C + 10% B	7%
38	7% C + 10% B	7%	89	15% C + 10% B	15%
40	7% C + 10% B	7%	93	10% B	
49	15% B + 10% M		96	7% C	7%
50	7% C	7%	99	10% M	
52	50% C	50%	100	7% C	7%

C = Climatic input
B = Corn borer attack
M = Miscellaneous causes of yield decline

Mean percent of potential crop yield allowed by climatic and other inputs:
Mean $\overline{X}$ = 94.55%, standard deviation s = 7.85.
Mean percent of potential pollen production allowed by climatic and other inputs: $\overline{X}$ = 97.41%, s = 7.92.

tude, and year of factors that reduce the potential yield of maize pollen and crops are computed (table 5.4). Each MAYAPOL simulation is run for one hundred consecutive years and the mean productivity calculated, since a pollen sample (or house mound) would integrate many years.

The results of several runs of program MAYAPOL representing 100-year periods and allowing but one type of agricultural practice are shown in table 5.5. Each agricultural system is a discrete entity. The prehistoric Maya did not use any one method, but probably selected those that best fit the diverse habitats we have shown surrounding a given site. The agricultural systems have been arrayed along two edaphic gradients, to determine the potential "maximal habitat" of each system (fig. 5.5) (Wiseman 1976). By combining the data produced by seven runs of the MAYAPOL program with the gradient analysis, we discover which methods are potentially competitive and which are complimentary in the Maya lowlands. Those methods that ecologically compete were assessed as to their stability (in terms of agricultural limiting factors) and productivity. More stable and/or productive systems were assigned greater weight in a multisystem reconstruction, to approximate better the apparent high productivity of past Maya agriculture.

I wish now to present a series of imaginary episodes in the history of agriculture in the Maya lowlands by combining the simulation results (table 5.5), the gradient analysis (fig. 5.5), and the simulated landscape (fig. 5.4). Although the values for productivity, pollen influx, and personnel are expressed in yearly terms, they are mean values for a 100-year run (table 5.4). Population figures are expressed as (1) producers (farmer + family), (2) persons supported (the mean maximum population that may be supported by agricultural productivity), and (3) persons per square kilometer (persons supported ÷ 100 square kilometers). Because so many assumptions must be made, the precision of this quantified reconstruction may be quite low. The simulation data are, however, useful for testing the various agricultural models that have been proposed against the evidence. When a model has been evaluated both through test implications generated by mathematical means, and through actual data, it can be considered verified (or not), and not before.

Table 5.5. Output of simulations: MAYAPOL program

Run	Type	Cycle (yr)	Array[a]	Pollen influx[b]	Productivity Maize	Ramon	Manioc	Population Producers	Support[c]
1	Milpa	5	0.5 km	8.6×10^{-4}	1.9×10^{4}			13	66
2	Milpa	5	Upland (70%)	1.1×10^{-2}	2.2×10^{6}			1,526	11,228
3	Chinampa	1	Bajo (20%)	2.8×10^{-2}	3.1×10^{6}				7,700
4	Monoculture	1	Upland (70%)	2.0×10^{-1}	1.1×10^{7}			7,630	39,500
5	Levee	1	Marsh				1.6×10^{4}		24
6	Ramon	1	Upland (70%)			7.6×10^{6}			
7	Artificial rain forest	1–2	Upland (35%)	4.0×10^{-5}	1.8×10^{6}	4.0×10^{6}	3.6×10^{6}		18,000

a. Distribution of fields within the simulation polygon. Run 1 had fields constrained to be within 0.5 km of the lake, run 2 had milpas scattered randomly within the upland zone, which covers 70% or 70 km^2 of the polygon.

b. Pollen influx is expressed as *Zea* pollen grains/cm^2/year falling in the central lake of the simulation polygon.

c. Population supported refers to the number of people that may be fed by the estimated agricultural productivity.

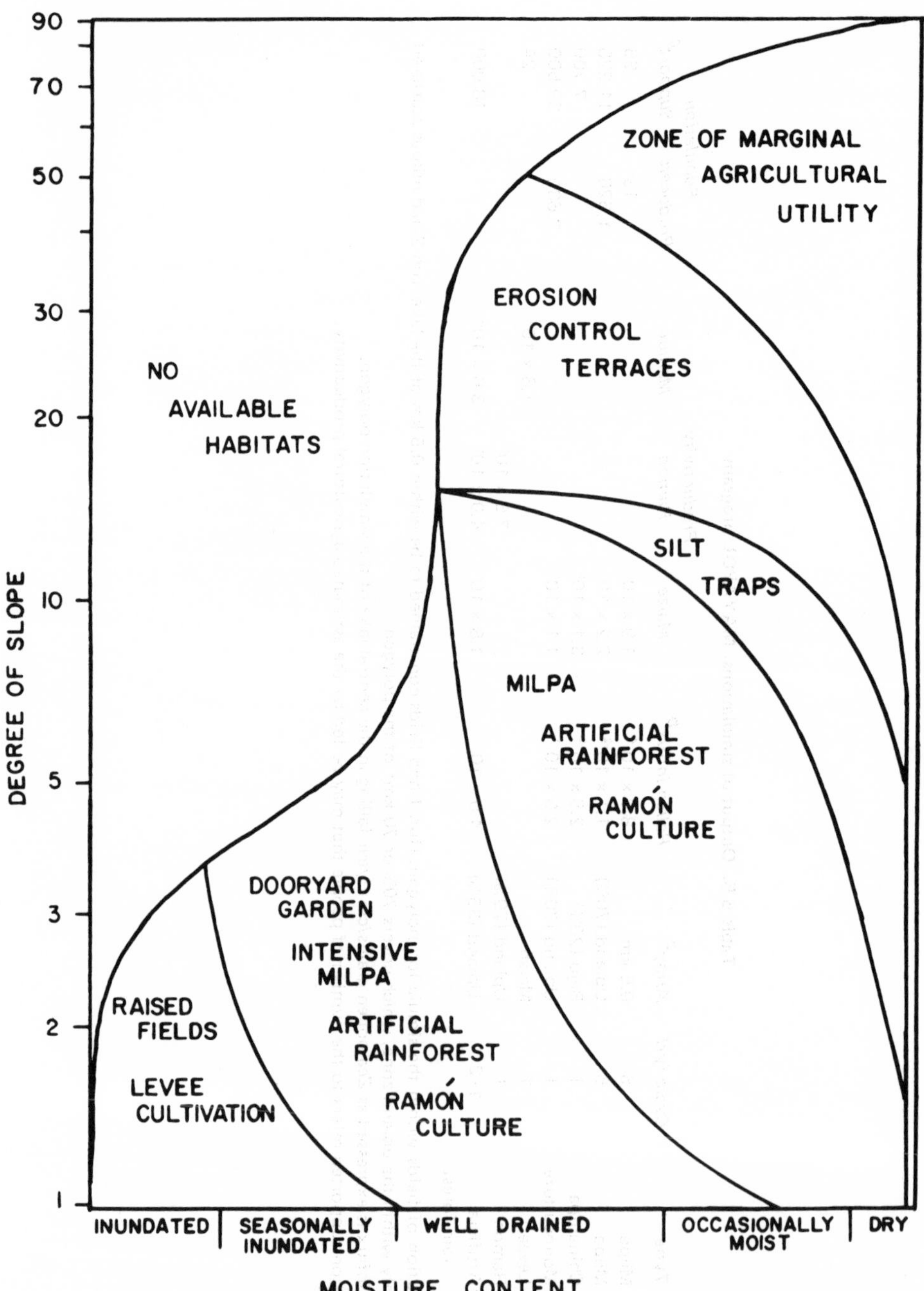

Figure 5.5. Tropical agricultural systems arrayed along two edaphic gradients.

Scene 1. Preclassic Agriculture: Simulation Run 1

A small hamlet of less than twenty structures was situated upon the shores of the central lake (of the simulation polygon). The inhabitants (approximately 15 producers) cultivated the 100-meter-wide band of marsh surrounding the lake. Raising mostly manioc, they harvested an annual average of 16,400 kilograms of tubers and some 500 kilograms of maize. Their neighbors raised crops in scattered upland swiddens within half a kilometer of the lake. They planted approximately twelve hectares of field each year, which were then let fallow for four years. The 13 (milpa) producers raised 19,000 kilograms of maize per year. The combined milpas and drained fields contributed 0.0109 *Zea* pollen grains per square centimeter per year to the lake sediments. Surpluses were the rule, since the supportable population was 66 persons, while there were only 31 producers. The maximum population density for the polygon was only 0.67 persons per square kilometer. Remains of 7–13 house mounds date to this hypothetical period (data from Puleston [1974b] were used to convert population to house mounds).

Scene 2. The Late Preclassic Expansion: Simulation Run 2

The small preclassic hamlet may have undergone a population surge during the centuries around the birth of Christ. Swidden technology now overshadowed marsh cultivation, and had spread throughout the upland forest zone of the simulation polygon at this early date. Of the total land surface, 14 percent was covered with productive field and 56 percent was covered with bush fallow. Only culturally spared trees, small patches of forest, and the unusable *bajos* remained untouched. Fifteen hundred producers, from numerous small hamlets, worked in the milpas, obtaining a mean annual harvest of well over two million kilograms of maize. The supportable population was 7,700 persons, or 77 persons per square kilometer, resulting in 17 structures per square kilometer dating from this episode.

The fields had a mean nearest-neighbor distance of 425 meters, separated by early secondary vegetation (less than four years old). I suspect that pest populations and leaching may have quickly become limiting to such a system. Unstable agriculture of this type probably caused increased competition for richer soils, or a beginning of intensive agricultural systems.

Scene 3. Classic Period Intensive Agriculture: Simulation Runs 3–7

Raised-field systems occupied the *bajo* soils which cover 20 percent of the simulation polygon. They provided the Classic Maya with a stable, highly productive agricultural option. The fields were continuously cropped, but probably needed more labor input per hectare than a milpa plot of similar size. Twenty thousand hectares of raised fields had a potential productivity of over three million kilograms of maize, if that were the sole crop raised. The supportable population of the raised fields was 11,228 persons, or 112 persons per square kilometer. Twenty-five hundred house mounds were left by the raised field cultivators and the people they supported.

The intensive swidden system occupied one-half of the upland forest zone (3,500 ha) on those soils to which it was best adapted. Terraces, erected on hillsides, were incorporated into this intensive system. Maximum yearly harvest of maize from the intensive milpas was slightly less than two million kilograms, since it was raised on but one plot in three, owing to crop rotation and/or fallow. The labor input of 3,600 producers supported over 6,500 persons. These inhabitants left behind 1,400 house mounds for archaeologists to discover, and 0.0018 *Zea* grain per square centimeter per year for the palynologist to find.

Half of the upland forest zone was occupied by artificial rain forest (Wiseman 1973) that provided, in addition to maize, beans, and squash, a host of minor cash crops such as vanilla, cacao, and other crops. Producers, numbering a little over 2,500 persons, tended the immensely stable and productive forests. Yearly harvest was four million kilograms of ramon, 1,800,000 of maize, 3,640,000 of manioc, and numerous smaller cash and subsistence crops. The population supported by the maize and manioc productivity was approximately 12,000 persons. The addition of ramon and other products probably made the figure closer to 18,000 persons (180 persons per square kilometer). Pollen influx into the central lake from the artificial rain forest was small, about 0.00004 *Zea* grain per centimeter per year.. The inhabitants lived in and around 4,000 houses that today are mounds, covered by the forest they sought to control.

Using the maximal-habitat concept, I wish to describe the total productivity and supportable population of the combined output of the artificial rain forest, raised fields, lakeside cultivation, and intensive swidden, which are ecologically complementary in the simulation polygon. Ten percent of the land was set aside for urban construction or nonusable lands. The combined harvest for the 100-square-kilometer simulation polygon was four million kilograms of ramon, 6,800,000 of maize, and 3,656,400 of manioc. These combined fields produced a pollen influx of 0.015 *Zea* grain per square centimeter per year in the central lake. This stable, diverse system supported a population of 35,758 persons (358 persons per square kilometer), who left a total of 8,000 scattered rural and suburban house mounds in addition to their art and monumental architecture.

THE TEST

Verification of such a systems analysis rests upon four distinct independent data bases: paleodemographic estimates, relic earthworks, botanical distributions, and palynology. First, the population estimates (table 5.6) may be considered independent data suitable for testing output from the simulations. The population estimates derived for the simulation polygon are not directly comparable to the archaeological figures, since house-mound survey is only possible in upland habitat situations. Demographic estimates often extrapolate upland habitat densities for the total area of the lowlands, whereas the simulation model integrates *bajo* and savanna into the predicted densities, giving a lower estimate than the archaeological. To accommodate this disparity, the population estimates derived here will be multiplied by the constant 1.25 (ratio of total land to upland). The converted minimum and maximum populations derived from the simulation are arrayed in table 5.6 according to agricultural method. The minimum is defined as the number of producers. The maximum is defined as the total number of persons supported by the method

Table 5.6. Comparison of Archaeologically Derived and Simulation-Derived Population Estimates

Type	*Minimum*	*Maximum*
Urban, archaeological		900
Intersite, archaeological		300
Rural, archaeological	40	200
Chinampa, simulation		140
Milpa, simulation	19	77
Artificial rain forest, simulation		225
Maximal habitat, simulation		448

and should most closely resemble archaeological reality due to the large number of administrators and other nonproducers in Maya society. The maximal-habitat system results are most in accord with the higher archaeological figures (table 5.6), indicating the distinct possibility that a combination of methods, each in its own niche, may have supported the population densities hypothesized by archaeologists.

The remains of terraces, raised-field systems, and artificially altered vegetation communities indicate that a series of subsistence options was used by the pre-Hispanic Maya in at least three ecologically distinct zones. These options are evidence for something approximating what I call the Maximal Habitat Model (Wiseman 1976).

Modern floral distributions give somewhat equivocal evidence of past multi-crop orchard systems, somewhat similar to the ramon model or to the artificial rain forest model. Since archaeological sites are edaphically different from unmodified land, these data must be viewed with caution.

Pollen Analysis in the Maya Lowlands

Perhaps the most appropriate tool in the reconstruction of past landscapes is palynology (Davis 1969). Pollen diagrams taken from Lakes Petenxil and Eckixil, Peten, have been presented elsewhere (Cowgill and Hutchinson 1966; Brooks et al. 1973; Wiseman 1974; Vaughan 1976), but these are not usually addressed to the Maya agricultural problem in more than a general way. Also, lowland pollen spectra have been interpreted with little or no reference to modern analogues, especially in agricultural situations.

Many of the vegetation sample stands described in the first section of this paper also served as modern pollen collection sites, so that correlations between coverage value and pollen productivity could be empirically determined. When pollen productivity was arrayed along the edaphic gradient (table 5.1), several factors became evident. First, pollen productivity and deposition (in soil samples) is low in tropical forest communities (about 400 grains/gram dry weight) because of the high incidence of entomophily (insect pollination) and the destruction of deposited pollen by soil organisms. As an example, a *Pseudobombax ellipticum* near Lake Petenxil had a coverage value in plot VT-1 of 30 percent, but contributed only 2 percent of the pollen found on the ground beneath it, a 15:1 underrepresentation. Such data indicate that most forest taxa, cultivated or not, are underrepresented in fossil pollen spectra.

Encinals and savanna formations have pollen more representative of their species composition, as well as higher absolute pollen density (about 2,000 grains/gram dry weight). Relative and absolute pollen density of lowland pollen taxa were plotted along the edaphic gradient. The absolute frequencies were more a function of local postdeposition degradation—a form of statistical noise obscuring the true patterns in the pollen data—and were rejected for these analyses. A second pollen-vegetion gradient was established at site VT-5, proceeding from uncut monsoon forest (VT-5A) to newly burned milpa (VT-5B) through regenerating forest (VT-5D) to advanced secondary forest (VT-5F) (Budowski 1970) in an attempt to follow pollen variables through a plant successional regime.

Both pollen gradients were evaluated through principal-component analysis to distill the main patterns from the data (Adam 1974; T. Webb 1974). The pollen information, arrayed as an M-by-N matrix, where $M=$ number of pollen taxa (variables), and $N=$ number of sites in the gradient (observations), was punched onto computer cards and processed through program PRINCI, an R-mode principal-component analysis program that standardizes the data before calculation of the correlation matrix. The resulting M eigenvectors are patterned representations of the original variables. Important eigenvectors (principal components) account for large amounts of variance in the original data and have potential paleoecological significance, while the less important eigenvectors describe residual noise, error, or variation caused by a closed percentage sum in the pollen counts. Each eigenvector consists of *M* weights associated with the original pollen taxa, so that the weight is proportional to the importance of a given pollen type to that eigenvector. Further manipulation of the eigenvector matrix results in a matrix of amplitudes of the principal components, arrayed as a function of sample (observation) rather than variable. The amplitudes can be a matrix through space, as in the gradient, or a time series (Adam 1974) expressed as goodness-of-fit coefficient of each site data set to that empirically derived principal component (eigenvector). As an example, if eigenvector 1 has heavy weights for pollen types *Pinus, Quercus,* and Graminae, and negative weights for *Alnus* and Compositae, and sample *A* has high percentages of the first three taxa, then its amplitude will be high. There is the same amount of information in the principal components matrix as in the original data matrix, but it is statistically distilled into independent patterns empirically describing most of the variance.

The gradient pollen samples consisted of grand means of up to ten subsamples (double fixed sum of 200 grains) collected from the top one-half centimeter of soil (Wiseman 1974; Adam and Mehringer 1975). Low local productivity meant that more subsamples were necessary to entiate the communities by their pollen than those in temperate zones. Due to statistical problems inherent in principal components analysis, the number of observations (samples) must be equal to or greater than the number of variables. Many pollen types were eliminated from analysis for this reason (T. Webb and Bryson 1972). Taxa rejected include extralocal pollen of *Pinus, Carpinus,* and *Myrica,* the purely lakeside genus *Typha,* and *Brosimum-Cecropia* and *Eugenia,* which do not have significant variance along the gradient (or low percentages). The remaining taxa, containing most of the information in the gradient but less noise, were counted as a second fixed sum of 200 grains, and used in the analysis. Since many of the modern pollen data have been presented elsewhere (Wiseman 1974), and detailed presentation of the results are in preparation (Wiseman n.d.), I will summarize only the results of the principal components analyses.

Results of the Gradient Analysis

Eigenvector 1 of the edaphic gradient, which accounts for 22 percent of the variance, has high positive scalars (weights) for Moraceae, *Terminalia*-type, *Achras,* and *Haematoxylan,* and negative scalars for Graminae, Cyperaceae, *Acaciae,* and high-spine Compositae (table 5.7). The amplitudes are highest in monsoon forest and mesic forest, and lowest in savanna and grassland, elegantly describing the transition from forest to grassland (fig. 5.6).

Eigenvector 2 (9 percent variance) seems to describe the presence or absence of oak forest, since it has high scalars on *Quercus* and high amplitudes in encinal and *aguada* forests, both of which contain *Quercus oleoides* var. *australis.* Unfortunately, the results of the climax-successional gradient are slightly equivocal. The first eigenvector, accounting for 17 percent of the variance, is uninterpretable in terms of the ecotone. It describes variance within the weed pollen from several sites, not along a successional

Table 5.7. Eigenvector Weights (Scalars) of 17 Selected Lowland Pollen Taxa

Taxon	*Vegetation Gradient* (E_1)	*Successional Gradient* (E_2)	*Petenxil Core* (E_1)	*Eckixil Core* (E_1)	*Habitat*
Nonarboreal Pollen					
Zea mays	−0.05	0.87	0.22	−0.71	Agriculture
High-spine Compositae	−0.28	0.71	0.52	−0.68	Disturbance
Low-spine Compositae	−0.12	0.52	0.09	−0.63	Disturbance
Graminae	−0.82	0.72	0.73	−0.71	Savanna
Chenopodiaceae	0.11	0.41	0.12	−0.52	Disturbance
Senecio-type	0.05	0.41	0.20	−0.50	Disturbance
Euphorbiaceae	0.08	0.36	−0.08	−0.16	Forest, disturbance, Savanna
Cyperaceae	−0.67	−0.11	0.68	0.06	Banks, savanna
Arboreal Pollen					
Quercus	0.11	0.11	0.64	−0.12	Encinal
Haematoxylon	0.59	−0.02	0.19	−0.09	Bajo, Savanna
Zanthoxylum	0.09	−0.20	−0.51	0.10	Forest
Bursera	0.33	−0.19	−0.22	0.12	Forest
Achras	0.67	−0.08	0.41	0.34	Forest, disturbance
Acacia	−0.69	0.19	−0.06	0.34	Forest, encinal, scrub
Celtis	0.23	−0.42	−0.49	0.51	Forest
Terminalia	0.62	−0.70	−0.82	0.61	Forest
Moraceae	0.70	−0.66	−0.66	0.72	Forest

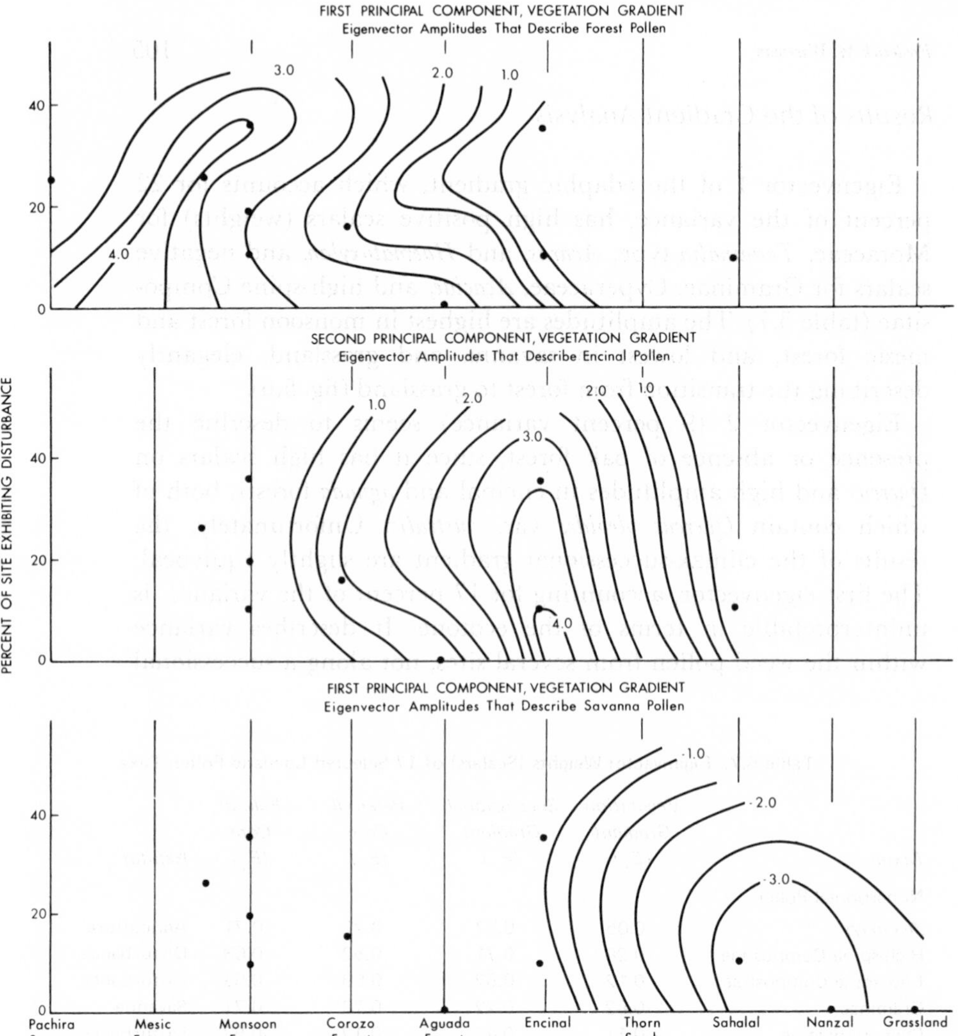

Figure 5.6 Eigenvector amplitudes of modern pollen sample sites, arrayed as a function of edaphic and successional gradients.

gradient. This result is due to the tremendous overrepresentation of weed pollen in all samples except for the mesic forest sites. Eigenvector 2, accounting for 8 percent of the variance (which is low but real in ecological terms), follows the trend and is similar but inverse to eigenvector 1 in the edaphic gradient. High positive weights occur on low-spine Compositae, Graminae, high-spine Compositae, and *Zea*, and negative weights on Moraceae and *Terminalia*-type. With these two analyses, one should be able to describe pollen variance through both edaphic and successional gradients in modern Peten, the necessary analogue for the fossil data.

The most significant result of the gradient analyses is the objective separation of savanna or grassland pollen (Graminae) from pollen produced as a by-product of agriculture (*Zea mays*, Compositae, Graminae, and to a lesser extent, "cheno-ams" [Chenopodiaceae and *Amaranthus*] and Euphorbiaceae). Past climatic change, which might cause expansion and contraction of grasslands, would probably produce a fossil pollen core eigenvector similar to that of the edaphic gradient, while change in agricultural intensity would resemble the successional gradient.

The Fossil Evidence

Mud-water interface samples from Lakes Petenxil and Eckixil contain pollen spectra statistically similar to those collected in analogue sites VT-1, VT-2, VT-5A, and VT-5F; in other words they resemble forest, as they should.

Eight cores were collected in 1975 to delimit the change from a man-dominated landscape to a more undisturbed postclassic landscape (Wiseman n.d.). Two cores taken in Lakes Petenxil and Eckixil were used for reconstruction of the Maya landscape. These two lakes were selected because each has a long core previously published with ^{14}C dates to allow tighter chronological control and the data are most familiar (Cowgill and Hutchinson 1966; Brooks et al. 1973). Pollen from each core was counted, using double fixed sums as described for the gradient analysis to facilitate statistical comparison with the analogues. It was assumed that the one-meter cores would intercept Classic-period pollen productivity, and that the herb-dominated spectra of that time would contribute enough data to the matrix to derive eigenvectors statistically comparable to the gradient analyses.

Petenxil core P_2, used in this analysis, did not intercept enough of the Late Classic deposition to allow a valid reconstruction of the vegetation of that time. From data published by Cowgill and Hutchinson (1966), cross dating indicated that the basal core sample was the only one from the Terminal Classic (zone G_2).

Pollen taxon weights for eigenvector 1 (E_1) are high positive on

Graminae and Cyperaceae (and to a lesser extent, on high-spine Compositae and *Quercus*), and high negative on Moraceae, *Bursera, Celtis* and *Zanthoxylum* (table 5.7). *Terminalia* was not significant on E_1 as expected, but appeared as a strong signal in E_3. The first principal component indicates an alteration of open and closed canopy vegetation throughout the Postclassic (fig. 5.7). The nature of these vegetation communities will be discussed later.

Owing to an apparently much slower sedimentation rate, the Eckixil core presents a clearer view of Classic period vegetation from those samples below approximately 0.44 meters that correspond to zone G_2 in the Petenxil core.

If the two lakes have watersheds somewhat similar in size, the slower rate is understandable, as Eckixil has more basin to adsorb the sediment. Eigenvector 1 scalars of the Eckixil core are high (+) on Moraceae, *Terminalia, Celtis* and Malpighiaceae, and low (–) on *Zea,* low-spine Compositae, Graminae, high-spine Compositae, and cheno-ams (table 5.7). As in core P_2, this eigenvector indicates an alternation of herbaceous and arboreal regimes.

To discover the nature of the arboreal and nonarboreal pollen inputs, a comparison of the core and the gradient data is necessary.

The method of comparison is Pearson's Product Correlation Coefficient (r) between eigenvector weights of the two analogues and the two cores:

$$r = \frac{\Sigma\ (x - \bar{x})\ (y - \bar{y})}{(N\text{-}1)SxSy}$$

where $x =$ eigenvector scalar (weight) on taxon A in the gradient, $y =$ scalar on taxon A in the core, $N =$ number of pairs of eigenvector scalars, and Sx and $Sy =$ standard deviations of the scalars.

Since the same taxa were used in all cases (table 5.7), and the constraint of orthogonality (independence of eigenvectors derived from one data set) does not hold between the cores and the gradients, regression of eigenvectors is a valid method for comparing modern and fossil pollen.

The results of the comparison of the gradient and the core eigenvectors are as follows:

vegetation gradient x Petenxil core $r = -.335, P < .1$,
vegetation gradient x Eckixil core $r = .279, P < .1$;
successional gradient x Petenxil core $r = .681, .01 < P < .001$; and
successional gradient x Eckixil core $r = -.916, P > .001$.

These data show no significant correlation between the vegetation-edaphic gradient and the core data and are evidence that change

Figure 5.7. Amplitudes of principal components from two pollen cores from the central Peten, Guatemala.

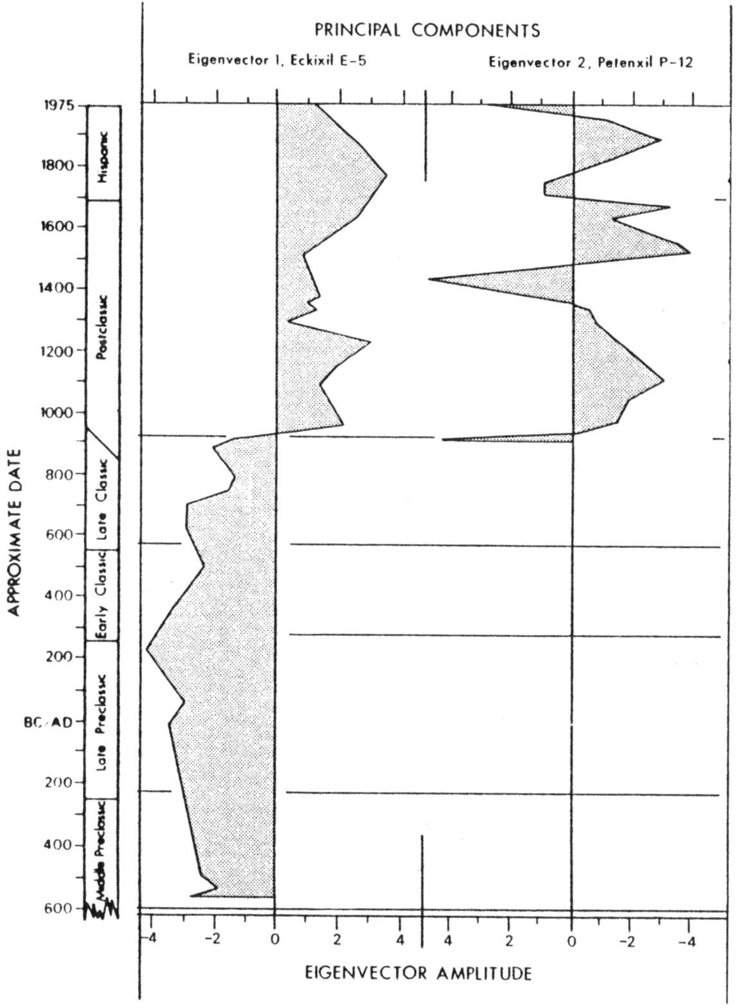

through time in natural vegetation was probably not the cause of the major patterns of variance in the core data. This tends to refute major climatic or edaphic change as being an important factor in the Maya lowlands during the Late Classic and Postclassic periods.

When compared to the cores, the successional gradients show significant correlation, implying that an alternation of agricultural and forest regimes accounts for the pollen variance. I have demonstrated, through the pollen analogue approach, that agricultural information is contained in the pre-Hispanic pollen data, but its nature needs to be discussed.

RECONSTRUCTION OF THE MAYA LANDSCAPE

The presence of *Zea* pollen in the cores indicates that Indian maize was raised in the environs of Lakes Petenxil and Eckixil. The absolute pollen influx, however, is much greater even in the Preclassic than that predicted by any run of the simulation, including total maize monoculture. Pollen transport mechanisms other than wind must therefore account for the discrepancy. Slopewash from fields surrounding the lake is the probable cause, and is evidence for maize agriculture within the watershed of the twin lakes. The nature of this maize agriculture is less clear. Significant correlation of *Zea* pollen with disturbance weed pollen is evidence that the fields were not cleared of weeds as they would be in modern agriculture in the United States. Tremendous overrepresentation of herb pollen may, however, render the weediness less real than it appears. If a short fallow period was used—say, a 1:1 cycle, then the fields may have been intensively fertilized and weeded, but overshadowed palynologically by neighboring fallow plots. Another scenario that fits the palynological evidence is that well-tended, intensive fields existed, but that weed-filled zones occurred in field borders or in areas of marginal usefulness.

Fragments of carbonized plant material are preserved in area sediments and presumably have a relation to fire frequency in the vegetation surrounding a lake. In the lake cores, no significant correlation exists between eigenvectors that describe agriculture and the relative frequency of carbonized fragments. This test of significance is evidence that traditional swidden agriculture is less likely than an intensive system as the actual form of pre-Hispanic Maya agriculture. Most fragments are probably grasses and sedges (Wiseman 1974). A distinct possibility is that the nature of the linear vascular tissue in monocot leaves renders them more easily preserved as charcoal than the more irregular dicot leaves. This dichotomy may result in a form of overrepresentation of grassland fires over woodland (or swidden) fires, masking somewhat the presence of slash-and-burn agriculture.

Although arboreal pollen is suppressed throughout the lower section of the Eckixil core, overrepresentation of herb pollen may mask considerable expanses of forest or orchard. Comparison of the pre-Hispanic palynological evidence with modern data (such as the *Pseudobombax* overrepresentation example cited above) indicates that up to 50 percent of the lake region may have been covered by forest, although alternating with open, herb-dominated vegetation. These data are compatible with models of ramon cultivation, artificial rain forest, and woodlots necessary for fuel. The output of agricultural simulations, when compared to the palynological evidence, allows critical assessment of models of the late Holocene landscape (500 B.C.–A.D. 1975). The following possible monocultural techniques were rejected:

1. Artificial rain forest. Weed pollen from the cores is much in excess of that from the simulation output, while arboreal pollen is below that predicted.
2. Intensive "weedless" agriculture. Simulation of intensively weeded cornfields produced a ratio of *Zea* to weed pollen much greater than that found in the core pollen spectra.
3. Swidden agriculture. No significant correlation was found between carbonized fragments and other agricultural indicators in the core sample matrix.
4. Ramon cultivation. Weed pollen from core samples was in excess of that predicted by simulation, and no statistically significant change was found in the frequency of the *Brosimum-Cecropia* pollen type through time.

Rejection of these techniques means only that none of them was the *sole* subsistence base of the Maya. Such analysis, however, leaves several options for reconstruction of an agricultural sequence for the lake region of Peten.

A PRELIMINARY AGRICULTURAL SEQUENCE FOR THE CENTRAL PETEN

Middle and Late Preclassic, ca. 500 B.C. (base of core)–A.D. 250

According to the simulation and palynological comparisons discussed above, maize agriculture covered the watershed of Lake Eckixil as early as the Middle Preclassic period. Such evidence supports an early riverine-lacustrine adaptation such as that postulated by D. E. Puleston and O. S. Puleston (1971), since the lake's immediate watershed was then as fully utilized as during the Late Classic period. The presence of abundant weed pollen during Preclassic times and the general lack of tree pollen indicate abundant secondary successional herbs and shrubs of the sunflower, pigweed, grass, and potato families. These Preclassic data palynologically resemble old field communities of the modern Peten—tangled, thorny, economically useless shrublands, one to four meters high, with occasional spared climax species. Whether these reconstructed secondary scrublands existed as part of a fallow cycle, as border communities, or independent from agriculture is unclear, but their presence is likely. Burning was sporadic during the Preclassic period but the presence of generally higher percentages of dicot carbonized fragments hints of significant woodland fires. It is tempting to combine the maize and weed pollen data and that of the carbon fragments into a swidden-type reconstruction. Indeed, uncritical comparison with the modern pollen data, in which swidden agriculture is a component, yields a Preclassic dominated by slash-and-burn agriculture. Although an early extensive system, slowly developing into intensive methods, is close to the heart of many researchers, diachronic analysis of the agricultural eigenvectors and charcoal frequencies renders such an interpretation equivocal. In summary, the Preclassic landscape in the immediate environs of Lakes Petenxil (original Preclassic data from Cowgill and Hutchinson 1966) and Eckixil was a mosaic of cornfields and scrublands, with occasional houses or hamlets, with a population of between 25 and 60 persons per square kilometer (data from the neighboring Lake Yaxha region from Rice 1976). This reconstruction is not unlike the scenario generated by the simulation for the Preclassic period, except that the uplands were generally unmodified until Late Preclassic times.

Classic Period, A.D. *250–850*

A combination of techniques (at least some of which were characterized by weedy undergrowth) or extensive short-fallow maize agriculture without significant burning are two options that seem to fit the Classic period data. The human population outputs from the simulations, as well as pest or nutrient problems, negate, to a certain extent, the short-fallow maize agriculture model. The population able to be supported by a 1:2 and 1:1 cycle may approach the archaeological population estimates if all upland forest is eliminated. The resulting nature and distribution of fields, however, is incompatible with modern plant-pest and nutrient-loss data as described in the first section of this paper.

Since this maximal model requires the virtual elimination of upland forest, the predicted loss of the characteristically underrepresented arboreal pollen does not occur. I therefore reject short-fallow agriculture as the sole method used by the Classic Maya.

In summary, it appears that no single agricultural technique, either actual or hypothetical, will satisfy the requirements of the demographic, ecological, and palynological data. The remaining option is the most likely when the derived simulation results are compared with real data. That is, a suite of agricultural techniques, each fitting into its own environmental niche, with differing "intensification" and productivity is the valid model of Classic period subsistence. The maximal habitat model for the Classic period central Maya lowlands is supported by the following data:

1. The simulation of the "maximal habitat model" (Wiseman 1976) supports populations similar to those derived from settlement surveys (Puleston 1974b).
2. Pest incursions are limited by differing crops, harvest times, and land use.
3. Erosion and nutrient loss are limited by terracing (B. L. Turner 1974a) and retention of tree or shrub cover.
4. The combination of weed and *Zea* pollen indicates maize agriculture, probably accompanied by either fallowing or other weedy plots, as one agricultural technique of the "maximal habitat" system.
5. The presence of terraces in the Peten, as described by B. L. Turner (1974a), indicates the use of a second technique, although the paucity of Peten terrace data must be recognized.

6. The correlation of *Brosimum alicastrum* (and other tree crops) and some archaeological sites may be evidence of a third technique.
7. Raised fields, which may exist in the environs of Tikal (Dahlin 1976b) and elsewhere, are a possible fourth technique.
8. No agricultural technique known will meet the criteria of the simulations and ecological evidence.

The "maximal habitat" hypothesis has been evaluated through its ecological, archaeological, mathematical, and palynological implications. It has met or exceeded the requirements of the modern and pre-Hispanic data.

The Maya Collapse, ca. A.D. 800–900

The collapse was not only a hierarchical phenomenon but also a general catastrophe that affected the bottom of the social pyramid, the Maya farmer. The change from an agricultural regime dominated by *Zea* and weeds to a forest-dominated landscape occurred rapidly (as shown in figure 5.7 at about 0.4 meters in the Eckixil core). Rapid depopulation of the central Peten, occurring over less than a century, was inferred from calculated sedimentation rates and from the stratigraphic positions of the last major agricultural episode and the first arboreal episode. If this change coincided with the cessation of temple construction, as I suspect, the event was truly an all-encompassing catastrophe, not a slow degeneration.

The Postclassic, A.D. 900–the Present

The forest-dominated Postclassic period was interrupted by a small episode of agriculture around the middle of the second millennium A.D. (approximately 0.2 meters in the Eckixil core, and 0.65 meters in the Petenxil core). This result may correspond to the recolonization of the lake region by the Postclassic Peten-Itza, the last flickering light of the Maya civilization, extinguished by the Spaniards in 1697 (Morley 1946).

The modern vegetation communities and pollen rain (fig. 5.7) of the Maya lowlands are returning to an agriculture-dominated regime under the present expansion of the highland Maya into the relatively untouched lowland forest. Perhaps lessons gleaned from the past will prevent a recurrence of the agricultural and social chaos that brought the Maya civilization to a close over 1,000 years ago.

NOTE

1. Partial support of this study was provided by National Science Foundation Grant BMS 72-01859 to E. S. Deevey, Jr.; NSF Grant DEB 75-13944 to P. S. Martin, and by the Department of Geosciences, University of Arizona. I thank T. Patrick Culbert, V. C. LaMarche, T. J. Blasing, H. C. Fritts, Linda Drew, A. M. Solomon, and R. M. Turner, who assisted in various parts of the study. I thank David P. Adam, Wayne Wendland, Emil Haury, Jack Ewell, Ken Petersen, and others for their helpful discussions, and Betty Fink for editing and typing services.

6

ALFRED H. SIEMENS
Department of Geography, University of British Columbia

Karst and the Pre-Hispanic Maya in the Southern Lowlands[1]

Limestone solution has played an important geomorphological role throughout the habitat of the lowland Maya. It is responsible for many aspects of the landforms and water regime of the Yucatan. Some of these characteristics are commonly referred to in descriptions of the Yucatan and recited by every tourist guide; others seem not to have been given the attention they deserve.

Bishop Landa observed the basic Yucatecan hydrographic fact many years ago: "Nature worked so differently in this country in the matter of rivers and springs, which in all the rest of the world run on top of the land, that here in this country all run and flow through secret passages under it" (Tozzer 1941:187). The resulting array of features, often referred to collectively as *karst,* has been studied extensively in northern Yucatan but less so in the classic core area to the south. A diagram from Robles's very useful essay on karstic geology and geohydrology in the north introduces the range of landforms commonly encountered and illustrates the general hydrological conditions (fig. 6.1). The cenote, a place of ritual and a source of water, a kind of window on the subterranean circulation system, has always been the most remarkable single landform in this landscape (Pearse, Creaser, and Hall 1936). Caves run a close second. They are standard components of virtually every karstic landscape and, indeed, are their most useful diagnostic features. Nevertheless, they seem to maintain a mystery and a very special allure. Henry Mercer's well illustrated classic, *The*

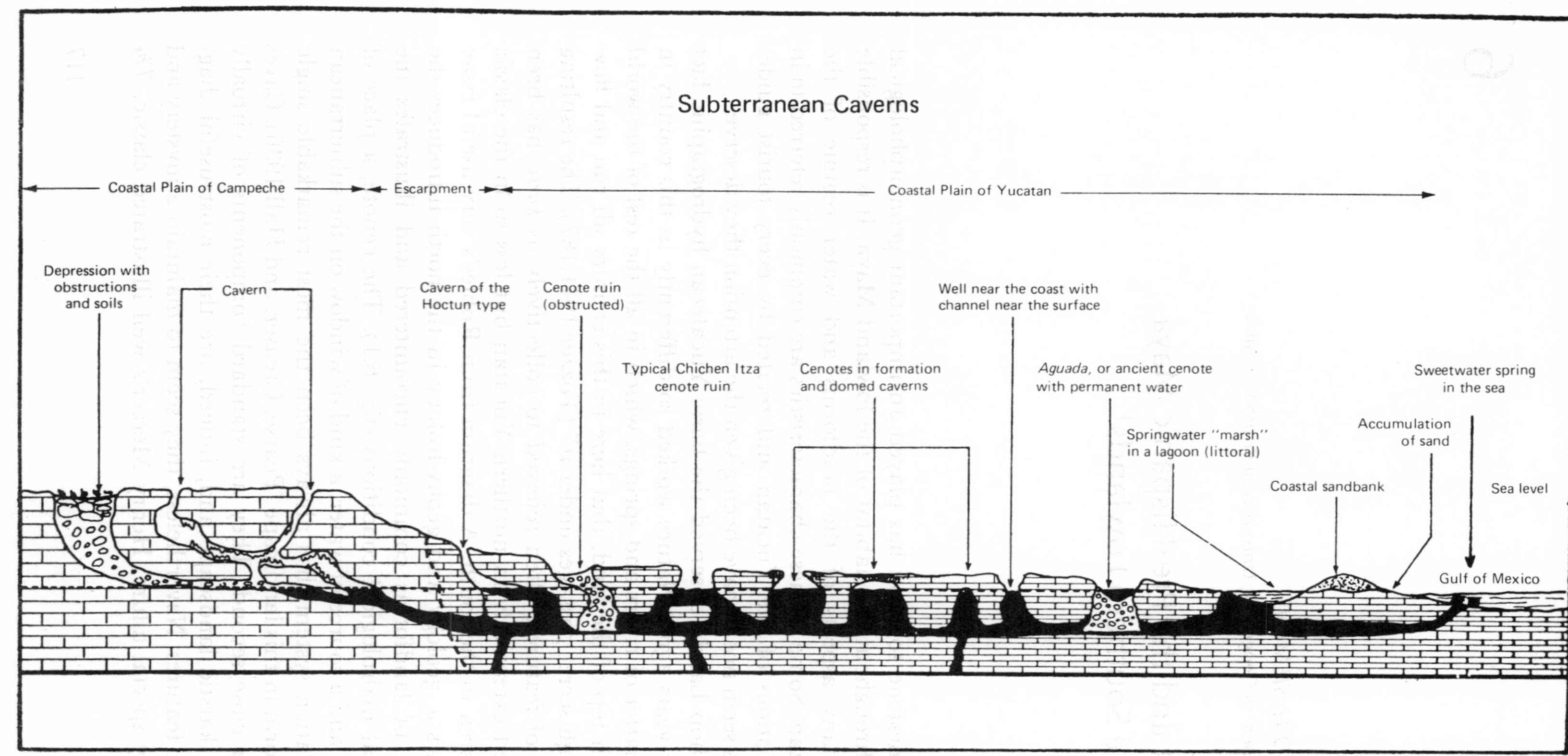

Figure 6.1. Schematic pattern of subterranean caverns on the Yucatan Peninsula. (Source: Robles 1958:59)

Hill-Caves of Yucatan, is quite irresistible (1896, republished 1975), as is Eric Thompson's interpretation of Yucatecan caves as prime sources of "virgin" water (1959).

Karstic landscapes are generally quite problematic habitats, and the Yucatan Peninsula illustrates a number of these problems (LeGrand 1973). Soils are sparse, more so in the northern than in the southern lowlands. In the north, the basal groundwater table, virtually at sea level, is relatively easily accessible through numerous cenotes. In the south, water is less easily accessible away from the few permanent surface streams; altitudes are higher and cenotes scarce. Local topographic relief is generally rugged, except in the *bajos,* and overland movement is difficult.

The environment is problematic also in other ways that would probably have been unknown or at least mysterious to the pre-Hispanic Maya. The permeability of karstic terrain varies greatly; homogeneous aquifers that make prediction of well depths and yields feasible are absent, especially in the higher terrain toward the south. Furthermore, water circulation through cavernous ground may be altered through such occurrences as subterranean stream capture or enlargement of channels. These events can add to or subtract from surface flow, making the streams, which may already be seasonally intermittent, that much less reliable. All these environmental problems, which proceed from limestone solution, added to the climatic and other rigors of the tropical lowland environment, make the achievements of the ancient lowland Maya that much more impressive and their choice of this habitat that much more intriguing.

Recently it has become apparent that carbonate terrains generally set rather severe constraints on modern socioeconomic development. Man-induced contamination threatens the peculiarly vulnerable water resources of the Yucatan Peninsula, especially in the densely settled north (Doehring and Butler 1974). Karstified aquifers do not seem to purify groundwater effectively, even where the lateral flow is as much as 20 kilometers. Typhoid bacilli, for example, are not effectively filtered (Brown and Ford 1973).

A number of karstic landscapes elsewhere in Middle America have been studied extensively. The *Kegelkarst* of the Cockpit Country of Jamaica, something like an upturned egg carton in its configuration, and the "tower karst" of Cuba and Puerto Rico, with its steep-sided limestone hills (*mogotes*) surrounded by alluviated plains, have come to epitomize tropical karst (Sweeting 1972:270–96). The limestone landscapes of Tabasco and Chiapas have also been incisively analyzed (Gerstenhauer 1960, 1966).

It is unfortunate for the interpretation of ancient Maya civilization that the karst of the peninsula's southern interior is not yet well known. The landforms involved have been prominently noted on Guatemalan topographic maps of the area and smaller-scale maps elsewhere (e.g., West 1964:71), but in very general terms. It would appear from our own air survey of a good deal of the Peten that spectacular cockpits or mogotes are scarce, and in places the limestone solution features appear as merely a superimposition on terrain dramatically controlled by folding or faulting. It is understandable, therefore, that this region has so far been relatively uninteresting to karst geomorphologists. Moreover, fieldwork under the forest cover of Peten is an intimidating prospect. These problems would seem to be outweighed, however, by what could accrue to the understanding of the human ecology of this ancient Maya heartland, as well as the geomorphology and hydrology of karst.

Relying, no doubt, to varying degrees on earlier materials, Puleston has made many very useful field observations of karstic features around Tikal (1973). Useful data are also provided in survey essays on physical landscape features of larger parts of the Yucatan, such as those by Robles (1958) and West (1964). Some petroleum geologists have provided us with a good geological map of the Peten and a north-south cross section (Lloyd and Dengo 1960). There has long been good 1:40,000 air-photo coverage.

Such information, however, as is available on karst in the southern Yucatan is evidently not yet comprehensive or forceful—or familiar—enough to figure explicitly in theoretical constructs about the ancient Maya in the southern lowlands. *The Classic Maya Collapse,* the collection of essays edited by Culbert (1973), probably best illustrates this lacuna. It shows that the investigation of the physical environmental aspects of pre-Hispanic cultural ecology in the Classic Maya habitat is out of phase with the relatively sophisticated inquiry into other aspects of that habitat. The volume is "ecological" at many points. It reviews the literature extensively and seems in many ways an important synthesizing statement on the Maya heartland, but only a few scant allusions to limestone solution features are offered and one call is made for hydrological research (Culbert 1973:494).

In view of the increasing focus on water use and management in examinations of the cultural ecology of the ancient Maya, and in expectation of more specialized studies, it seems beneficial to engage in discussion here of several related topics. First, the usefulness of explicit reference to karstic processes in the interpretation of some recently observed features of the southern lowlands, particularly certain aspects of their hydrology, will be discussed. Various suggestions will emerge as to what might have been the attractive as well as the problematical aspects of a karstic habitat in pre-Hispanic times, and how hydrological conditions may have changed in the last two millennia. The discussion of Maya water management and the logistics of waterborne trade will also be carried a few steps further. Throughout the discussion some of the well-known environmental basics of the southern lowlands will be integrated with analogous material from other regions and some new firsthand observations about the Maya region. No new scenarios will be offered for the rise or the fall of this enigmatic civilization, but some suggestions will be made about factors that should be included in the construction of such scenarios.

Approaching the Maya central zone from the flanks of the peninsula, the peculiarities of the river regimes with catchment basins in karstic terrain become apparent. Some peculiarities are readily observable; others may be deduced from data on river levels, the most obvious clues to river behavior (fig. 6.1). Six collection stations provide data on river levels in the region. Three stations, Boca del Cerro, Agua Azul, and Salto de Agua, are on streams with catchment basins that are in areas of impervious lithology. The other three stations, San Pedro, Subteniente López, and Candelaria, are on rivers that issue out of karstic areas. The statistical run is not very long for any of these stations, but the indications are interesting nevertheless (table 6.1).

Traveling along lowland karstic streams, one soon becomes aware of their peculiarities. The water is hard; soap will not lather. Groundwater in adjacent areas presents a similar problem, and is also subject to seawater intrusion (Versey 1972:10–12). Terrain with any relief at all may show karstic solution features: an occasional cave or even cenotes, such as the magnificent examples on Albion Island in the Hondo. The streams themselves may be

Table 6.1. River Levels in the Southern Lowlands (Meters)

Station	*Year*	*Annual High*	*Annual Low*	*Difference*	*Arithmetic Mean of Difference*
1. Boca del Cerro (Usumacinta River)	1949	9.11	1.72	7.39	
	1950	11.61	1.66	9.95	
	1951	9.76	1.62	8.14	
	1952	11.64	1.87	9.77	
	1953	11.20	1.80	9.40	
	1954	11.48	2.16	9.32	
	1955	11.70	1.80	9.90	
	1956	11.50	1.95	9.55	
	1957	9.80	1.97	7.83	
	1958	10.18	1.73	8.45	
	1959	8.82	2.34	6.48	
	1961	10.43	2.34	8.09	
	1962	10.18	2.36	7.82	
	1963	10.68	1.78	8.90	
	1964	9.96	1.84	8.12	
	1965	11.32	1.77	9.55	
	1966	11.96	2.48	9.48	
	1967	11.50	2.07	9.43	
	1968	10.81	2.06	8.75	
	1969	11.68	2.07	9.61	8.83
2. Agua Azul (Usumacinta River)	1960	16.08	4.70	11.38	
	1961	14.88	4.80	10.08	
	1962	14.20	4.38	9.82	
	1963	15.00	4.01	10.99	
	1964		incomplete		
	1965	17.00	4.00	13.00	
	1966–69		incomplete		11.05
3. Salto de Agua (Tulija River, Grijalva system)	1954	9.87	2.16	7.71	
	1955	14.17	1.88	12.29	
	1956	13.36	2.03	11.33	
	1957	11.90	1.97	9.93	
	1958	12.53	1.85	10.68	
	1959	13.52	2.29	11.23	
	1960	11.74	1.92	9.82	
	1961	12.70	2.15	10.55	
	1962	11.83	2.09	9.74	
	1963	12.31	1.98	10.33	
	1964	13.14	2.12	11.02	
	1965	10.97	2.07	8.90	
	1966	11.91	2.16	9.75	
	1967	15.58	2.12	13.46	
	1968	13.28	2.93	10.35	
	1969	13.57	2.94	10.63	10.48
4. San Pedro (San Pedro River)	1953	2.81	1.60	1.21	
	1954	2.96	1.66	1.31	
	1955	3.10	1.63	1.47	
	1956	3.00	1.69	1.31	

	1957	2.42	1.68	.74	
	1958	2.45	1.57	.88	
	1959	2.60	1.66	.94	
	1960	2.81	1.73	1.08	
	1961	2.77	1.97	.80	
	1962	2.35	1.92	.43	
	1963	3.14	1.72	1.42	
	1964	2.62	2.01	.61	
	1965	2.93	2.02	.91	
	1966	3.30	2.15	1.15	
	1967	2.83	2.18	.65	
	1968	3.12	2.19	.93	
	1969	3.20	2.28	.92	.99
5. Subteniente Lôpez	1949	.68	.05	.63	
(Hondo River)	1950	.87	.00	.87	
	1951	.94	.00	.94	.81
6. Candelaria	1954	6.04	4.77	1.27	
(Candelaria River)	1955	6.23	4.72	1.51	
	1956	6.18	4.81	1.37	
	1957	5.62	4.77	.85	
	1958	5.34	4.72	.62	
	1959	5.12	4.78	.34	
	1960	5.38	4.73	.65	
	1961	5.21	4.76	.45	
	1962		incomplete		
	1963	7.64	4.58	3.06	
	1964	5.16	4.75	.41	
	1965	5.16	4.62	.54	
	1966	5.26	4.62	.64	
	1967	5.37	4.69	.68	
	1968	5.71	3.05	2.66	
	1969	5.56	4.72	.84	1.06

Sources: Secretaría de Recursos Hidraulicos 1962; Sweeting 1969.

enlarged dramatically by substantial springs, like that near the Colonia Miguel Hidalgo on the Candelaria—as fine a swimming hole as may be found anywhere. Karstic rivers generally have lower banks than nonkarstic rivers, as might be expected from the water-level data. Along the Usumacinta (Boca del Cerro station), the arithmetic mean of variations between annual extreme high and extreme low water levels is around ten meters. The mean variations on the Hondo (Subteniente López station), Candelaria, and San Pedro rivers, on the other hand, are of the order of one meter.

The behavior of the second group of rivers illustrates what might be called a reservoir effect. A considerable fraction of precipitation in karstic areas moves directly into the groundwater reservoir, reappearing gradually downstream via springs and seepage to keep minimum discharge relatively high. Precipitation highs in the catchment basin are transmitted to such streams through the subterranean reservoir in a subdued fashion; only a minor fraction of even the wet-season discharge is likely to be direct surface runoff (Jennings 1971:67; Chow 1964:3–4). This factor makes for rivers that are relatively placid and reliable —usually; vagaries of subterranean flow, such as stream capture, may introduce substantial variations.

These peculiarities of the karstic rivers of the Yucatan became quite interesting a few years ago in the examination of ancient Maya raised fields in the floodplain of the Candelaria and nearby *bajos* (figs. 6.2–6.5; also see Siemens and Puleston 1972). It was apparent that the yearly rise and fall of the stream and groundwater nearby had been manageable enough to allow intensive land use and canalization. Toward the end of a dry season, a trench was cut across what remained of one of the prehistoric canals. It showed that even under the current hydrological regime—and there is evidence of recent downcutting in the river's profile—the waterway probably could have been negotiated by a dugout at low water. Remains of ancient raised fields on the same floodplain were identified. They were submerged at highwater in the next rainy season. At their earlier well-maintained and higher levels, however, the fields were probably not flooded, and if they were, such silting as occurred was probably beneficial. The Candelaria fields were clearly an impressive food-producing area, with a well-developed waterborne transportation infrastructure, good access to the sea, and, judging from the current discussion of Maya trade routes, good links by water or land or both to the central zone. The ancient Nahuatl name given to the region in which the fields occur was Acalan, the place of the canoes (Scholes and Roys 1968:50).

It was obviously important to find out how widespread such intensive production systems might have been in the southern lowlands. It was postulated that river-level data would provide some early clues as to which other water systems might usefully be surveyed from the air. Such quantitative and qualitative information as was available indicated that the Hondo River had a regime about as placid as that of the Candelaria. In due course, extensive

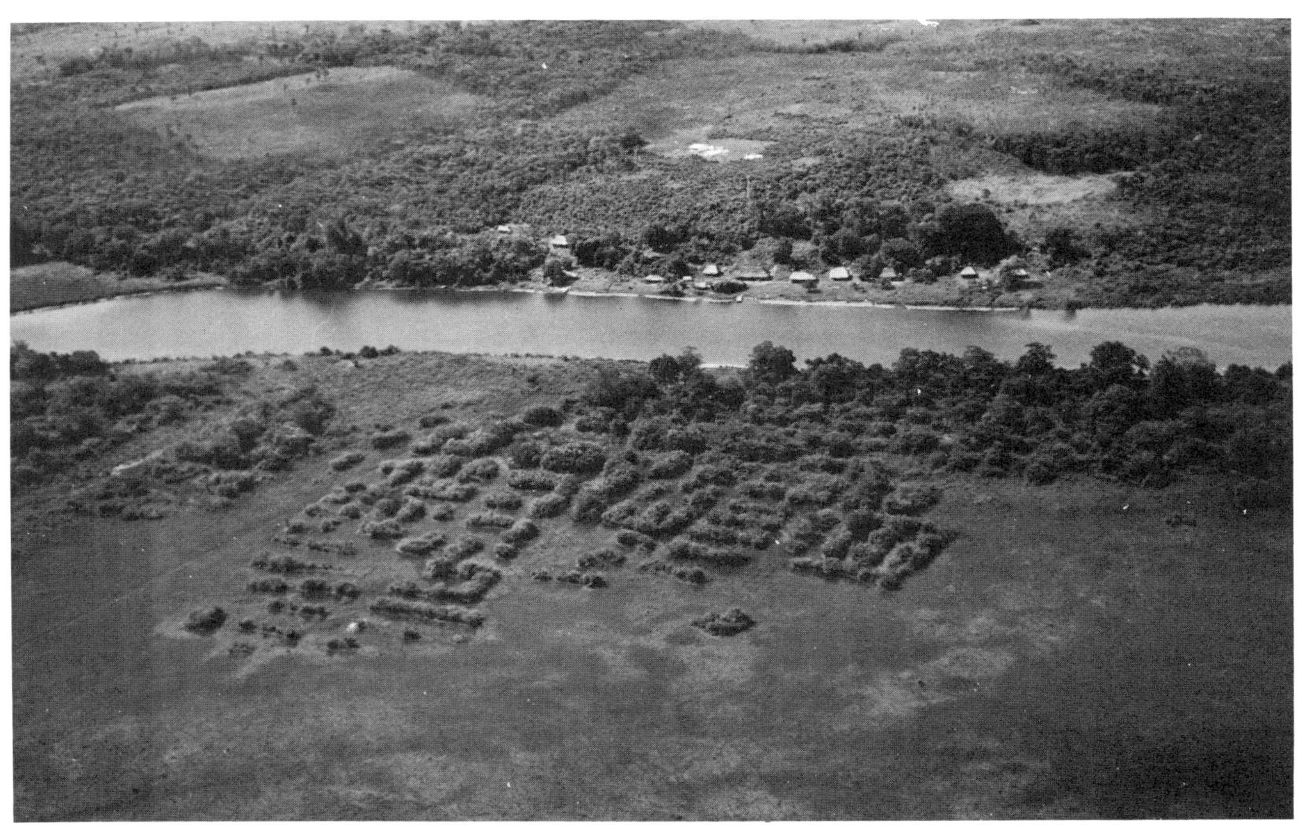

Figure 6.2. Raised fields along the Candelaria River, Campeche. The tops of the fields have been colonized by tree growth. The water level is low, the photograph having been taken at the end of the dry season. Behind the modern settlement of El Tigre is the site believed to be Itzamkanac.

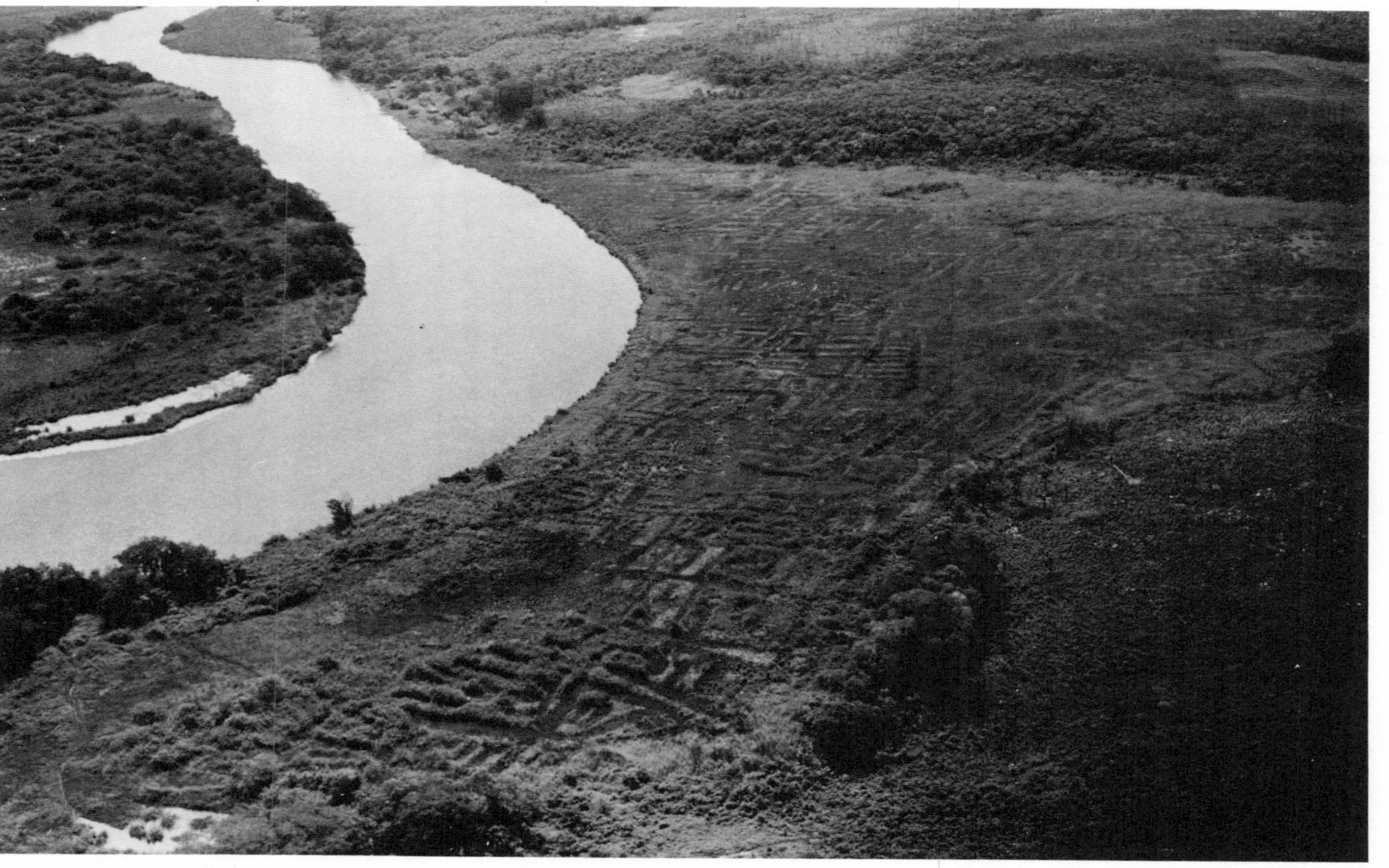

Figure 6.3. The vestiges of raised fields represented by variations in tone and height in the high saw grass, downstream from El Tigre on the Candelaria River.

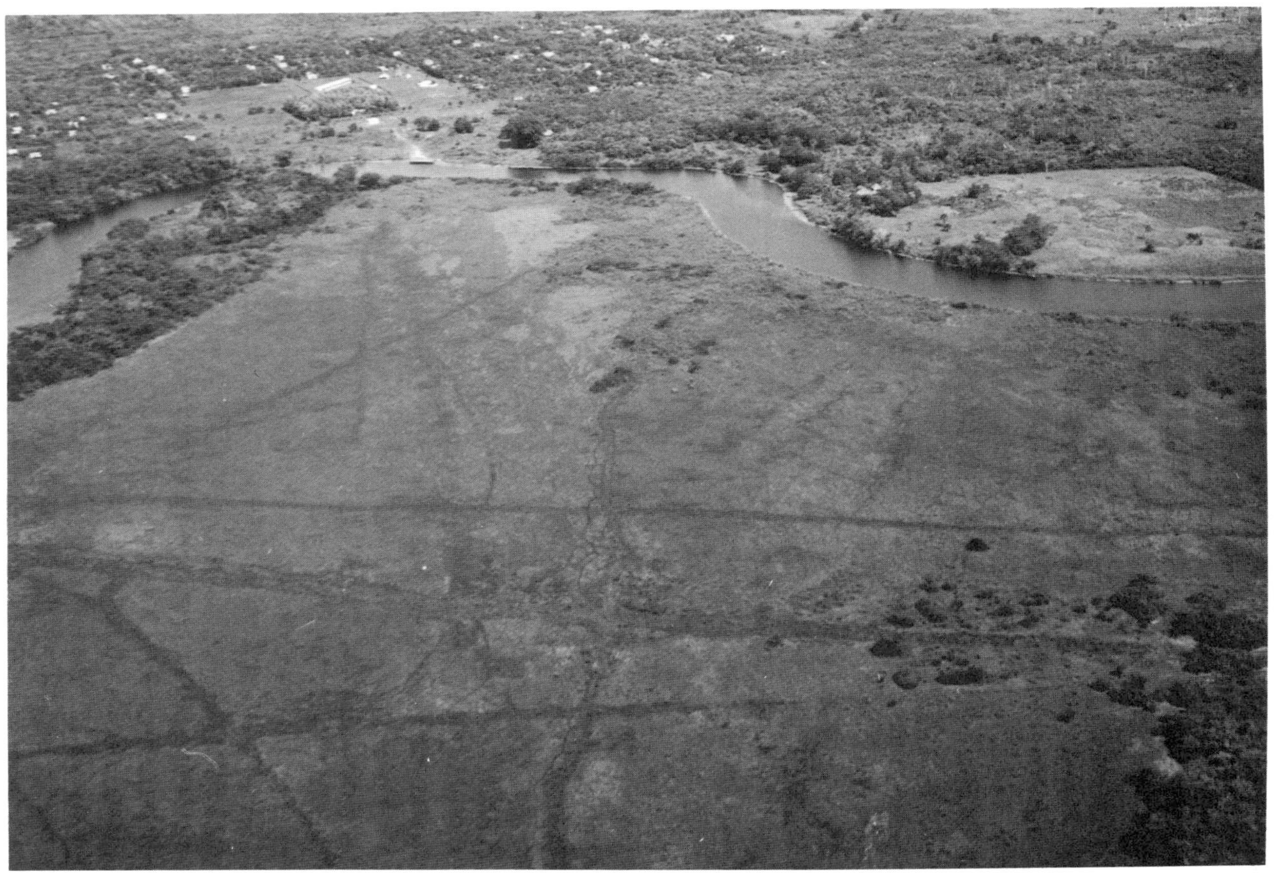

Figure 6.4. Canal lines across the floodplain of the Candelaria, upstream from El Tigre, opposite one of the six new colonies recently established along the river.

Figure 6.5. Enigmatic tracings across a particularly wide portion of the floodplain of the Candelaria. The diagonal, light-toned lines may represent ancient fisheries; the transverse lines may be the remains of canals providing access between the river (off to the left) and firm ground (on the right).

complexes of raised fields and associated features were in fact found in the floodplains and nearby *bajos* of both the Hondo and the New rivers (figs. 6.6–6.9). Here was clearly an even more impressive agricultural region, as well linked to both the sea and the interior as the floodplain of the Candelaria (Siemens and Puleston 1977).

The significance of karst for the interpretation of culture history in the core of the southern lowlands is considerably more enigmatic. Intensive specialized study would almost certainly yield critical new insights. At this point, one can only suggest some possibilities.

Although the Guatemalan topographic maps label only the knobby hill lands as karst, the intervening flatlands are just as influenced by limestone solution as the hills. In fact, any discussion of karstic landforms tends to emphasize the depressions. In this case it soon focuses on the *bajo,* the lowest of the lowlands, a rather sinister landscape, difficult to negotiate. The *bajo* is characterized in the literature as an interstice sufficiently forbidding to constitute a natural defense, as perhaps at Tikal (Puleston 1973:112), and also as an attraction (W. Coe 1965:10), a source of water and fish, as well as a medium of transportation–all of which may have been complementary functions. Lundell's forecast that "the exploration of [these] uninviting yet interesting swamps will repay in discoveries all effort devoted to them" (1937:29) is becoming more and more plausible, but it is still mostly a promise.

The *bajos* of the southern lowlands, especially the Peten, have often been described. It is instructive to pull together various lines of evidence on their hydrology. A very general southwest-northeast alignment that reflects folding and faulting (West 1964:71) is apparent in the *bajos* of the eastern Peten, the central zone during the Classic period (Culbert 1973:5). Their successive floors drop in level as one moves northward and eastward from Lake Peten. Their physiography immediately suggests possible water routes, probably discontinuous, from the classic heartland via the Hondo, New, and Belize rivers to the sea, as already intimated by J. E. S. Thompson (1970:129–30). Northwesterly water routes to link up with the Candelaria are, at first sight, not as clearly indicated. In fact, even the pre-Columbian overland route sometimes postulated from Acalan in a southeasterly direction across the base of the peninsula has been set in doubt (J. E. S. Thompson 1970:132). If,

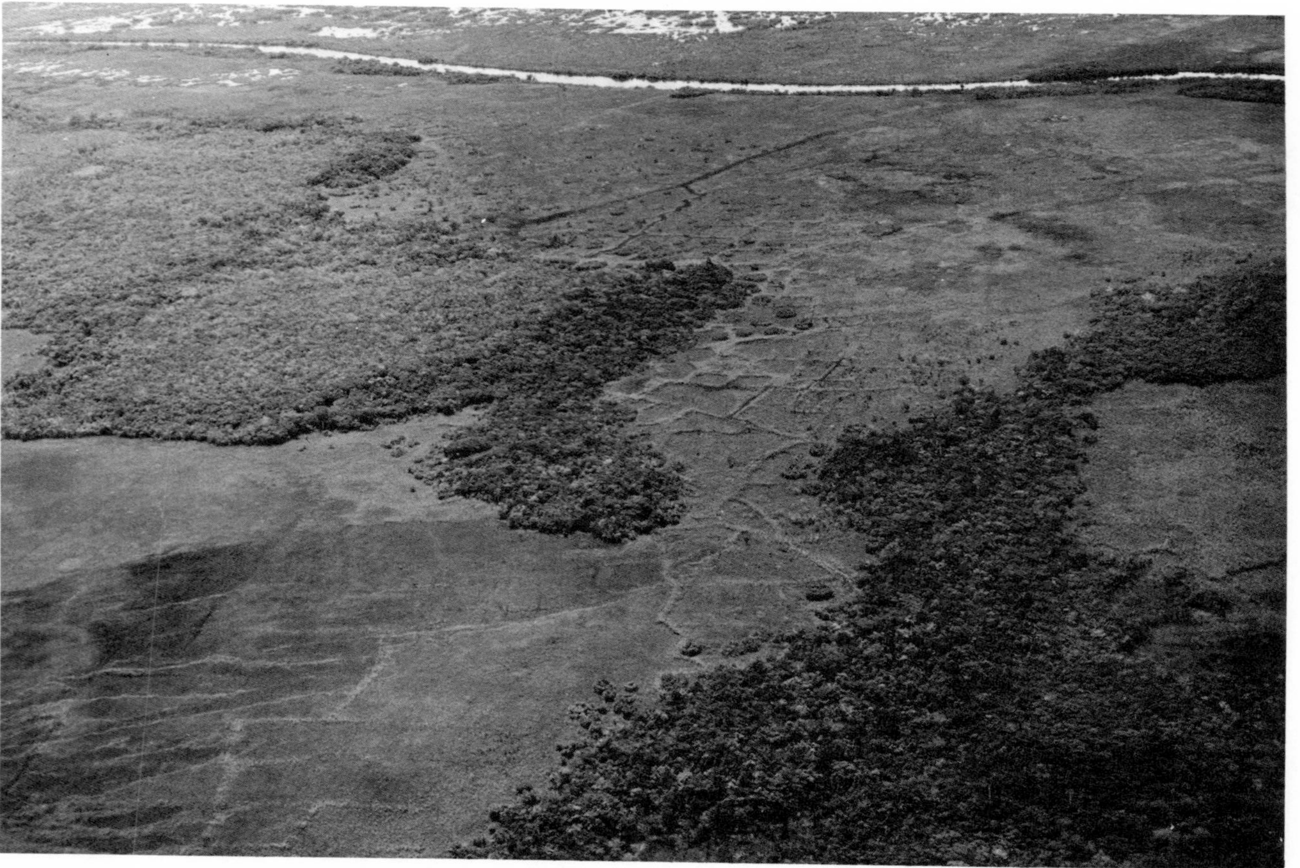

Figure 6.6. The remains of raised fields along the Hondo River, which constitutes the boundary between Mexico and Belize.

Figure 6.7. Raised fields around Pulltrouser Swamp, east of the Hondo floodplain, in Belize.

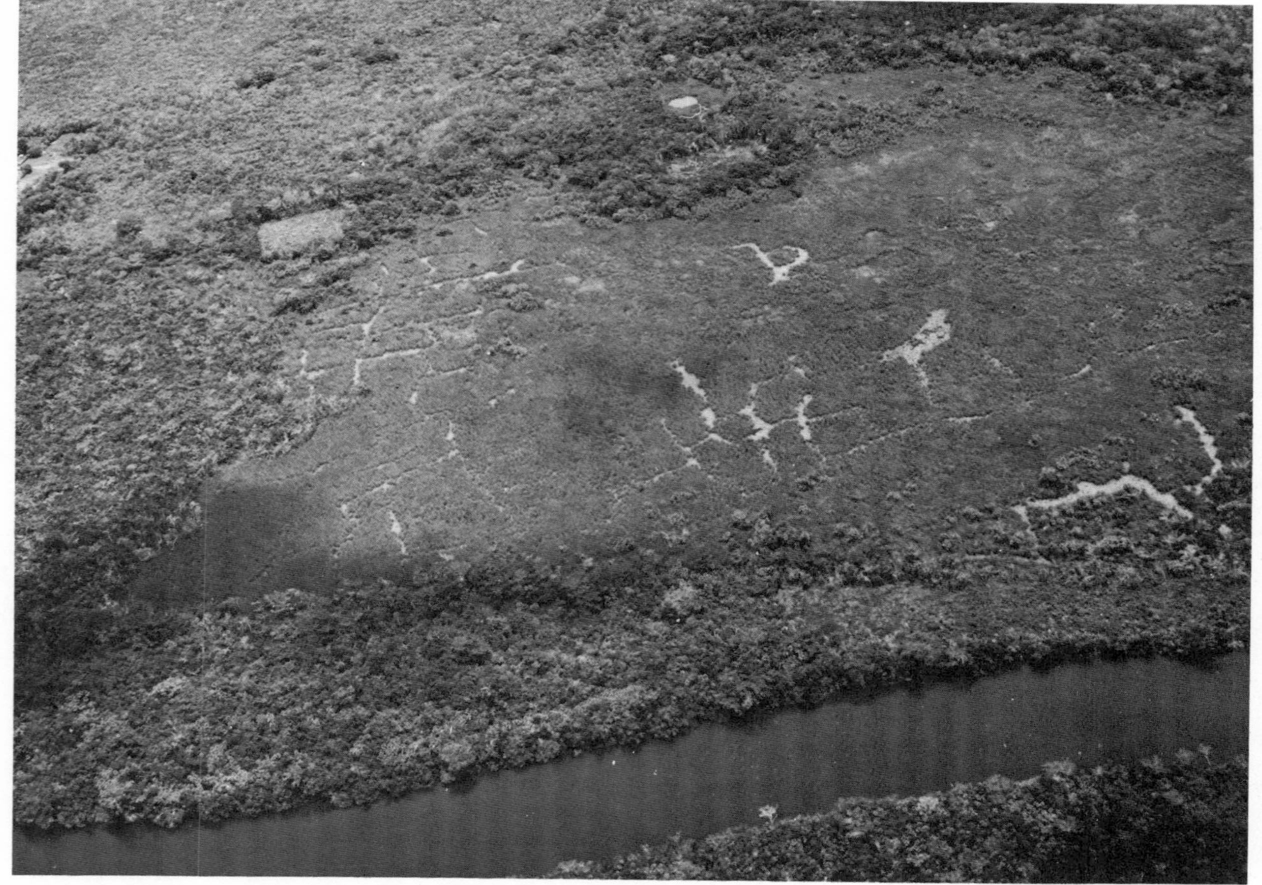

Figure 6.8. Raised fields on the Hondo floodplain, just north of the village of San Antonio.

Figure 6.9. Raised fields in a bend of the Hondo River.

however, the 1:250,000 Guatemalan topographic coverage is even generally reliable in its rendition of the hydrography—and our own air surveying suggests it is—an interesting possibility becomes apparent as one traces some permanent stream channels from the northwest into the Peten. A portage of no more than 10 kilometers could conceivably have linked the Candelaria to the Chocop, which in turn flows into the San Pedro. The last of these becomes intermittent about 30 kilometers from Tikal. A fairly direct route over this distance would have coincided for at least 15 kilometers with one large attenuated *bajo.* Some corroborating evidence for prehistoric movement along this route will be suggested below.

The topographic, hydrographic, and vegetation features of *bajos* may perhaps be elaborated with the help of figure 6.10, a diagram of a hypothetical *bajo.* It is part speculation, part synthesis.

Bullard noted a recurrent topographic asymmetry in *bajo* floors years ago (1960:357). This asymmetry is probably related to a dominant southeast-northwest dip in the limestone beds (Lloyd and Dengo 1960:210). The lowest parts of the *bajos* are frequently near escarpments on the western or northern margins. A number of examples of the diagrammed situation are to be found around Tikal, although the most striking example may be at Uaxactun. Such low points are often the sites of major natural *aguadas,* distinguishable from the air by the remains of open water as well as a low vegetation of shrubbery or sedges. The margins of *bajos* generally seem to have been considered suitable for modification into artificial *aguadas* (Puleston 1973:281).

The higher topography around most *bajos* of the Peten represents only an approximation of what is called *Kegelkarst* (cone karst) in the basic literature on tropical limestone solution (Lehmann 1954; Gerstenhauer 1960). The crumbled contour lines indicative of this type of intricate topography are, however, massed in broad swaths over maps of the region. They frequently show irregular, closed depressions, and these often contain natural *aguadas.* This higher terrain represented prime agricultural land for the Maya; it is on such topography that the rendzina and related soils are found. Stevens has pointed out that they "are not inclined to severe erosion, but it is feasible that the calcareous Lithosols may now be undergoing rejuvenation after a former period of intensive cultivation and accelerated erosion" (1964:301). Evidence for serious erosion during the occupancy of Tikal has

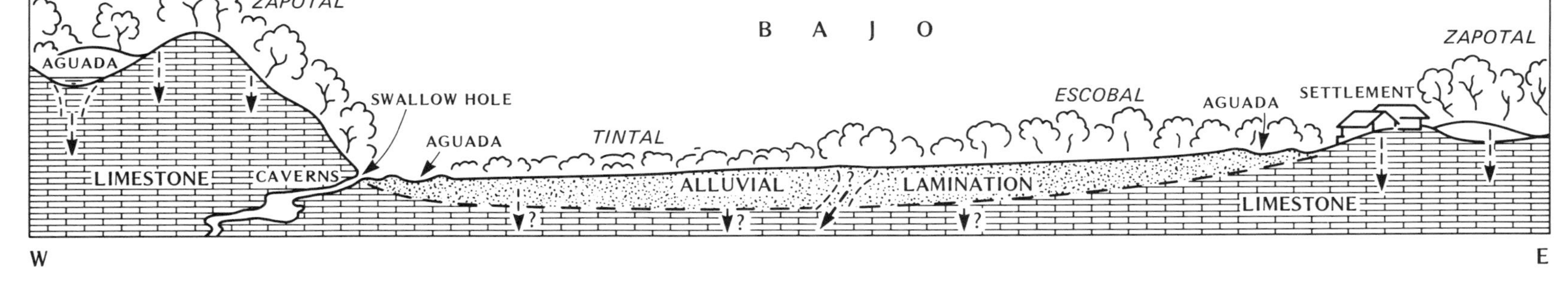

Figure 6.10. A schematic section of a hypothetical *bajo*.

been cited by Olson and Puleston (1972:35). We shall return to this point later.

The typical *bajo* may be considered a *polje* (Derek C. Ford, personal communication; Lehmann, Krömmelbein, and Lötschert 1956:186; Sweeting 1972:193), which simply denotes a more or less flat surface, enclosed or almost enclosed by karstic uplands. A catchment basin for noncalcareous debris, it is normally floored by alluvium. It is subject to seasonal flooding and is drained by intermittent surface streams as well as swallow holes of various types. Each polje has its own hydrological regime; one is thus reminded of the predominantly vertical nature of the limestone solution. Any exact correlation of water levels between poljes is not feasible. The levels of a group of poljes may be linked in a very general way, as has been noted for the *bajos* of Peten, but one must remain aware of the possibility of "kinks" in the drainage profiles as well as differences from *bajo* to *bajo* in the record of sedimentation.

The karstic perforations of the landscape represented in the typical *bajo* (fig. 6.10) seem to have been somewhat neglected in the descriptions of the lowland habitat of the Classic Maya, even though they seem critical to its understanding. The terminology that surrounds them is somewhat confusing. The common Spanish terms are *sumidero* (Robles 1958:84) and *resumidero* (West 1964:72), both words meaning an opening through which water drains away. The association made by West (1964:72) and by Puleston (1973:85, 234) with *dolines* or *sinkholes* is perhaps misleading since it identifies the *sumidero* too closely with the *cenote.* The latter feature is a closed topographic depression often resulting from subterranean collapse in carbonate terrain with a groundwater table not many meters below the surface (see fig. 6.1). The term *ponor* is often used in the literature on karst. The graphic English term, *swallow hole* (Sweeting 1972:122–28), seems preferable here.

Several kinds of swallow holes are apparent in the *bajos* and related stream valleys of the Peten. One type takes the form of a permeable segment in the bed of an intermittent water course. It may have little or no topographic expression; it is simply an area where the water filters through alluvium into the joints and bedding planes of the bedrock. The movement of this water is vertical, toward the zone of phreatic water that lies below the basal water table, which is roughly at sea level (Williams 1969:271). When the runoff is less than can be absorbed by these swallow holes, the streams are reduced to a series of pools. Such intermittent stream flow and ponding has been well described for some of the arroyos around Tikal (Puleston 1973:249–50).

A more spectacular variety of swallow hole is that found against a limestone escarpment (fig. 6.10). Here water visibly and dramatically drains away in the form of a stream. Robles characterizes it as "an opening whose entrance is no more than a meter in diameter and gives access to the depths, where generally the cave grows wider" (1958:84). Given the large volume of the organic debris and the sediments carried in the water entering these swallow holes in the flood season, there seems likely to be a characteristic slight rise up to the actual orifice, in front of which an *aguada* is formed, or where artificial *aguadas* may be created, as at Uaxactun. According to local informants, the ancient artificial *aguada* there, still the modern village's main water supply, drains out through the swallow hole when filled to overflowing with the onset of rains. It is obviously in an optimal location to preserve some of the last of the *bajo's* surface water during the dry season.

It seems possible that water also filters out of the *bajos* through perforations other than the rather dramatic swallow holes on their lower margins. This brings up the rather intriguing subject of gilgai, a type of microrelief that is often patterned polygonally. It is caused by shrinkage and subsidence in clay soils that are subject to alternating wet and dry conditions. The most striking aspect is a network of cracks that may go down from 5 to 10 meters (Hallsworth, Robertson, and Gibbons 1955; Edelman and Brinkman 1962). Gilgai has been recognized in the Peten by Gerald Olson (1976, personal communication). An intriguing question is whether or not its formation leads to perforation of the *bajo* to bedrock. Discussion of the subject by the authors just cited strongly suggests it does. Since the surface over such a perforation becomes something of a zone of collection, it may produce wetter patches in the vegetation. This just possibly could be the explanation for the strange "age marks" in the vegetation of the *bajos* when observed in the 1:40,000 vertical air coverage of Peten. F.-D. Miotke (1973), in his intriguing diagramatic cross sections of depressions in Puerto Rican karst, may be showing a somewhat similar kind of perforation.

The *tintal* vegetation of the *bajos* has been described as the wettest of the circum-Tikal associations, aside from that of the *aguadas* (Puleston 1973:280). Lundell observed long ago that *tintal* species also show "all protective defences against intensive insolation and excessive evaporation . . ." (1937:29). The terrain is alternately flooded and parched, which might well make any association of plants schizoid. During the dry season evaporation certainly contributes heavily to aridity. Edaphic factors that make some of the remaining moisture inaccessible may contribute to aridity too, as Puleston points out. Subterranean drainage of one kind or another seems also to be a basic factor, although neither author mentions it in this connection.

The water regime of the *bajos* is a surficial system perched high above a basal water level that may be near sea level. The Tikal well drillers' famous dry hole, which was finally stopped at 180 meters (Puleston 1973:238), might well have had to be pushed down 100 meters more before striking water. Between the levels of the swallow holes and the assumed basal water level, there must be a labyrinth of caverns. Puleston cites some corroborating evidence out of the experience of petroleum drillers (1973:238). Whether or not these caverns are accessible to speleologists is an open question, but it might be worthwhile to try to find out. There are few references in the literature on the Maya to caves in the higher terrain of the southern lowlands. Local informants often apply the term *cueva* to chambers in ruined structures, introducing a potential confusion.

The Maya seem to have managed their water resources rather skillfully in various ways. The construction of *aguadas* with clay as a liner has been alluded to here and in many other places. The artificial *aguada* may be seen as an imitation and a modification of the *bajo* itself. It seems frequently to have been placed just within the perimeters of the *bajos.* The suitability of these zones for *aguada* construction has been interpreted as a possible major reason for the concentration of settlement on the edges of *bajos* in many places (Puleston 1973:281). This might be seen as an alternative to Harrison's (1977) revival of C. Wythe Cooke's theory that the *bajos* were desiccating lakes.

The management of swallow holes is also conceivable. Dams may have been built to retain water in the impermeable sections of intermittent-stream beds, as in the case of the Naranjal Aguada at Tikal (Puleston 1973:250). The cliffside swallow holes may have had to be unplugged or enlarged when flooding threatened; more likely it would have been desirable to plug them or shore them up in order to conserve water.

Water levels presumably were of great concern to traders operating in the southern lowlands. J. E. S. Thompson has maintained that "Peten traders who dominated the commerce of the peninsula almost surely went by land only when they could not go by water" (1970:134). He maintains that similar constraints may well have obtained earlier in the history of the Maya, too. The three commodities considered "necessary for successful maize agriculture in rainforest environments are igneous or hard stone for grinding tools, obsidian for razor-sharp cutting tools, and salt" (Rathje 1972:368). Stone and salt are bulky and heavy items; their transport would have been tremendously facilitated by waterways. In addition, it seems likely that waterways would have facilitated warfare, at least seasonally. During high water, canoe-borne attackers, properly guided, could have moved quickly to within striking distance of the settlements. Defenders could have made the flooded or canalized terrain, which would usually be considerably obscured by vegetation, extremely hazardous.

Picking a way by canoe through the tangle of a flooded *bajo* would be no easy task. It would be considerably facilitated by clearing the fallen wood and other debris from a suitably direct route. Some deepening by scooping muck out onto the sides might be worthwhile as well, since it would lengthen the trading season.

Stimulated by various intimations, including those made by Harrison (1977) and an enigmatic photograph published in *National Geographic* (Stuart 1975:785), as well as by my own 1972 sightings in the *bajos* near Chetumal (fig. 6.11; see also Harrison 1974, 1975, 1977), Bruce Dahlin and I undertook extensive air reconnaissance in March 1976. Some conceivably artificial lineation, first reported by Harrison in 1975, become apparent in the vegetation of the *bajos* around Tikal. We were well aware that forest or shrub vegetation is notorious for lining up in spurious ranks when viewed obliquely from the air, especially if the viewer is looking for something rectilinear. Nevertheless, when the same lines, expressed as regularities in vegetation heights, appeared to both of us on repeated flights over a given *bajo,* we were prepared to take them seriously. Several of those elusive lines, furthermore, seem to match up with faint, dark gray lines on the vertical air coverage. These gray lines, in turn, often do not seem to follow

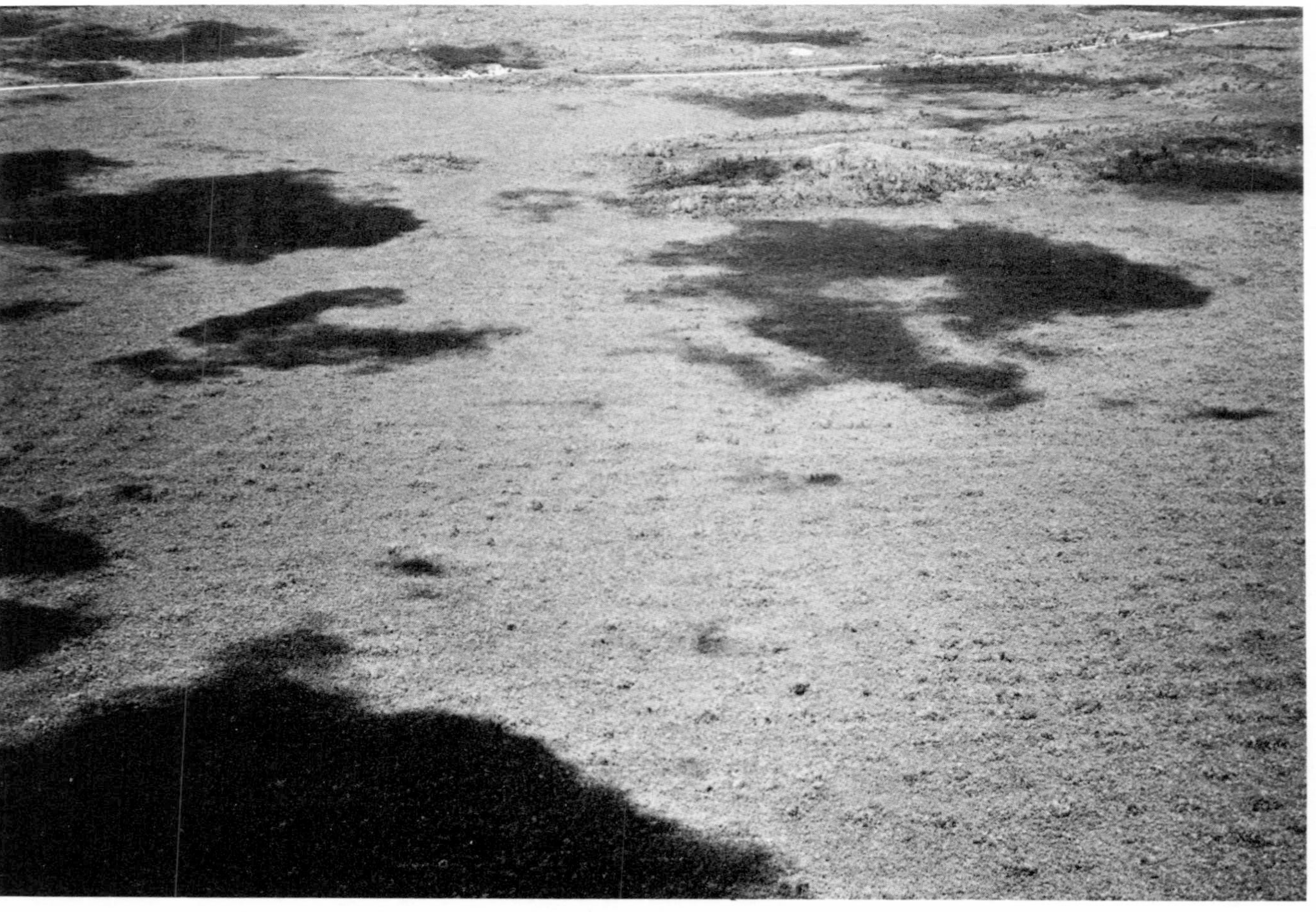

Figure 6.11. Raised fields in a *bajo* west of Chetumal.

what one would expect to be the natural direction of drainage. They are most numerous to the east and the southwest of Tikal. It may be that they are visual evidence of channel clearance long ago to facilitate trans-*bajo* canoe transportation. They are not illustrated here because further reproductions would probably make a mockery of the evidence that can just barely be coaxed out of the contact prints of the original negatives. It is clear that some serious attempts will need to be made to find these coquettish lines on the ground and to cut trenches into them for possible stratigraphy. They are reminiscent of the lines that cross the floodplain of the Candelaria (Siemens and Puleston 1972). The latter are visually clearer, by and large, and have been verified as man-made.

Various investigators have raised the possibility that the *bajos* of the Peten may have been used for intensive agriculture, especially with raised fields. There is striking evidence for raised fields in several extensively forested *bajos* to the west and north of Chetumal, Quintana Roo. These *bajos* look vegetatively similar to those of the Peten when seen from the air (Harrison 1974, 1975, 1977). The Quintana Roo fields are practically at sea level, however, and must share in the hydrological regime of the Hondo River, along which the vestiges of numerous raised-field complexes are also clearly evident.

The perched water tables in the perforated *bajos* of the Peten, if they behaved in prehistoric times as they do today, would seem to have fluctuated too much to allow raised-field agriculture, except perhaps in the areas that remained flooded longest. For the maintenance of crops, enough water had to be in the canals between the fields at the height of the dry season to float a canoe. During the planning of the March 1976 air survey, we expected that if we were to find raised fields anywhere in the Peten it would be in the floodplain of the San Pedro, a tributary of the Usumacinta that shows a yearly variation in level as slight as that of the Candelaria or Hondo. Some visual evidence was apparent for canalization, but none for raised fields.

The importance of fish in the nutritional equation of the ancient Maya has become an intriguing question recently in connection with the investigations of raised fields (J. E. S. Thompson 1974). Fish may have been a considerable resource in the *bajos* of the Peten, even with a highly seasonal hydrological regime similar to that of today. An adaptation to running as well as standing water can be expected of various tropical freshwater fish (Lowe-McConnell 1975:9).

As has been intimated already, it is possible that the water regime of the central zone was not always what it is today. One recalls the rather idyllic view held some time ago that the "bajos were open lakes of fresh water teeming with fish and waterfowl and permitting a brisk commerce by canoe" (Morley 1938:5). This view has been generally discredited, largely because of the weakness of some of the early evidence for the presence of lakes (Ricketson and Ricketson 1937:11) and the apparent acceptability of the Cowgill and Hutchinson evidence against it (1963a). It should be remembered that the latter was derived mainly from one pit in the Santa Fe *bajo* at Tikal and that it is probably risky to generalize past hydrological conditions in a swarm of poljes on the basis of evidence from one. Some corroboration elsewhere would be very reassuring.

Harrison (1977) has recently reassessed the proposition that the *bajos* were once lakes. He emphasizes not the lakes themselves, but the usefulness of the idea for the clarification of various key aspects of Maya settlement and subsistence, and his arguments are rather impressive.

There is reason to believe, at the very least, that the *bajos* once did hold water more efficiently than they do today. Various authors have commented on the relationship of erosion and plant cover in karstic tropical lowlands (Gerstenhauer 1966:39; Cowgill and Hutchinson 1963a:275–76; LeGrand 1973:863). A full forest cover absorbs much precipitation, supplementing the reservoir effect of karst and helping to even the flow of karstic streams. With the expansion and intensification of cultivation during the Maya ascendancy, it is likely that heavy rainfall accomplished considerable erosion. The sediments carried into the *bajos,* while "silting up" the postulated lakes to a certain extent, probably also enhanced the lamination of the *bajo* floors and thus contributed to more efficient water storage. Furthermore, it is reasonable to suggest that the seasonal length and level of *bajo* flooding decreased with the reduction of erosion and with reforestation after the collapse. The annual reinforcement of the *bajos'* seal was probably diminished, whereas the yearly cracking resulting from desiccation, and the related soil churning (gilgai), continued. Gradually the *bajo* floors were perforated like the bottom of a rusty kettle, helping to bring about the current hydrological regime.

A decrease in the efficiency of *bajo* water storage may have occurred earlier and contributed to the collapse in the southern lowlands. The shrinkage of the water supply may have happened through down-cutting in stream channels such as that of the Holmul, consequent on the uplift that seems to have been continuous in recent times (Maldonado-Koernell 1964:24). The effects of such a relentless diminution of a basic resource, together with population increase, social problems, and warfare, are not difficult to imagine. We lack the supporting evidence, however.

Two other suggestions regarding desiccation in the Peten may be applicable to the period of the collapse or pertain mainly to the subsequent centuries. The first relates to lake levels. The Ricketsons (1937:25) reported evidence for a general drop in lake levels in Peten. I recently noticed long flights of abandoned shorelines around lakes just to the south of the San Pedro River. The increased permeability of the depressions in this karstic landscape might well be deduced from the vegetation in and around the natural *aguadas* in front of swallow holes. The forest seems to be advancing in on them. In other places former *aguadas* seem already to have been entirely covered with low forest.

Several very strong images from ancient Maya art imply some change in the hydrography of the central zone since Classic times. These images are incised decorations on bones found in a tomb in Temple I at Tikal. They have been enlarged magnificently and hung as murals in the Tikal museum. One of them depicts gods in a large canoe, plying some mythical waterway (Sabloff and Rathje 1975:77). On another, a figure stands behind a canoe, up to the waist in water. On his back is a creel with a fish in it, and a huge catfish is in one hand (J. E. S. Thompson 1966:295). If these scenes reflect the surroundings of the site where they were found, the implications are very interesting, indeed.

NOTE

1. I owe special acknowledgment to Canada Council, Ottawa, for financial support through various grants, and to Dr. Olav Slaymaker, Department of Geography, University of British Columbia, for his help in the early conceptualizations of parts of this paper.

7

ALAN P. COVICH
Department of Zoology, University of Oklahoma

A Reassessment of Ecological Stability in the Maya Area: Evidence from Lake Studies of Early Agricultural Impacts on Biotic Communities

Among the many groups of plants and animals now living in the Mesoamerican lowlands, some species are perhaps much more common than they were prior to the beginnings of Maya agriculture. Other taxa may be more scarce, or even extinct. Many ecologists have long held that the tropics represent a biologically stable, well-buffered ecosystem that slowly evolved for more than 60 million years into a highly diverse, complex set of interacting species. This "naturally stable" ecosystem was thought to have undergone extensive agricultural deforestation, which led to soil erosion, filling of lake basins, and the creation of swamps and savannas. The view that *all* agricultural productivity required extensive deforestation was the only concept considered. Before ecologists can correctly evaluate the impact of ancient agriculture on natural tropical ecosystems several questions must be answered: How stable were the diverse tropical ecosystems *prior* to agriculture? How diverse were intensive agricultural methods, and how extensively were the natural ecosystems changed?

As a basis for predicting the impact of both ancient and modern agriculture, it is necessary to know whether preagricultural ecosystems were exposed to intense or minor fluctuations in species compositions. If natural communities were highly uniform in composition and only adapted to minor changes in rainfall, nutrient cycling, and burning, then the onset of extensive slash and burn cultivation by ancient farmers would probably devastate these uniform, stable biotas while more intensive but restricted farming of raised mounds (without frequent burning) could be less detrimental. If, however, the preagricultural biotas were dynamically changing in species composition in response to varied climatic conditions, they would be resilient and relatively well adapted to environmental changes caused by indigenous cultivation. Some evidence now exists to support this latter hypothesis, but more data are needed from many independent sources of paleoecological information to substantiate this possibility. Before evaluating evidence of biotic changes in the Maya area I will review some current concepts of ecological stability and some methods of extending ecological studies into very long sampling periods. Documenting environmental conditions during preagricultural times and sorting out early man's impact on natural ecosystems from those changes caused by climatic and biotic parameters is only possible from analyses of the records preserved in lake sediments. Paleolimnological studies can provide much insight, but interpreting information obtained from sediments requires consideration of many lines of evidence. Fortunately, progress is being made and simultaneously a great deal of new information on ancient population estimates and techniques of cultivation is now available from archaeological and geographical studies (e.g., B. L. Turner 1974a; Matheny 1976).

DIVERSITY AND STABILITY

The relationship between biological diversity and ecosystem stability is no longer as simple and obvious as it once was thought to be. Currently, some ecologists (Gardner and Ashby 1975; May 1973, 1976) are questioning the assumption that complex systems composed of diverse assemblages are more stable and well buffered than simple systems made up of only a small number of interacting species. One contention is that as the number of linked biotic components increases, the chances that some links will be disrupted by random events also increases. Thus the entire network, although highly complex is vulnerable to perturbations and very prone to drastic changes in species composition; localized extinctions occur frequently, for example, and the ecosystem is unstable. Although these discussions refer to model ecosystems rather than to naturally coevolving ecosystems, the previously assumed resiliency of diverse natural communities must be reexamined (Botkin and Sobel 1975; Goodman 1975; Orains 1975; Webber 1974). There is no general theoretical maxim that dictates that diverse natural assemblages will remain uniform or continuously retain resiliency. It is possible that natural ecosystems such as the tropical forests or tropical streams and lakes could undergo abrupt changes in species composition independently of any human-created disturbance.

What evidence exists for determining whether preagricultural ecosystems did undergo drastic changes? The studies reviewed below demonstrate that at least some data support the hypothesis that preagricultural ecosystems in the neotropics underwent major but rather infrequent changes in species abundance. Conclusions regarding the relative impacts of different agricultural methods, however, are difficult to draw, and many more data are needed before any conclusive interpretations can be reached.

PALEOECOLOGICAL APPROACHES TO TROPICAL ECOSYSTEMS

Historical records deposited in lake sediments are currently being unraveled by analyses of micro- and macrofossils and by a broad array of chemical parameters, ranging from isotopic analyses of ^{14}C dating (Fleming 1976) and ^{18}O enrichment (Covich and Stuiver 1974) to studies of fossil plankton (Deevey, Vaughn, and Deevey 1977). Some of these recent studies (A. S. Bartlett and E. S. Barghoorn 1973; Covich 1976; Deevey in press; Graham 1975, 1976) may provide evidence of marked oscillations in long-term patterns of rainfall and evaporation. Apparently many terrestrial and aquatic ecosystems in lowland areas of the neotropics underwent changes in species composition in response to large fluctuations in sea level, groundwater flow, and seasonally variable rainfall. Because much of the Maya lowlands are composed of limestone and are readily weathered by hydrological processes, the increase in sea level (see fig. 6.1) has had a considerable effect on the inland solutional lakes and marshes. These dynamic responses created a complex mosaic of biogeographic distributions among many taxa of plants and animals (Terborgh 1974; Vuilleumier 1971; Graham 1975, 1976).

Pollen Analysis

Extracting fossil pollen grains and matching the identifications with those from plants of known ecological distributions provides some of the most important paleoecological data for environmental reconstructions. Because many flowering plants are relatively long lived and immobile, their presence as represented by fossil pollen can yield a great deal of information about rainfall, soil chemistry, and disruptions such as fire and deforestation. The distribution of some plants is restricted to a limited habitat; their fossil pollen grains can be interpreted as indicator species. However, because pollen are very minute and often windblown over considerable distances (especially arboreal pollen), it is necessary to compare distributions of *many* species (both nonarboreal and arboreal) known to constitute natural communities. Rarer pollen types from insect-pollinated species of plants often have considerable value in documenting the presence of a particular assemblage. For example, Bartlett and Barghoorn (1973) determined changes in sea level by counting changes in frequency of mangrove pollen deposited in long cores as well as by analysis of rarer species associated with the dominant mangroves. Generally, the presence or absence of a particular species is not as informative as overall trends in changing patterns of pollen distributions over time. The displacement of a large number of marsh-inhabiting plants by those characteristic of a drier upland forest is convincing evidence of a major ecological change, such as sea level lowering or succession, whereas shifts in abundances of only a few species could result from many factors and are therefore difficult to interpret.

Major methodological questions arise in counting fossil pollen grains. First, how many should be counted? Obviously, the larger the sample size, the more reliable is the interpretation of an entire assemblage. Often a single dominant species is the major pollen producer and rarer species are infrequently encountered. The search for complete ecological communities is time-consuming but essential. Once the pollen grains are counted, how are the numbers best analyzed? Previous studies relied on percentages to express relative abundances; these values can lead to multiple and conflicting interpretations because if only one of ten species changes greatly in absolute abundance (while the other nine remain constant in quantity) all species will change in relative abundances and percentages can shift considerably. In other words, a slight increase in numbers of individuals of a species which produces large quantities of pollen may be interpreted as a major change in community composition and climatic conditions, when actually the community has changed very little. Such difficulties are avoided by counting *absolute pollen frequencies* (APF) in which the total pollen per unit volume is analyzed (Faegri and Iversen 1964). As M. B. Davis, Brubaker, and Webb (1973) point out, these APF values can be calibrated by comparisons with the modern pollen rain obtained from sediment traps or exposed microscope slides.

Another kind of error—one more difficult to work around—occurs because some species have thinner, less readily preserved pollen grains than others. Some important components of natural communities are thus completely lost owing to lack of preservation or degradation during the extraction and cleaning process. Comparisons, then, between absolute pollen frequencies of modern pollen rains and ancient pollen preserved in sediments will never directly correspond, but analysis of deposition of preservable pollen in modern lakes allows for accurate estimates (M. B. Davis 1973). In many tropical lakes, however, the sediments are frequently well oxygenated, and pollen preservation under these conditions is negligible.

Another problem is determining stratigraphic integrity. If lake levels drop, the sediments may become oxygenated and prevent uniform preservation of pollen; but even more complex and long lasting mixing of subsurface sediments occurs as a result of burrowing activities of benthic invertebrates (R. B. Davis 1974). The blurring of temporal relationships may be more of a problem in well-oxygenated tropical lakes where the benthic macroinvertebrates can become very numerous. Fortunately, the presence of laminated structures in lake sediments is usually a reliable basis for discounting the effects of major redeposition of pollen and other microfossils. There is increased awareness among paleolimnologists that large numbers of cores are needed from different depths of water in a single lake. Replication is particularly needed if the basin is steeply sloped and prone to sediment slumping or redeposition of fine sediments from frequent resuspension by wind-driven currents. Steep, cylindrically shaped lakes, such as some solutional sinkholes or cenotes, will accumulate sediments at a relatively linear rate, with only infrequent erosion of loose rock and soil from the steep, parallel limestone walls. Conical basins, however, may accumulate sediments faster in the deepest, central portion of the basin than in the shallow margins. Likens and Davis (1975) and Lehman (1975) term this latter type of redeposition *sediment focusing.* Recent studies further substantiate that sediment accumulation rates in a single core are not linearly related to sediment deposition in the entire basin (Deevey, Vaughn, and Deevey 1977).

Microfossils

In addition to pollen grains, plant and animal remains are preserved in lake sediments. David Frey (1964) reviews the animal taxa and discusses the use of fossil assemblages in interpreting lake histories. Only a few studies of microcrustaceans and insects, however, pertain to the impact of Maya agriculture (see Cowgill and Hutchinson 1966). In summarizing several of his studies of chydorid Cladocera, a major component of the littoral zooplanktonic community, Clyde Goulden (1969) notes that the long period of agricultural disturbance around the shores of Laguna de Petenxil, Guatemala, is represented by minimum values of chydorid species diversity.

The siliceous cell walls of diatoms, other algae such as dinophyceae and chrysophyceae, and sponge spicules add to the variety of biotic information stored in lake sediments. Siliceous deposits (phytoliths) produced in grass epidermis may be preserved in lake sediments and could possibly be used to document the presence of maize and related grasses in ancient time horizons. Although species determinations are still tentative, size-frequency analyses of phytoliths demonstrate the presence of maize in soil horizons from archaeological sites in Ecuador (Pearsall 1978). Calcareous-encrusted cell walls of charophyte oospores, calcite structures of foraminifera, and ostracode valves (see below) are also encountered in lake sediments but are only infrequently studied. By far the most work has focused on siliceous diatoms; much of this research is reviewed by R. Patrick and C. W. Reimer (1966). John Bradbury (1971) discusses some methodological problems of interpreting the impact of early hydrologic changes brought about by pre-Columbian agriculture in the Valley of Mexico. Work now in progress by Bradbury and Puleston on lake sedimentary cores from the Orange Walk district of Belize and by Edward Deevey and his colleagues in the Peten will undoubtedly yield additional information on lacustrine changes related to early Maya agriculture.

Macrofossils

Changes in plants and animal distributions are also traced by analysis of macroscopic fragments preserved in lake sediments. For example, the abundances of charred grass washed or blown into a lake increase dramatically after a fire. Changing concentrations of grass fragments in sedimentary cores thus can document frequencies of burning. Identification of grass species is even sometimes possible if the stomatal cells of the leaf epidermis are distinctive and well preserved (Goulden and Hutchinson 1966). Seeds, leaves, and woody stems can also be extracted for ^{14}C dating of the sediments if the organic material was covered over by mud before it could decompose.

Macrofossils such as snail and bivalve shells often occur in considerable abundances, especially in hardwater lakes. My own work has focused on these molluscan groups and their changes in distribuitons in the Yucatan Peninsula (Covich and Stuiver 1974; Covich 1976). My longest record of deposition extends 12 meters into the bottom of Laguna Chichancanab and has a ^{14}C date of greater than 28,000 years B.P. One species of snail (*Cochliopina infundibulum*) is known to have gone locally extinct in this lake following a long period of reduced lake levels. On the basis of several independent lines of evidence, I hypothesized that this marked reduction in lake volume occurred during a period of lower sea level in the Caribbean, which lowered the groundwater table. As the sea level began to rise again some 10,000 to 11,000 years ago, the lake slowly refilled but the assemblage of molluscan species was somewhat different. Apparently during the last 8,000 to 9,000 years there has been a large oscillation in lake levels in the Yucatan Peninsula, but the molluscan assemblage has remained quite uniform and no localized extinctions have occurred. This is an example of long-term instability prior to agricultural development accompanied by another sequence of long-term stability during a period of extensive agricultural development (although the intensity of agriculture in the drainage area around Chichancanab was probably relatively low). Other groups of associated fossils, such as the ostracodes, can supply additional information about chemical conditions in the ancient lake. L. G. Price (1974) established three zones in the upper 2.5 meters of a core from Chichancanab, delimiting them on the basis of marked changes in distributions of four dominant species of ostracodes that have different ecological requirements and tolerances of salinity changes. These zones suggest that some distinct fluctuations in salinities and water levels have occurred during the past 2,500 years.

Other workers have also used changes in distributions of gastropod shells to document shifts in use of mollusca as food and trade ornaments (E. W. Andrews IV 1969; M. D. Coe and Flannery 1967; Voorhies 1974) as well as to interpret land-use changes (Hammond 1977) in the limestone-rich areas of the neotropical lowlands. Shell densities of small species can exceed several hundred per cubic centimeter in some sediments from hardwater lakes (fig. 7.1; Covich 1976), and shells are often found in archaeological deposits where calcium concentrations are high in the environment of deposition. Such high densities give the impression that complete molluscan communities are preserved. However, just as pollen grains undergo differential preservation so, too, can shell material be corroded prior to and after deposition. Once the thin organic periostracum is decomposed, the shell carbonate can be weathered by weak carbonic acid produced by heavy rainfall. Some species of thin-shelled gastropods can be more susceptible to corrosion than other, thick-shelled taxa during a period of slow deposition and corrosion, while perhaps all will be preserved during a time of rapid deposition. In this instance, the

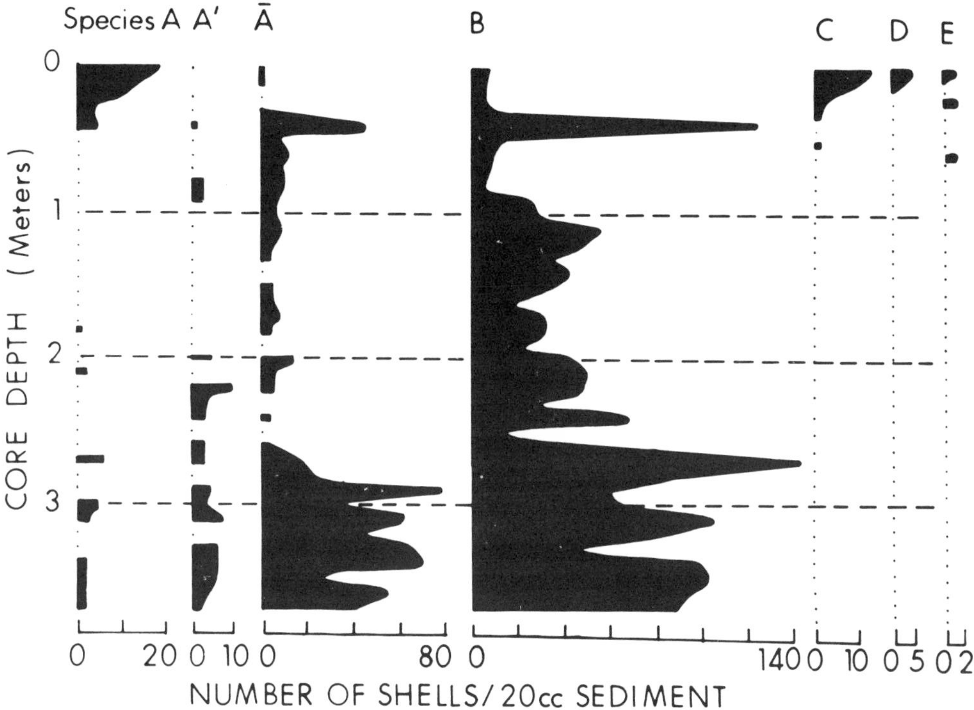

Figure 7.1 Gastropod population dynamics, Lake Peten.

death assemblage of subfossil shells would be different even though the live community of gastropods did not change in composition.

Before interpreting any changes in densities of shells it is essential to document independently the uniformity of the environment of deposition. Another factor of considerable importance is the destruction of live mollusca by their predators. It is possible that many thin-shelled mollusca could be thriving in a habitat and none would be preserved even in rapidly sedimenting environments if the live gastropods and bivalves were being ingested by predators (fishes, turtles, birds, crayfish, crabs). Many of these difficulties have been reviewed by Evans (1972) in his discussion of land snails, but much more information is still needed on rates of shell deposition in modern environments before this potential source of paleoenvironmental information can be completely interpreted.

Chemical Analysis

When tropical soils are exposed to heavy rainfall, the leaching of minerals results in increased concentrations of major ions in lake sediments. Leaching is accelerated when drainage basins are deforested and burned, so fluctuations in chemical compositions of lake sedimentary profiles document the impact of various types of agricultural development. These data provide independent comparisons for analyses of micro and macrofossils, and because there are distinct differences in the mobilities of many different chemicals and isotopic forms of ions, the amount of information potentially available is very great (Cowgill and Hutchinson 1966).

One of the most informative and easily measured ionic concentrations is calcium. Because it is abundant and quickly leached it undergoes rapid, large-scale changes. These shifts are often correlated with fluctuations in other major cations such as magnesium and sodium (Covich 1976). When changes in calcium concentrations are compared with the large-scale fluctuations that occur among ratios of oxygen isotopes in calcium carbonates, it is possible to analyze long-term changes in lake levels. In closed lakes—those that lose their water primarily through evaporation rather than from outflowing rivers (Covich and Stuiver 1974)—the rate of ancient evaporative enrichment of heavier isotopes is measurable by analysis of fossil shells, which precipitate and retain the ratio of heavy to light isotopes of oxygen (^{18}O:^{16}O) in their calcium carbonate.

CONCLUSIONS

How important is it to determine the ecological stability of the preagricultural neotropics? Given all the possible complexities of paleolimnological data, it is essential for ecologists to agree upon the importance of attempting to interpret long-term environmental conditions. Without this geological and evolutionary perspective it is difficult to evaluate the validity of modern-day ecological studies. While most biologists recognize that the modern tropical ecosystems are rapidly being cleared away for large-scale agriculture and ranching (e.g., Golley and Medina 1975; Gomez-Pompa, Vazquez-Yanes, and Guevara 1972), it is difficult at present for ecologists to determine just which habitats have undergone long periods of secondary succession and which are relatively undisturbed or natural ecosystems. As Graham (1976:837, 841) points out, the neotropical rainforest may actually be

> a delicately balanced ephemeral assemblage that has undergone greater changes in range and composition during the late Cenozoic than more northern temperate biotas closer to the glacial boundary. . . . The natural origin and antiquity of the Low Semi-Evergreen Selva, Savannas, and Palm Stands . . . have never been satisfactorily resolved. The prevalent view is that the present extent, if not the origin, of these associations resulted from agricultural practices of sedentary populations. . . .

That many biotic communities are cultural artifacts is becoming increasingly apparent from paleolimnological studies (Tsukada and Deevey 1967; Vaughan 1976), and much more can be learned from the large number of still unstudied lake basins. Unfortunately, time for conducting these studies is limited by the rapid, drastic changes resulting from deforestation and modern agriculture.

8

T. PATRICK CULBERT, PAMELA C. MAGERS, and MARA L. SPENCER
Department of Anthropology, University of Arizona

Regional Variability in Maya Lowland Agriculture

The study of prehistoric Maya agriculture is coming of age as new data force a rejection of traditional assumptions. Discrepancies between estimates of prehistoric population based upon archaeological data and the projected support capacity of the long-fallow swidden system of agriculture used by modern peasant cultivators in the area have not disappeared as data accumulate. Mayanists are consequently forced to the conclusion that earlier assumptions about the nature and potential of prehistoric agriculture were wrong. The failure of the traditional model of Maya subsistence is not really surprising. It was based upon two premises that are simplistic in the extreme: first, that almost no variation in subsistence practices was possible and, second, that the Maya lowlands were uniform, so that information from any part of the lowlands could be extended to the entire area. The purpose of this paper is to focus upon the question of regional variability. We believe that such variability has received more lip service than actual consideration, and that even recent research has often tended to act as though large areas of the lowlands constitute a uniform environment, even though the researchers undoubtedly understand that such is not the case. Much of the problem lies in a lack of data, for it would be impossible to create a sophisticated model of regional variability on the basis of information currently available. But until such data are accumulated, we are confined to simplistic models that will probably prove to be unsatisfactory.

The case we will use to illustrate our point happens to relate to variation within lowland swidden agriculture. We must emphasize forcefully, however, that this does *not* mean that we reject or denigrate recent suggestions about more intensive techniques that seem to have been used in prehistoric times. We do believe that the Maya practiced such intensive techniques. We also believe that there is little solid information about the potential and possible variations of swidden agriculture and that continued investigation of extensive practices is as necessary as research into more intensive techniques.

The particular issue to be raised here concerns the potential for multiple cropping within the Maya lowlands. In traveling through the southeastern section of the lowlands for an archaeological survey during February and March 1974, we observed extensive stands of maize approaching the harvest stage (Culbert, Spencer, and Magers 1976). This evidence contradicted the widely held assumption that the Maya lowlands can produce only a single summer crop harvested in September through November. The area in which the winter crop was observed is large, extending from the point at which the trans-Peten road leaves the Guatemala City–Puerto Barrios highway to the town of Dolores, about 135 kilometers northwest. Less frequent winter crops were observed for an additional 25 kilometers to the town of El Chal.

Intrigued by the question, we began informal interviews with *milperos* in and around the town of Poptun. Almost invariably, these informants reported that they did plant two crops a year of maize and that the production of the second crop was equal to or only slightly less than that of the rainy-season crop. Unfortunately, we were unable to obtain the maize-yield data necessary to substantiate these claims. Our observations, however, suggest that the second crop actually does offer a significant contribution to subsistence. We also have no information on year-to-year variation in yields, but we can report that winter rainfall at the two weather stations in the area was below normal for the winter in question, so the observations we made cannot be the result of a year of unusually heavy rainfall. Our only claim is that the question of multi-cropping in the southeastern Maya lowlands seems worthy of investigation and that objections based upon data from other parts of the Maya lowlands or the assumption that winter cultivation is everywhere unsuccessful are examples of precisely the kind of uniformitarian thinking to which we object.

Our own observations, of course, are not the only report of attempted multi-cropping in the Maya lowlands. Reina's (1967) study of swidden farmers in the community of San José on the shores of Lake Peten Itza indicates the possibility of fall and winter plantings in addition to the rainy-season crop. Both of these additional plantings, however, are reported to be emergency measures that return a low yield. Interestingly, however, Nicholas Hellmuth (1971) cites colonial documents suggesting very successful double cropping in the same zone around Lake Peten Itza. Further north in the Rio Bec region, B. L. Turner notes that a second crop may be planted but that "most local farmers . . . agree that winter maize crops are too risky to justify unnecessary cultivation" (1974b:33). William Carter (1969) has studied a community of Kekchi-speaking Maya who have recently settled at Chichipate, south of Lake Izabal. He indicates that all of the members of the community attempt double-cropping, but that the results of the second planting are disappointing. In addition, there are reports in the oral tradition among Mayanists that triple-cropping is possible in the southwestern sector of the Maya lowlands at the base of the Cuchumatanes mountain massif, and Robert Rands (1973:166) reports an area of double-cropping in the zone of heavy rainfall bordering the Chiapas highlands near Palenque.

It is clear that multi-cropping is known over a widespread area in the Maya lowlands. In much of this area, however, reports suggest that the practice is associated with low yields and high risk. None of the reports provides a quantitative estimate of yield, and it would seem wise to obtain actual yield figures before dismissing multi-cropping as insignificant. If the results of dry-season plantings averaged only 25 percent of the yield of summer crops, the potential contribution to food supplies at times of demographic stress would be considerable.

When consideration of Maya subsistence turns to such variations in cultivation routines as multi-cropping or to many of the more intensive alternatives that have been suggested recently, we encounter situations in which the Maya lowlands are marginal in terms of environment. In such conditions of marginality, both regional and local variations take on greatly increased importance, for even small differences in critical variables such as rainfall, soil, and slope may make the difference between success and failure. In this context, it seems wise to consider regional rainfall patterns in the Maya lowlands in relation to their possible effect upon the potential for multi-cropping. A summary of these patterns may be gleaned from the precipitation data of a number of weather stations in the southern part of the Maya lowlands (table 8.1). The data show the expected pattern of increase in annual precipitation from north to south. More important for the topic of this paper, comparable differences in winter rainfall exist. The most northerly stations, those in the Rio Bec area, show very low November-January precipitation, although the figures from the Nicolás Bravo station suggest a fair amount of local variability. Winter rainfall increases to the south, with a significant increase south of Lake Peten Itza. The stations south of the lake, in the area where we received reports of successful second plantings, show half again as much winter rainfall as the station at Flores and those in the northern Peten. Differences of this magnitude may well be of significance for agricultural routines, and we consider the general neglect of regional weather data to be another symptom of the failure to come to grips with regional variation in subsistence potential.

Finally, if research should prove the existence of significant regional variation in subsistence practices and productivity within the Maya lowlands, such variability would have an important impact upon questions of demography, trade, and economic and political patterns. A number of researchers already have made suggestions about variation between the densely occupied area of the northeastern Peten and other, more peripheral parts of the lowlands. Rathje's core–buffer zone model (1971, 1973) attacks this problem from the standpoint of differences in resources and organization necessary for trade with areas outside of the lowlands. Sanders (1977) has suggested that the greater density of sites in the core area may relate to differences in soil and slope. Rands (personal communication) comes closer to the problem considered here with his suggestion that the zone of multi-cropping near Palenque may have been a source of subsistence support for other parts of the lowlands. Yet all of these suggestions suffer from the lack of data appropriate to test them. Only when Mayanists accept the challenge of variation and undertake detailed ecological studies in several parts of the lowland area will progress be possible on models of regional interaction.

Table 8.1. Precipitation in the Maya Lowlands[a]

Station	*Years of Data*	*Av. Ann. Precipitation (millimeters)*	*Nov.*	*Dec.*	*Jan.*	*Feb.*	*Mar.*	*Apr.*	*May*	*June*	*July*	*Aug.*	*Sept.*	*Oct.*
Silvituc	11	1,161	36	30	45	25	18	46	97	121	166	173	260	144
Zoh Laguna	17	1,240	65	50	35	25	20	65	110	220	178	115	200	160
N. Bravo	12	1,377	115	58	71	42	32	54	134	154	162	147	226	182
Carmelita	5	1,327	127	84	61	25	43	45	128	183	97	125	232	177
Uaxactun	5	1,192	83	88	48	28	37	37	126	216	163	113	120	132
El Paso	11	1,762	121	89	49	41	31	53	171	236	199	191	303	278
Fallabon	5	1,328	96	157	98	32	114	27	50	239	168	83	122	142
Flores	10	2,006	88	99	50	36	45	179	240	249	240	214	362	204
Poptun	8	1,690	152	147	73	59	45	44	174	178	210	176	194	236
Machaquila	3	1,504	190	127[b]	86	54	51	34	80	124	168	156	215	210
San Luis	5	1,773	169	123[b]	91	48	55	24	161	208	208	212	286	188
P. Barrios	26	3,074	304	258	197	115	100	133	213	276	485	311	313	370
Quirigua	22	2,255	189	157	110	63	65	64	186	308	293	250	339	230

a. Data for Silvituc, Zoh Laguna, and Nicolás Bravo from Turner (1974b); data for Machaquila and San Luis from Fomento y Desarollomento del Peten (FYDEP) offices in the towns in question; data from all other stations from Comite Coordinador de Hidrolgia y Meteorologia (1968).

b. FYDEP offices do not record data between Dec. 20 and Dec. 31, the annual vacation period for all employees. The December rainfall figures and annual averages for Machaquila and San Luis have been adjusted to make provision for the missing period.

9

B. L. TURNER II
Department of Geography, University of Oklahoma

Ancient Agricultural Land Use in the Central Maya Lowlands

The traditional view of lowland Maya Classic civilization as consisting of a small, scattered populace limited by a uniform and hostile environment to a subsistence based on swidden (slash-and-burn) agriculture is unacceptable in light of recent discoveries. New evidence indicates that at various times in the past the lowland Maya maintained large, densely settled populations which subsisted by intensively cultivating several diverse physiographic zones.[1]

This paper presents an initial assessment of the pattern of ancient agricultural land use in the central Maya lowlands of the Yucatan peninsular region of Mexico, Guatemala, and Belize (fig. 9.1). Several physiographic zones in the central lowlands and the principal techniques used by the Maya to cultivate these zones are identified and discussed. Relics of cultivation techniques, terraces and raised fields, and remnants of field demarcation are used to delimit local patterns of agricultural land use. These local patterns are evaluated in terms of the distribution of Maya sites occupied during the Late Classic period (ca. A.D. 550–1000) in order to project a likely pattern of agricultural land use for the entire central lowlands.[2]

The term *physiographic zone* refers to the principal physical characteristics of a specified area. Each of the physiographic zones identified here is a composite of several physical qualities, includ-

Figure 9.1. Central Maya lowlands.

ing drainage, slope and soil, and vegetation, that create differing circumstances for agricultural activities. In this perspective, the central Maya lowlands may be categrorized in terms of drainage characteristics as either well-drained uplands or poorly drained depressions. Including slope and soil differences, the uplands may be divided into five physiographic zones: northern ridge lands, southern ridge lands, flank lands, flatlands, and mountain pine ridge. Three physiographic zones, based primarily on soil and vegetation characteristics, are identified among the depresssions: *bajos,* savannas, and river valleys.

These eight major physiographic zones are not exclusive and are subject to change in accord with the scale of investigation or by restructuring the emphasis placed on the various physical characteristics (also see Wilson in press). Furthermore, they are not physically uniform, and they often overlap. They do, however, reflect the more prevalent physical qualities of certain areas within the central lowlands. Undulating terrain, for instance, dominates the ridge-land zones, although savannas, *bajos,* and flatlands are common in the ridge lands as well.

Climatic distinctions are not particularly important to the classification of the major physiographic zones. All the central Maya lowlands are dominated by warm temperatures and a seasonal precipitation regime. Temperatures range from about 10°C to 32°C annually, although temperatures in parts of the Maya Mountains may dip below 5°C in the winter. The entire region is characterized by distinctive wet and dry seasons, the dry season being more pronounced and longer in duration in the north. Total annual precipitation decreases from 2,000 millimeters in the southern sections to 1,200 in the northern sections. The major effect of this precipitation difference is a more xerophytic vegetational response to the north.

Implicit in the arguments that follow is the assumption that the environmental conditions described for the present-day physiographic zones in the central lowlands are comparable to the conditions that existed during the Classic period (ca. A.D. 250–1000). Meager evidence tends to support this assumption, although the paleoclimatic picture is unclear. Pollen and sedimentation studies suggest that the central lowlands have not incurred major climatic changes since about 2,000 years ago, but slight fluctuations in rainfall may have occurred (Cowgill and Hutchinson 1963a; Tsukada and Deevey 1967). The significance of these fluctuations for agriculture has not been determined. Vegetational changes have occurred but were probably induced by the Maya through the destruction of the upland and *bajo* forests for agricultural activities. Contemporary soil and climatic conditions, then, are probably representative of conditions during the entire Classic period, but further paleoecological studies are necessary before this interpretation can be substantiated.

PHYSIOGRAPHIC ZONES AND RELIC AGRICULTURAL FEATURES

Ridge and Flank Lands

The undulating ridge and flank lands are the dominant physiographic zones in the northern and southern sections of the central Maya lowlands (fig. 9.2). These upland zones share numerous physical characteristics, especially sloping terrain, well-drained soils, and seasonal tropical forests. Major differences between these zones are the increased elevations and steepness of slopes in the southern ridge lands and the flank lands.

The slightly karsted northern ridge lands cover the south-central portion of the Yucatan Peninsula, extending along the Campeche–Quintana Roo border as far south as central Peten. Relief is dominated by elongated limestone ridges that increase in elevation to the south. In Campeche the northern ridge lands rarely exceed an elevation of 330 meters above sea level, but elevations in northern Peten may approach 400 meters. Slope gradients in this zone display considerable variety, ranging up to 50°, but slopes of 10° to 25° are more common. The northern ridge lands also maintain a variety of floristic and soil types (Lundell 1937; Simmons, Tarano, and Pinto 1959). In a broad scheme, however, they are characterized by a subevergreen or humid seasonal forest situated on shallow (generally 50 centimeters or less) calcareous loams that comprise mostly Lithic and Typic Troporendolls as well as several varieties of Mollisols.[3]

The geological terminus of the Yucatan Peninsula lies just north of Lake Peten Itza, near the parallel of 17° north latitude (fig. 9.1; H. Waddell 1938). Here, too, the northern ridge lands give way to the southern ridge lands. The latter are an extension of the folded and faulted ranges of Chiapas that sweep across central and southern Peten along an east-west axis, ending abruptly at the Maya Mountains. Basically limestone in composition, the southern ridge lands reach elevations of 500 meters above sea level in west-central Peten and 600 in southern Peten. Rugged terrain is often encountered. Soil types are varied, but numerous Mollisols, especially Troporendolls, are present. The precipitation in this zone allows the development of humid forests that often approximate rain-forest conditions.

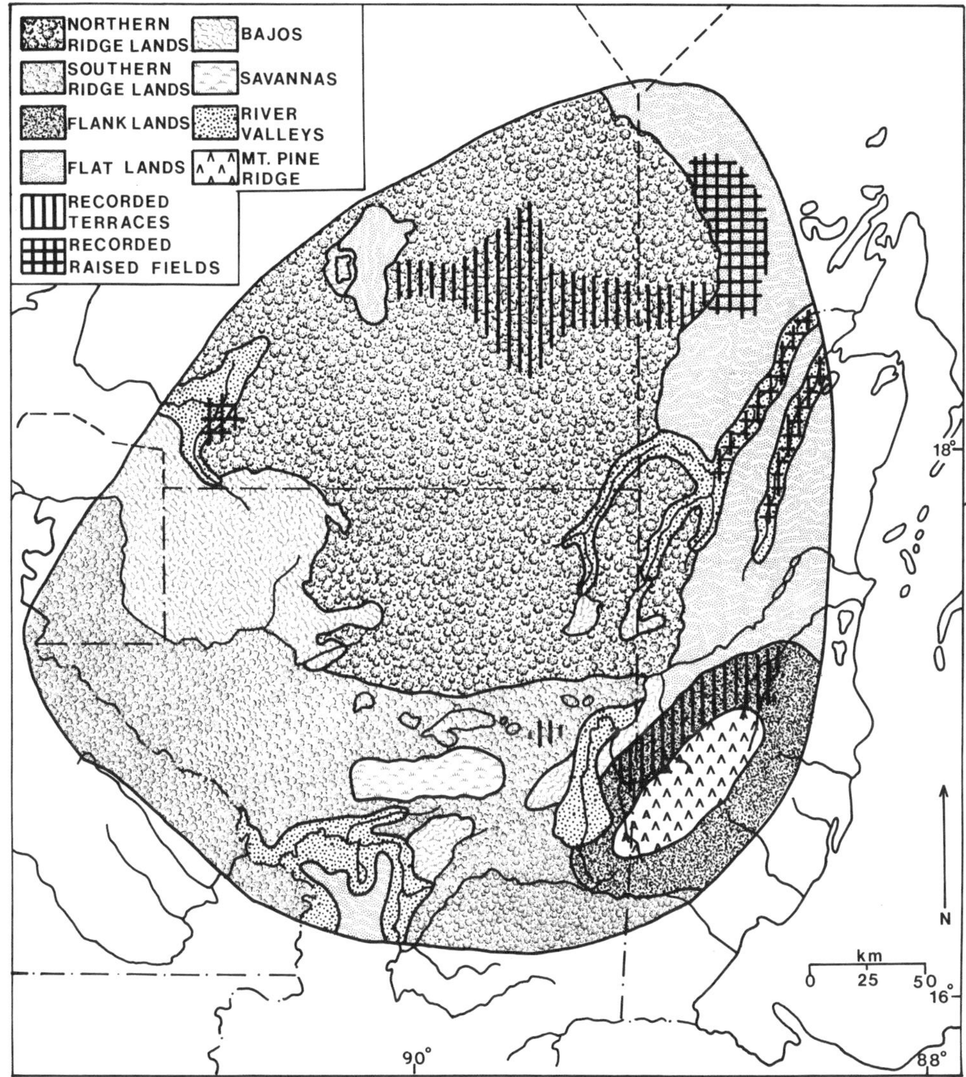

Figure 9.2. Physiographic zones and identified relic agricultural features.

The region designated as the flank lands comprises the limestone flanks or foothills of the Maya Mountains of central Belize and the southeastern sector of the department of Peten in Guatemala. This physiographic zone is similar to the ridge lands but displays marked increases in elevation and slope (see Wright et al. 1959). The flank lands approach elevations of 900 meters above sea level. Steep slopes are common in Belize, gradually diminishing in gradient as the flank lands extend south and west into Peten.

Vegetational responses in the flank-land zone are similar to those in the southern ridge lands. Well-drained, calcareous loams (Rendolls) are the predominant soils.

These upland zones share several physical characteristics that create common problems for the development of intensive agriculture. The calcareous soils are generally fertile, particularly the Rendolls, and can sustain lengthy periods of continuous cropping if proper nutrients are replaced, especially phosphorous (Simmons, Tarano, and Pinto 1959; Turner 1974b; Olson 1975). When continually cleared for cultivation, however, the shallow slope soils are vulnerable to erosion. To minimize soil erosion, either a type of long-fallow swidden system of cultivation must be pursued or terraces must be constructed. Apparently the intensity of agriculture in the uplands during ancient times considerably exceeded the long-fallow system of cultivation, and large-scale terracing was implemented throughout the two zones.

Relic Maya terraces have been recorded over an extensive area of southern Campeche and Quintana Roo (fig. 9.2; Turner 1974b). This sector of the northern ridge lands, referred to as the Rio Bec region, displays hundreds of thousands of relic terraces and related stone works that cover an approximate contiguous area of 10,000 square kilometers.[4] The exact areal extent of Rio Bec terraces is uncertain, but the features have been recorded in east-west and north-south transects across southern Campeche and Quintana Roo of 174 kilometers and 159 kilometers, respectively (Turner 1974b:119). Terrace works probably exist farther north and south of the Rio Bec region, following the uplands. Stoneworks similar to the Rio Bec terraces have been observed in the Chenes region of Campeche and near the Peten-Campeche border.[5] Indeed, relic terraces have been identified as far south as central Peten in the southern ridge lands, about 35 to 40 kilometers southeast of Tikal (fig. 9.2; Turner 1974a:124).[6]

Relic Maya terraces have been recorded over an extensive portion of the flank lands (fig. 9.2). Ower (1927:384, 1929:1) observed terraces throughout the entire northwest corner of the flank lands of the Maya Mountains between the Belize and Sibun rivers.[7] J. E. S. Thompson (1931:228–29) and Lundell (1940:9) expanded this zone of terracing to include the western flank lands; an area demarcated on the north by Benque Viejo, on the south by Mountain Cow (Tximin Tax), on the east by the Macal River, and on the west by the Rio Chiquibul of Peten. Lundell (1940:9) estimated that the entire zone of terracing in the western flank lands covers approximately four hundred square kilometers.

The number of relic terraces in the flank lands may exceed that of the ridge-land zones. Ower (1927:384) reported that the terraces in the northwestern section of the flank lands occur "wherever it was possible to retain a few yards of soil." J. E. S. Thomspon (1931:228–29) has made a similar observation concerning the relic terraces in the western flank lands; the same features of which Lundell (1940:9) reported, "Everywhere the land is terraced . . . terracing was found whenever the terrain was sloping. On one hillside I counted no less than 51 terraces, and this was not an exceptional case."

Terracing in the central Maya lowlands was probably implemented in an attempt to retain soils on slopes, to expand the land area under cultivation, to manipulate soil-moisture conditions, and to create an adequate soil depth for cropping.[8] The terraces may have served several secondary functions as well (Turner 1978). The presence of small stone walls that angle across the terraces and of slightly noncontoured terrace embankments that probably acted as water deflection devices suggests that runoff control may have been a function (Turner 1974b:140–41). The terraces may have assisted in maintaining a more consistent moisture content of the soil, improving the chances of producing a dry-season crop or of saving a crop during periods of drought. Also, the terraces may have assisted in increasing the low phosphorus content of the slope soils by retaining organic materials on the hillside (Wright et al. 1959:113; Wright 1962:9).

Regardless of their precise functions, the terraces in the central lowlands were undoubtedly constructed in order to facilitate intensive agriculture, probably an annual or near-annual cycle. The time, expense, manpower, and organization necessary to construct and maintain the large-scale terrace systems were too great to have been wasted on a system of cultivation that merely approximated or slightly improved the swidden cycle. The studies of Urrutia (1967) indicate that lengthy cultivation can be accomplished on various soil types in the central lowlands if proper care is taken. Indeed, the Troporendoll soils of the uplands constitute one of the best agricultural soils in the tropics (Sanchez and Buol 1975). Furthermore, the Maya probably possessed the knowledge to care for the soils through the application of mulches, manures, and ash, and by tilling. Snail shells from terrace soils near Cubietas Viejas, Belize, suggest that the terraces may have been filled or at least fertilized with alluvial soils.[9]

Flatlands

Large tracts of relatively level (or minimally sloping) terrain are common in eastern Quintana Roo and in segments of the ridge lands (fig. 9.2). These flatland zones are not to be confused with the plane surfaces created by karst activity that occur in depressions, although depressions do occur in these zones. Indeed, small but numerous *bajo* depressions are present in the flatlands of Quintana Roo. The flatlands share most of the physical qualities of the ridge lands with the exception of prevalent sloping terrain. Indeed, the well-drained flatlands may constitute the best agricultural zones in the central Maya lowlands, in that the calcareous loams (often Rendolls) are fertile for cultivation but do not suffer serious erosional or inundation problems.

Generally, the flatlands are well suited for agricultural activities that the Maya could have pursued without the construction of major stoneworks or earthworks. Nevertheless, remnants of stone walls abound in the flatland zones, especially in the Rio Bec region (fig. 9.2). These walls, often incorrectly termed ridged fields, occur not only on more level terrain, but on terraced hillsides as well. Varying in width and height, the cut limestone walls divide the land into compact rectilinear and curvilinear segments.

Stone walls occur in profusion in the southern sectors of Campeche and Quintana Roo and have been thoroughly mapped around the site of Becan (Turner 1974b).[10] Lundell (1933a:73) reports that stone walls occur west of the Becan area near Tuxpeña, Campeche, and Shufeldt (1950:224–29) has suggested that similar features are common throughout the Campeche and Peten areas of the central Maya lowlands. The stone walls probably represent precise land division or field demarcation resulting from intensive land use, presumably for agricultural purposes. Interestingly, permanent field demarcation suggests some type of individual or group ownership or control of the land, a tenure situation not prevalent among extensive, swidden farmers.

Most likely, the demarcation of fields was spurred by population pressure (or production pressure) that resulted in intensive agricultural activities within the demarcated plots.

The specific functions of the stone walls in the flatter lands are subject to speculation. They may have acted as deterrents to pests, both domesticated and wild. Larger walls may have been used as walkways to facilitate movement during the wet seasons. Also, the walls may have been used to protect crops from strong winds associated with hurricanes, which frequently pass over the peninsula.

River Valleys and Bajos

Seasonal inundation is characteristic of several physiographic zones in the central lowlands, including river valleys and *bajos* (fig. 9.2). The principal watersheds that are subject to seasonal flooding are the Hondo-New, the Usumacinta-Pasión, the San Pedro, and the Candelaria drainage systems which envelop all but the northern peripheries of the central Maya lowlands. Situated between the watersheds and the interior ridge lands are major zones of *bajos* extending from southern Campeche and Quintana Roo into the central and southern sections of Peten.

The river valleys display several microvegetational responses that are related primarily to soil-moisture conditions. The vegetation of the lower alluvial terraces of the valleys, which are regularly flooded, is characterized by herbaceous growth. The higher and dryer sections of the valleys are dominated by woody species (see Lundell 1937). Acidic clays, Entisols and Inceptisols, are prevalent (Olson 1975). *Bajos* are depressions that have slow interior drainage, resulting in various degrees of seasonal inundation. The vegetational response to these conditions is a low scrub forest that has adapted to the sticky clay soils. *Bajo* soils in the Rio Bec region tend to be Mollisols, mostly the Haplaquoll variety (Turner 1974b:96).

Soils in both the river valley and *bajo* zones are seasonally inundated and hence generally too wet and sticky for cultivation. During the dry season, cultivation is often possible on the dryer margins of either zone. For the most part, however, cultivation necessitates the creation of cropping surfaces above the level of inundation by draining the zone and/or by constructing raised fields. The central lowland Maya used both methods.

Siemens (Siemens and Puleston 1972) was the first to report relics of raised fields in the Maya lowlands, situated in the Rio Candelaria valley of southwestern Campeche (fig. 9.2). About fifteen small complexes of raised fields, covering a total area not exceeding 1.5 to 2.0 square kilometers, were identified upstream from the settlement of Candelaria. The individual raised surfaces appeared as rectangular platforms, and the field complexes formed a lattice pattern when viewed aerially. Also identified in the region were a large number of relic canals or large ditches that occur in conjunction with and isolated from the raised fields. On the opposite side of the peninsula, in the Hondo and New valleys of Belize, Siemens and Puleston have discovered much larger complexes of relic raised fields. Initial data indicate that the field systems cover at least 75 square kilometers in the vicinity of San Antonio, Belize (Puleston 1977; Olson 1974:3; Olson et al. 1975:9–12).

Perhaps the largest complexes of raised fields have been located in the *bajos* of the flatland zones of southern Quintana Roo. A 120-square-kilometer area containing relic fields has been identified in the *bajos* situated north and east of Nicolás Bravo; about 62 square kilometers of this area are confined to the Bajo del Morocoy.[11] Subsequent reconnaissance indicates that the ancient field systems extend considerable distances north and east of the Morocoy fields. Harrison (1975, 1977) reports that every *bajo* between the settlements of Morocoy and Ucum is filled with relic raised fields and that the fields extend as far north as Uomuul, Quintana Roo. The fields appear to be rectangular platforms separated by large and small canals and ditches. The complex of platforms and ditches produces a lattice pattern, similar to the fields in the Candelaria River Valley.

The dominant form of raised fields found in the central lowlands—rectangular platforms—is not unique to the Maya area but is common in other parts of the tropics, especially in Southeast Asia and Oceania (Denevan and Turner 1974:25). Initial descriptions of relic fields near San Antonio, Belize, indicate that the Maya constructed the platforms with the use of marl and topsoils that created a planting surface about one meter or more above water level. Ditches and canals, often exceeding a depth of one meter or more above water level, were dug around each platform (Olson et al. 1975:10).

Raised fields provided several functions that allowed the Maya to cultivate inundated terrain. The platform provided suitable soil-moisture conditions and adequate soil depth for cultivation. The apparent method of field construction, the digging and piling of soils, produced a pulverized cropping medium that improved aeration and allowed deeper root growth than was obtainable in the unimproved soils of the river valleys and *bajos.* Furthermore, the concentration of topsoils and the probable application of muck from the surrounding ditches created a more fertile soil for cultivation. Initial data indicate that organic materials were applied to the Hondo Valley fields to maintain fertility (Olson 1974:3).

The canal and ditch system associated with Maya raised fields provided drainage that impeded the waterlogging of platform soils during periods of maximum inundation. The canals, especially those in the river valleys, may have functioned as irrigation devices during the dry season. Water from canals and ditches may have penetrated to the root level of the crops planted on the fields due to capillary rise, or water could have been thrown on the fields with the use of baskets or pots, much in the manner currently employed by the highland Maya (Puleston 1977). Indeed, the great number of large ditches or canals recorded in the Candelaria Valley may represent attempts by the Maya to facilitate drainage and/or irrigation of the raised fields and of the margins of the valley. If sufficient water was maintained, the larger canals and ditches may have been used for water transportation.[12] The large size of the main canal that runs through the raised fields of the Bajo del Morocoy suggests a function other than drainage, perhaps irrigation or transportation.

Savannas and the Mountain Pine Ridge

Other major physiographic zones in the central Maya lowlands include savannas, both well-drained and seasonally inundated, and the mountain pine ridge. Savannas are found scattered throughout the lowlands, often in depressions that may retain standing water. The largest zone of savannas in the lowlands is situated south and west of Lake Peten Itza (fig. 9.2). This area, referred to as the central savanna zone, comprises both well-drained and poorly drained grasslands interspersed with small, often dome-shaped hills. Forests cover the hills and occasionally spill over into the flatter lands. Most of the level terrain, however, is dominated by grasses. The savanna soils tend to be deep acidic clays, often Haplaquolls, especially in the seasonally inundated savannas of southern Campeche. Many lowland savanna soils are fertile for cultivation if tilled and properly treated.

The Maya apparently had the ability to cultivate the savanna zones with the use of raised fields. This cultivation technique is commonly utilized by so-called primitive farmers to cultivate tropical savannas. Indeed, most relic raised fields in the New World have been found in grasslands (Denevan 1970). Despite the potential of the savannas to sustain cultivation and the possession by the Maya of an appropriate technique with which to cultivate grasslands, no clues have been uncovered to indicate that the savanna zones in the central lowlands were utilized for major agricultural activities.[13]

The mountain pine ridge zone dominates the higher interior section of the Maya Mountains of Belize and southeastern Peten (fig. 9.2). The predominant vegetation is a pine-oak-grass cover associated with leached loams and sandy loams (possibly Rankers). Pine-ridge soils, generally infertile, are avoided by contemporary cultivators. Ruins are not abundant in the mountain pine ridge, and evidence of major occupation of the zone during ancient times is absent.[14] Agricultural activities by the Maya in the mountain pine ridge of Belize, for instance, would have necessitated major soil preparations for probably marginal returns. The Maya had the capabilities to undertake such preparations but the pressure to obtain agricultural production probably did not reach a sufficient level to justify the high costs.

In sum, eight major physiographic zones may be identified in the central Maya lowlands. Relic agricultural and related features indicate that the ancient Maya manipulated at least six of these zones—northern ridge land, southern ridge land, flank land, flatland, river valley, and *bajo*—in order to pursue intensive agriculture. The more obvious problems confronting agricultural intensification in these zones were the maintenance of soil fertility, the impediment of soil erosion, and the improvement of inundated soils. Direct evidence concerning the manner in which soil fertility was maintained is lacking, so we can only speculate on fertility-sustaining practices by the Maya. In the ridge-land and the flank-land zones, erosion was controlled with terraces, and inundation in the river valley and *bajo* zones was circumvented by drainage and raised fields. Agricultural activities in the savanna zones and the mountain pine ridge zone are uncertain. The savanna zones may have been utilized for agricultural activities but it is doubtful that the mountain pine ridge was ever a major zone of cultivation.

PROJECTED PATTERN OF AGRICULTURAL LAND USE

The established pattern of agricultural land use in the central Maya lowlands is restricted to several areas for which evidence has been uncovered (fig. 9.2). A projected pattern for the entire central lowlands might include the extension of the limits of field demarcation, terraces, and raised fields throughout the several physiographic zones with which these features are associated. It is unlikely that such a pattern existed, however, as agricultural land use is the result of a more complex set of circumstances.

Projection Bases

Agricultural land use is established by the interplay of various economic, social, and environmental factors. The pattern of agricultural land use that developed in the central Maya lowlands probably was the result of production pressure (the pressure to produce agricultural goods), technology, types of crops, soil, drainage, and the orientation of the agricultural economy. Our knowledge of these factors is limited and hinders any projection of ancient land-use patterns. Nevertheless, the more prominent facets of the pattern may be projected with minimal assumptions by focusing on several key factors—population density, agricultural technology, and physiographic zones—for which evidence is available.

Systematic studies of contemporary subsistence agriculturalists in the tropics indicate that a strong relationship exists between population pressure (population density) and agricultural intensity (Brookfield, 1962:242–54; Turner, Hanham, and Portararo 1977). Population pressure is one form of production pressure that is taken to be a major determinant of agricultural intensity, although several secondary factors may modify the relationship (Brookfield 1972; Turner, Hanham, and Portararo 1977). Assuming that the agricultural economy of the lowland Maya Classic civilization was primarily subsistence oriented, a projection of agricultural land use can be established based on the population pressure–agricultural intensity relationship. The evidence of field demarcation, terraces, and raised fields indicates the more intensive modes of Maya agriculture and the physiographic zones in which they were utilized. Ruins, ranging from major civic-temple centers to individual house sites, indicate the areas of large and densely settled populations that probably required intensive cultivation as a means of support.

The more densely occupied areas in the ancient lowlands were probably those that possessed a large number of civic-temple centers (sites). Numerous studies have demonstrated that civic-temple centers in the central lowlands were centers of population concentration and that the regions that surrounded these centers often were occupied densely (Puleston 1974b; Turner 1974a). Although population densities in the central Maya lowlands have shifted both temporally and spatially, peak populations for the entire area probably occurred in the Late Classic period (ca. A.D. 550–1000).

The distribution of Late Classic sites in the central Maya lowlands suggests at least two major areas of population concentration and one minor (fig. 9.3).[15] By far the largest number and greatest density of sites occurs in an oblong-shaped wedge that covers the entire eastern segment of the central lowlands from southern Campeche to southern Peten. Site density is especially heavy in the northeastern portion of Peten, spaced at an average distance of about ten kilometers. Site spacing increases to an average of about twenty kilometers in southern Campeche and southern Peten (Hammond 1974a:320). These sites tend to follow the upland zones, indicating on a macro scale the areal association between Maya settlements and the fertile Mollisols of the central lowlands. This areal relationship has also been demonstrated on a micro scale for several sectors of the Maya lowlands (Voorhies

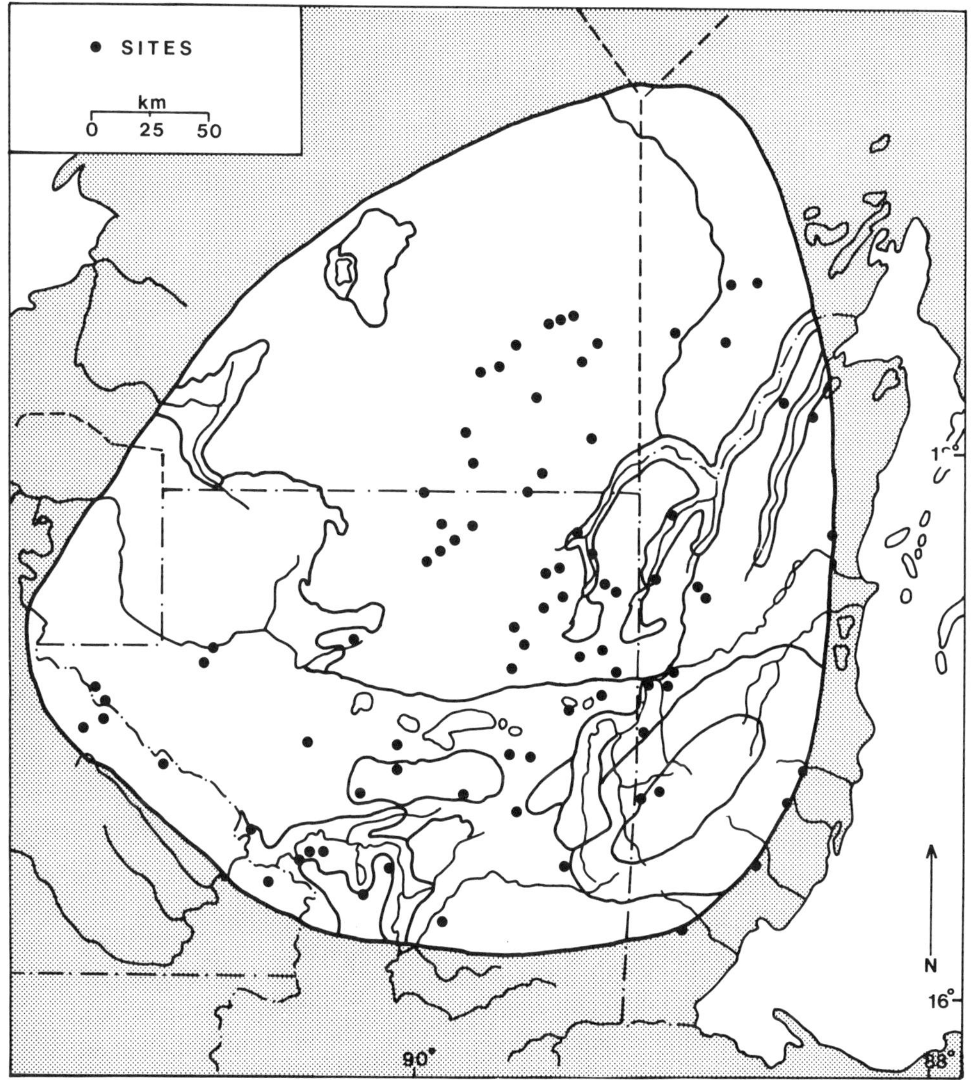

Figure 9.3. Physiographic zones and the distribution of Late Classic sites.

1972; Green 1973). The site-situation relationship in the uplands probably reflects the ancient practice of settling on or near prime, well-drained, agricultural land, although numerous sites are situated near zones of fertile but poorly drained soils.

The second major area of site concentration is along the Usumacinta and Pasión river valleys, especially in the southern ridge land bordering the lower Pasión Valley. The eastern flank lands of the Maya Mountains constitute a subsidiary zone of site concentration that may have developed in the Late Classic period in response to crowded conditions in the interior ridge land zone.[16]

Projected Pattern

Correlating the physiographic zones and the corresponding relic agricultural features with the site distribution, the following agricultural land use pattern is projected for the Late Classic period (fig. 9.4).

Large-scale field demarcation and terracing. These techniques were probably operative throughout the uplands, especially east of Lake Silvituc and southward into the flank-land zone of Belize. Terracing may also have been important in the southern ridge lands bordering the Pasión and Usumacinta rivers and in the eastern flank lands of Belize. Field demarcation, without terracing, may have been significant throughout the well-drained level terrain within the ridge-land zones and, especially, in the flatland zone of eastern Quintana Roo and the western segments of Campeche.

Raised fields. A large number of raised-field complexes may have been constructed throughout the *bajos* of the flatland zone of Quintana Roo and the *bajos* of the northeastern segment of Peten.[17] Also, many of the river valleys penetrating the eastern segments of Peten and portions of the Usumacinta and Pasión river valleys were likely zones of raised-field cultivation. Finally, raised-field cultivation near the civic-temple centers situated along the San Pedro River was a distinct possibility.

Small-scale terrace and raised-field works. These may have been operative in various other locales in the central lowlands, particularly in conjunction with more isolated sites or population concentrations. The raised-field complexes of the Candelaria River Valley may have been a case in point. This mode of agriculture probably supported the population concentration of Itzamkañac; the apparent absence of other major sites in the vicinity may explain why more field complexes have not been identified in the area.

Other techniques. Those sections of the central lowlands that were sparsely settled may have been used for various types of swidden

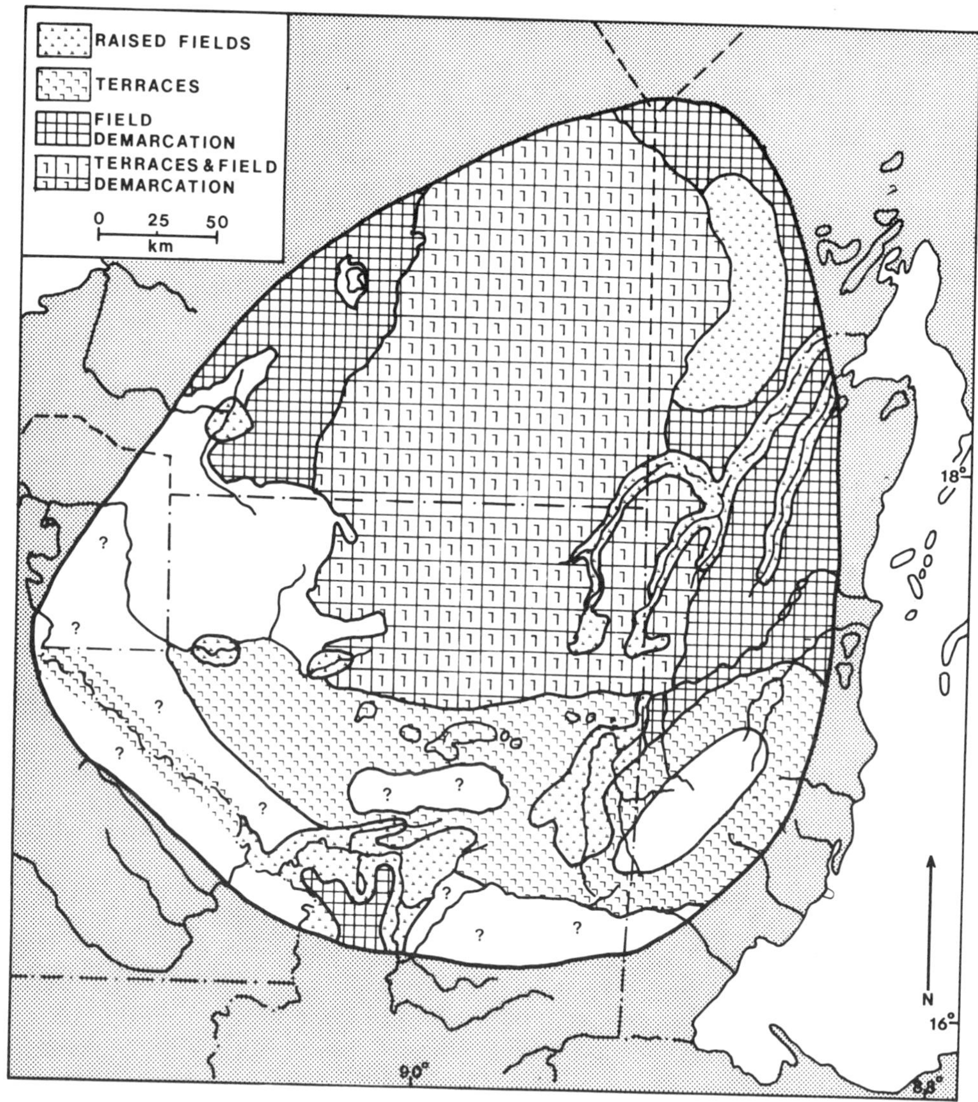

Figure 9.4. Projected zones of intensive agricultural land use.

cultivation or not used for agricultural activities of any kind. The coastal strip east and south of Altun Ha in Belize and the northwestern portion of Peten are likely areas of minimal agricultural activities. Land use in the central savanna zone remains a puzzle. The one area probably not subjected to any cultivation during the Late Classic period is the mountain pine ridge.

PERSPECTIVE: PROJECTION PROBLEMS

Clarification of the numerous subsistence patterns and activities in the central lowlands is essential to understanding Classic Maya civilization. Assessments of agricultural land use can now be projected with some measure of factual support, thanks to the recent increase in agricultural evidence from the central lowlands and to the emphasis placed on site and settlement patterns in the same region. Such projections are nevertheless still tenuous and primarily serve as a foundation for further reconnaissance and research of ancient agriculture in the central lowlands.

Field research on relic agricultural features and their distribution is a relatively recent development, and numerous sectors of the central lowlands have not been adequately examined. As a result, the agricultural land-use pattern posited here is based on the assumptions that (1) the known distribution of sites is relatively accurate and reflects Late Classic population concentrations; (2) the Maya basically maintained a subsistence economy in terms of agricultural staples, the staples being grown and consumed within the central lowlands; and (3) transportation problems were such that long-distance external trade of agricultural staples was not economically feasible and, therefore, exogenous pressures on agricultural production were minimal. Evidence that any of these assumptions are incorrect may necessitate alterations in the suggested pattern.

Although most of the major sites in the central lowlands probably have been identified, the density and distribution of small sites, especially hamlets, are not well known (Hammond 1974a:319). Further research may identify Late Classic population concentrations in areas of the central lowlands thought to have been sparsely settled, such as the northwestern segment of Peten. Such identification probably would entail an expansion of the projected agricultural land usages according to the physiographic zones in which the population concentrations were located.

Most of the staple crops that supported the Late Classic populace in the central lowlands were probably grown and consumed locally. This assessment is based, in part, on the assumption that long-distance trading of major staples was not economically feasible, although specialty crops, such as cacao and cotton, may have been traded. Transportation facilities may have been sufficient, however, to allow adjacent sectors of the central lowlands to supply one another with staples, especially with the use of canal systems and improved walkways. If a canal system were operative, for instance, the swamp and *bajo* land in northwestern Peten could have supplied the heavily occupied eastern portion of the central lowlands with agricultural goods. It is possible that the raised fields in the Hondo Valley supplied the Tikal area with produce that was transported inland by way of the river and canals to the Tikal region. Terrace cultivation in flank lands may have supplied staples to Peten sites. The flank-land zone borders the eastern Peten and is only 60 to 70 kilometers from Tikal, a reasonable distance for the transportation of staple crops; it is mostly downslope, and it crossed a densely settled region in the Late Classic period.

The nature of Maya agriculture in the central lowlands is the best evidence that most staples were grown for local consumption near major population concentrations. Intensive cultivation during the Late Classic period undoubtedly demanded a large work force to supply the labor necessary to crop the land, to maintain soil fertility, and to construct and maintain the large complexes of walls, terraces, and raised fields. It seems unlikely that a sparsely settled region would have had a sufficient work force to provide for these requirements. It is possible, however, that the agricultural surplus from such areas was transported to civic-temple centers. Finally, the relics of intensive agriculture in the central lowlands found thus far are situated within or near regions that maintained large and densely settled populations. This evidence supports the subsistence argument and suggests that the projected agricultural land-use pattern is representative of conditions during the Late Classic period.

POSTSCRIPT

A few remarks are warranted concerning the possibility of finding evidence of intensive agriculture in the northern lowlands, where pre-Hispanic Maya population densities were quite large. To date, little direct evidence of ancient agricultural pursuits has been located in the northern lowlands, despite several attempts to find some (Hester 1954). The flat, highly karsted northern plain and eastern coastal lands are unlikely zones in which to find either terraces or raised fields. Intensive agricultural activities could have been conducted by the Maya in these zones without large-scale stoneworks or earthworks, although raised fields would probably have been required to cultivate the savanna zones. Field demarcation may be abundant, as is suggested by the reports of Bishop Landa and by the presence of stone walls in the vicinity of Tulum (Tozzer 1941:97; Sabloff and Rathje 1975). The Puuc Hills pose an interesting problem. Although they were once densely settled and possess sloping terrain suitable for terracing, relics of agricultural features have not been identified in the zone. Interestingly, however, evidence suggesting some sort of hydraulic agriculture has been found immediately south of the Puuc Hills, at the site of Edzna (Matheny 1976; chapter 10, below).

NOTES

1. Evidence and arguments concerning population and settlement patterns of the lowland Maya Classic civilization have been presented elsewhere and are not treated here (Willey et al. 1965; Haviland 1969; Turner 1976b).

2. The chronology used here was developed by Ball (1973) to include the Rio Bec region or the northern portion of the central Maya lowlands.

3. The soil classification used here has been developed by the Soil Conservation Service (1970).

4. Rio Bec terraces were first reported as check dams by Ruppert and Denison (1943:13, 50). This identification went largely unnoticed until several members of the Middle American Research Institute's 1969–71 Becan project recognized the features, particularly Eaton (1972).

5. Personal communication with Jack D. Eaton, University of Texas at San Antonio, who has extensively explored portions of southern Campeche and Quintana Roo.

6. Ancient terraces have also been reported in Peten by Blom (1946:5).

7. I have credited Ower with the first report of terraces in the Maya lowlands. An earlier note of terraces in the eastern flank lands does not appear to refer to agricultural terraces (Joyce 1926:226–27).

8. Soil erosion is an acute problem in the tropics, especially where land is continually cleared for cultivation. Averaged data from the tropics indicate a soil loss of about 1,000 kilograms per hectare and 4,000 kilograms per hectare on slopes ranging up to 5 percent and 10 percent, respectively (Ochse et al. 1961:243).

9. This assessment was offered by Arthur A. Saxe and Henry Wright, and was reported by J. W. Hopkins (1968).

10. The map of the Becan area has been compiled by Prentice M. Thomas, Jr. and is to be published by the Middle American Research Institute, Tulane University, New Orleans.

11. Turner (1974a:121) was in error in assigning the entire 120-square-kilometer area of raised fields to the Bajo del Morocoy (see Harrison 1975).

12. Siemens and Puleston (1972:235) suggest that the canals of the Candelaria Valley

that are not directly associated with raised fields may have been used as accessways for canoes. J. E. S. Thompson (1974) challenges this interpretation, arguing that the features may have been fish ponds. While the fish pond thesis is plausible, especially in regard to the canals, it is tenuous when applied to the raised fields proper. The latter features were probably constructed initially and primarily for cultivation purposes and not for the creation of ditches for the rearing or trapping of aquatic life.

13. Savanna zones constitute a considerable portion of the central lowlands and, as such, deserve much more scrutiny for past use than they have hitherto received.

14. Natural, nonstone embanked terraces occur in the mountain pine ridge but are not to be confused with the agricultural terraces in the flank lands (see Wright et al. 1959).

15. The distribution of Late Classic sites is not complete and is taken largely from Norman Hammond (1974a).

16. Hammond (1974a:316, 330) notes that Lubaantun, a major site in the eastern flank lands, was only occupied during the latter stages of the Classic period in conjunction with population expansions in the central lowlands.

17. The outline of possible raised fields in the *bajos* near El Mirado was recognized by Peter D. Harrison and E. Wyllys Andrews V on viewing photographs taken by the National Geographic Society. The existence of raised fields near Tikal has been suggested by several scholars.

10

RAY T. MATHENY
Department of Anthropology and Archaeology, Brigham Young University

Northern Maya Lowland Water-Control Systems

That water-control systems in the Maya lowlands were integral features of settlements is now established fact (Siemens and Puleston 1972; Matheny 1976). Water requirements, especially for large sites, must have constituted a major problem for Maya town planners. It is now known that ceremonial centers without an appreciable resident population were rare and that most have house remains within a reasonable distance (Willey and Bullard 1965:368–77). Many of the so-called ceremonial centers I prefer to call towns or cities, in agreement with George Andrews (1975) and Jorge Hardoy (1973). Where large settlements were planned, a water system had to be developed before a significant population could be expected to thrive. Therefore each city or ceremonial center should show some evidence of constructions designed to accumulate and store water. This evidence is scarce for Maya lowland sites and still requires serious investigation.

My thesis in this paper is that the peoples of the northern lowlands were skilled in hydraulic engineering, insofar as we can extend the concept of engineering to mean a useful knowledge of landforms, soil, vegetation, water, and slopes for the accumulation, storage, conservation, and dispersal of water. Water controls are construed to refer not only to reservoirs, canals, and drains, but also to terraces, raised fields, including chinampas, embankments, garden beds, and other constructions designed to alter the normal flow of water in soil. This definition may be too broad for some readers, but it is felt that the end result of greater utilization of water than that associated with natural conditions qualifies as a water control. Water can be controlled for human consumption, food production, transportation, defense, and ritual use. Each of these purposes will be discussed as they apply to water-control systems.

WATER AND THE KARST FORMATIONS OF THE NORTHERN YUCATAN PENINSULA

Underground water is accessible on the Yucatan Peninsula through numerous cracks and caverns in the limestone bedrock. Water level changes seasonally and varies from area to area. In Cenote Xlacah, at Dzibilchaltun, Yucatan, it is only 2 meters below the cenote rim, whereas at Santa Rosa Xtampak the water level is over 75 meters below the surface. Water at Xcalumkin, Campeche, was once obtainable in a karst cenote at 7 meters below the surface, as evidenced by a shelf and numerous remains of water jars. In 1968, the water level here was about 54 meters below the surface, but we were informed by local inhabitants that the level is usually several meters above that. Before the Mexican government drilled a well in the nearby settlement of Cumpich, the inhabitants went down into a cavern for water where a large ceiba tree was growing. The water level in the cavern was reported to be approximately 30 meters below the surface.

A number of references from Stephens (1843) illustrate the difficulties of water procurement on the northern peninsula in the nineteenth century. One instance similar to that at Cumpich was related by Stephens (1843:1:211ff.) that demonstrates the great difficulty in obtaining water at Xcoch, not far from Ticul, Yucatan, in 1842. At this site water was obtained by descending into a cavern on a well-worn path cut into the rock, crawling through narrow passages, and climbing down an uncertain ladder to a deep basin. Stephens commented, "This account may not be perfectly accurate in all the details, but it is not exaggereated." He continued,

> As a mere cave, this was extraordinary; but as a well or watering-place for an ancient city, it was past belief, except

> for the proofs under our own eyes. Around it were the ruins of a city without any other visible means of supply.

At the Rancho Shawill, four leagues from Nohcacab, Stephens (1843:2:3–4) complained to the Maya alcalde

> against the charge of two reals for watering our horses, but the excuse was satisfactory enough. In the rainy season they had sources of supply in the neighbourhood, and these were perhaps as primitive as in any other section of the habitable world, being simply deposits of rain-water in the holes and hollows of rocks, which were called *sartenejas.* From the rocky nature of the country, these are very numerous; during the rainy season they are replenished as fast as they are exhausted, and at the time of our visit, owing to the long continuance of the rains, furnished a sufficient supply for domestic use, but the people were not able to keep horses or cows, or cattle of any kind, the only animals they had being hogs. In the dry season this source of supply failed them; the holes in the rocks were dry, and they were obliged to send to the rancho of Chack, the well of which they represented as being half a mile underground, and so steep it was reached only by descending nine different staircases.

In exploring the "well" at Rancho Chack, Stephens (1843:2:17 ff.) described the extreme difficulty in obtaining water. Large ceiba trees that grew at the mouth of the cavern were indicators of water. Stephens remarked,

> We noticed that there were no women, who, throughout Yucatan, are the drawers of water, and always seen around a well, but we were told that no woman ever enters the well of Chack; all the water for the Rancho was procured by the men, which alone indicated that the well was of an extraordinary character.

In the "well" at the Rancho Chack, the men made a vertical descent of about 200 feet via ladders, in torchlight. Below the ladders it was necessary to crawl on hands and knees near

> a great chasm at one side, and beyond we came to another perpendicular hole, which we descended by steps cut in the rock. From this there was another low, crawling passage, and,

> almost stifled with heat and smoke, we came out into a small opening, in which was a basin of water, being the well.

Stephens's notes were in poor condition because of profuse sweating and the smudge of the torches. He said, "The distance as we traversed it, with its ladders, ascents and descents, winding and crawling passages . . . by measurement . . . was not quite fifteen hundred feet. . . ." He noted further that this well was not as at Xcoch, the "occasional resort of a straggling Indian," nor the mere traditional watering-place of an ancient city. It was "the regular and only supply of a living population."

According to Stephens (1843:2:19), the village of Sabachshe had no water supply. Water was obtained "two leagues or six miles distant" and transported on the backs of Indians. At Kewick, another Puuc site, Stephens was taken to an *aguada* where the banks and bottom had been exposed during the dry season, showing "the remains of stone embankments still visible, made, as they supposed by the ancient inhabitants" (1843:2:52).

Stephens (1843:2:55) also reported a well dug at Xul, 200 feet deep, plus "large and substantial cisterns, equal to any we had seen in the country, for the reception of rain-water . . ."; he further mentioned seeing a fountain (1843:2:57). He stated that after traveling two leagues, he

> reached what was called a hebe or fountain. It was a large rocky basin, about ninety feet in circumference and ten feet deep, which served as a receptacle for rain water.

While visiting the town of Bolonchen ("nine wells") in late February 1842, Stephens found that the water level was 10–12 feet from the surface (1843:2:95 ff.). Informants reported that water remained in the wells for seven or eight months; the "time was approaching, however, when these wells would fail, and the inhabitants be driven to an extraordinary cueva at half a league from the village" (1843:2:96). This cave (fig. 10.1) was known to the Indians at the time as Xtacumbi Xunan ("lady hidden away"). A complicated system of ladders provided access to a depth estimated by Stephens as 450 feet and approximately 1,400 feet from the mouth of the cave (fig. 10.2). Stephens (1843:2:96) noted that

> the great point was the fact, that from the moment when the wells in the plaza fail, the whole village turns to the cave, and

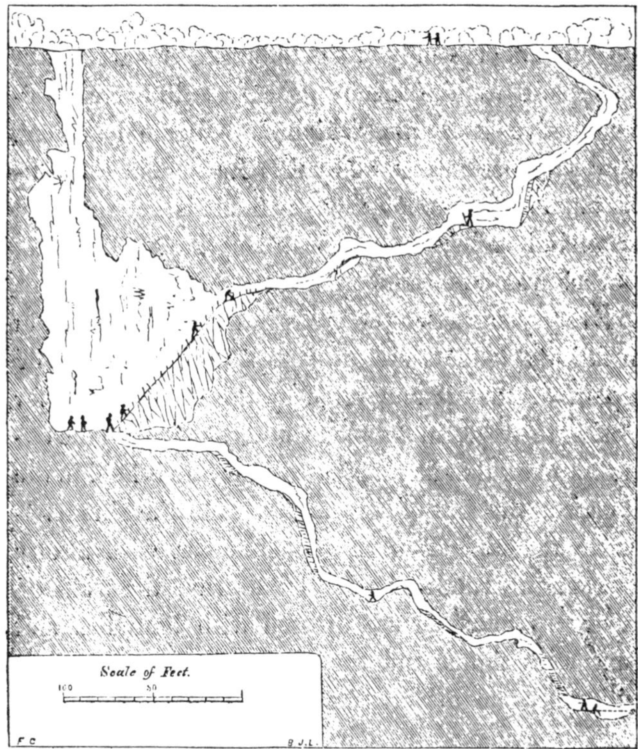

Figure 10.1. A cross section of the cavern at Xtacumbi Xuman, Yucatan. (Source: Stephens 1843)

> four or five months in the year derives from this source its only supply. . . . It was the sole and only watering-place of one of the most thriving villages in Yucatan, containing a population of seven thousand souls.

Small depressions, referred to as *aguadas* in the Maya region, are associated with karstic terrain. *Aguadas* in the northern Maya lowlands usually hold rainwater for only a few months and then dry up. Stephens (1843:2:148) noted an *aguada* at the Rancho Jalal that "was covered with water weeds like a carpet of vivid green." Ten years before, he reported, this *aguada* was dry, and an excavation revealed

> a square at the top, and beneath was a round well, faced with smooth stones, from twenty to twenty-five feet deep. Below the first well is another square platform, and under the latter another well of less diameter, and about the same depth. . . .

Figure 10.2. Cavern of Xtacumbi Xuman, Yucatan, drawn by F. Catherwood. (Source: Stephens 1843)

> upward of forty wells were discovered differing in their character and construction. . . .

Stephens illustrated a badly silted-in *aguada* that had wells and chultunes typical of Maya construction at the bottom (fig. 10.3).

The point was well made by Stephens that water was very precious on the peninsula and that people went to great lengths of labor and ingenuity to obtain it. An extreme case is the town of Bolonchen, where about 7,000 people depended on water from the famous cavern nearby for four or five months of the year. The difficulty of obtaining water was further emphasized by Stephens in his descriptions of *aguada,* well, and chultun development.

It seems unreasonable to assume that the ancient Maya could have sustained themselves at the apex of their population development with the hydraulic schemes that Stephens reported. With our new knowledge of Maya population size and agronomic skills, I believe the stage is set to explore the ancient water systems of the Maya, especially in the more arid northern lowlands.

LOWLAND WATER SYSTEMS

The Maya controlled water in at least three ways: (1) by draining excess water from inundated lands; (2) by conserving soil moisture; and (3) by collecting and storing water.

W. M. Denevan (1970:647) discusses various types of wetland cultivation involving water controls and specialized construction. He mentions

> (i) soil platforms built up in permanent water bodies; (ii) ridged, platformed, or mounded fields or seasonally flooded or waterlogged terrain; (iii) lazybeds or low, narrow ridges on slopes and flats subject to waterlogging; (iv) ditched fields, mainly for subsoil drainage; (v) fields on naturally drained land, including sandbars, river banks and lake margins; (vi) fields diked or embanked to keep water out; and (vii) aquatic cultivation, in which complete drainage is not attempted and plants are grown in water.

To these techniques we may add large and small structures in which water was stored for use in pot watering (Matheny 1976).

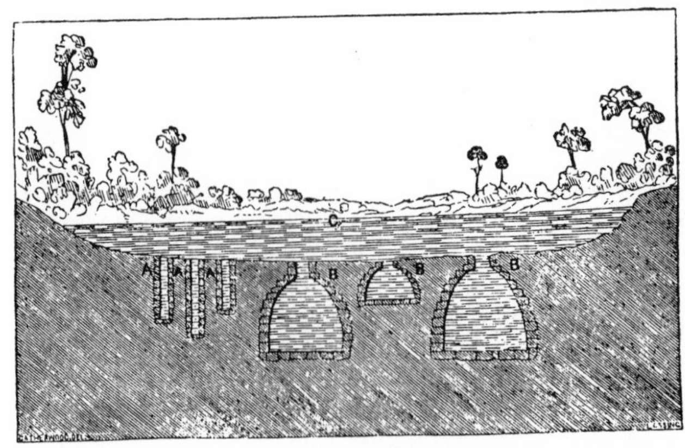

Figure 10.3. *Aguada* at the Rancho Jalal, Yucatan, with wells (A) and chultunes (B) noted by Stephens.

It is true that not all of these water-control techniques have been identified in association with Mesoamerican cultures, but most of them do apply. It is not unreasonable to expect more evidence of these and, perhaps, other such techniques to be forthcoming. Clearly, multiple methods of water control were practiced in the northern Maya lowlands; they were large in scale and designed for land and water use in food production, transportation, defense, and possibly ritual.

Canals Along the Candelaria River

Canals along lowlands near rivers were probably made for drainage. I have catalogued many such canals on the Tabasco Gulf Plain, along the Grijalva and Candelaria rivers, and I have seen similar drainage canals along rivers in Veracruz. The canals always occur on the floodplains where the rivers are sluggish and meandering. J. E. S. Thompson (1974) presents an argument that the canals on the Candelaria River were used for pisciculture, but I am not convinced that all were so used. Several of the canals along the Candelaria were cut from bend to bend in the river, affording a more direct passage by canoe by avoiding sandbars and other difficulties encountered in certain parts of the river (fig. 10.4). Siemens and Puleston (1972:238) report that some stretches of the river would be reduced from one-third to one-quarter in distance by use of direct connecting canals. On the other hand, much of the land around the river is flooded for long periods

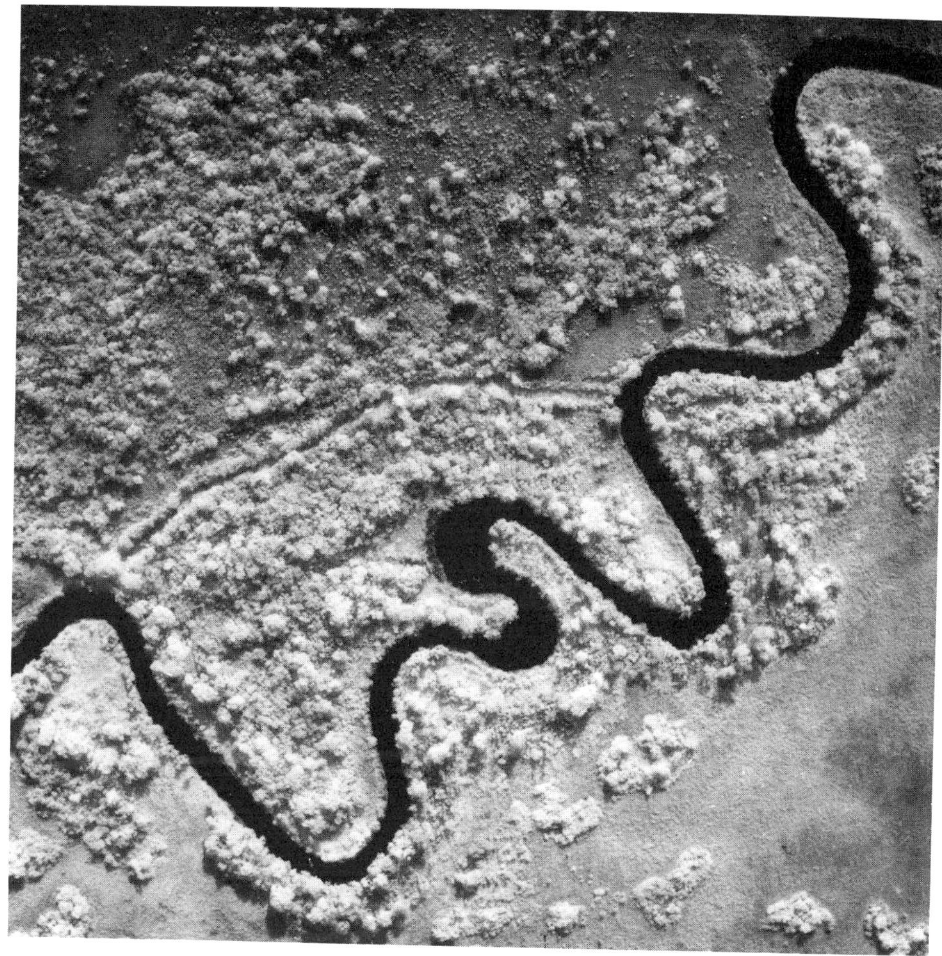

Figure 10.4. Black-and-white infrared aerial view of the Candelaria River, Campeche, showing an ancient canal.

during the rainy season. The small parallel lines seen in aerial photographs represent artificial canals made in pre-Columbian times for several purposes, but the draining of low-lying areas may have been of prime importance. Much research, including on-the-ground investigation, is needed on these water controls.

Hundreds of small, narrow canals (3–10 meters wide, 1–2 kilometers long) are known to exist along the Candelaria (fig. 10.5). A huge quantity of fish could have been raised in them, but other possible uses for the canals also suggest themselves. Rich riverbank soil from the narrow canals may have been used to construct the raised fields reported near the riverbanks, but on

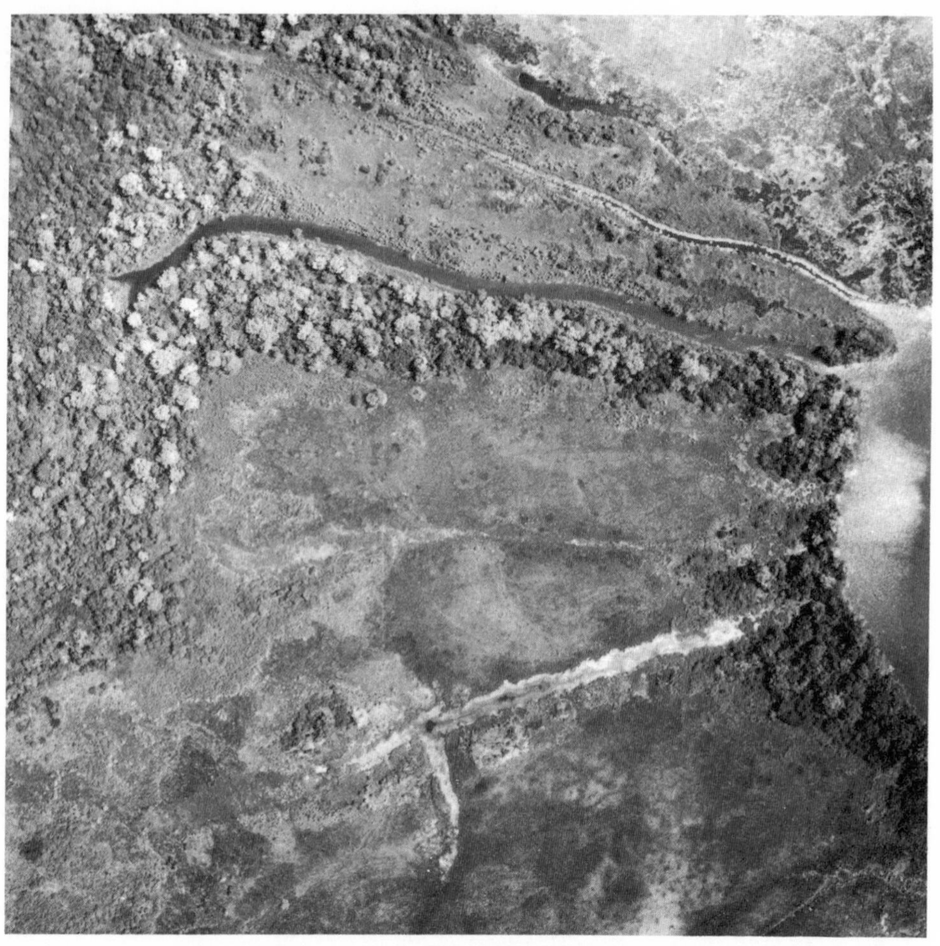

Figure 10.5 A cluster of canals on the Candelaria River, Campeche.

higher ground. If this interpretation of the evidence is correct, then two crops a year may have been obtained by cultivating the raised fields in the rainy season and the dry land near the river during the dry season. The raised fields could have been accessible during periods of inundation by canoes traveling between the ridges (Steggle 1977). If they were deep enough, narrow canals could have been used to bring water from the river to strips of land between canals for some sort of hand watering process. In any case, the small canals and raised fields are evidence of the control of water for some economic purpose.

Labor investment, of necessity, was large for the constructions discussed above. It is probable that surveying, planning, and a cooperative labor force were required to construct the canals and raised fields. Along the Candelaria and San Pedro rivers, for example, near the site of El Tigre, Siemens and Puleston have identified approximately 180 kilometers of canals.[1] Most of them are of the narrow type, but a few are wide. What it means to construct so many canals can be understood by calculating the man-days required for such an enterprise. Using C. J. Erasmus's (1965:285) figures for earth removal, we can calculate that over 10^6 cubic meters of excavation, involving nearly 500,000 man-days of labor, were required for the construction of the canals. This figure of earth removal is ten times greater than the volume of the Pyramid of the Sun at Teotihuacan. The labor estimate takes into consideration only direct removal of the earth from the canal—not planning, surveying, sustenance of the labor force, transportation of the soil, and other labor factors. Long, narrow, nearly parallel swales and ridges, unevenly spaced, about 1.5 kilometers long, also are found near the site of El Tigre. These features also required considerable labor to construct.

Sufficient evidence exists to demonstrate that the Maya in the Candelaria River area, which is thought by Siemens and Puleston to be the location of the historic Acalan of the Spanish chronicles, manipulated their environment to an astonishing degree. This manipulation appears to have centered around the control of water by the construction of canals and other features. Once this important resource was controlled, it could have been used in pisciculture, agriculture, transportation, and perhaps for defense.

Coastal Canals

A surface indentation cut perpendicular to the shoreline has been observed by F. R. Hauck (1975:114–20) about eight kilometers north of the city of Campeche. Hauck describes this indentation as a canal that extends nearly two kilometers inland to a site that dates at least to the Postclassic period. This canal is about two and one-third meters wide, but as it approaches the sea it widens to three meters. Hauck estimates its original depth as one and three-quarters meters; he reports that heavy lateritic clay from the original excavation was thrown up to form banks. Because ground elevation from the head to the mouth of the canal was slight, he discounts the idea that the canal was constructed for drainage purposes. It was probably used to provide direct access from the site to coastal water, thereby solving a basic transportation problem.

Our aerial reconnaissance flights along the coast of Campeche revealed many such canals connecting the shoreline to points about one to three kilometers inland. Although these canals have not been mapped or counted, our impression is that a hundred or more may exist between Campeche City and the Peninsula of Celestun. We can discern a pattern of canals leading from the shoreline to round clumps of trees (fig. 10.6). In some instances, a second canal emerges from the opposite side of a clump or at another angle and continues a short distance before disappearing into the landscape. Often two clumps of trees are connected by the canals. Other canals bypass clumps of trees and lead to obscure surface features. Several connect with small, shallow meandering tidal channels known as *esteros* (West 1957:67). It is clear that natural waterways were utilized until they could no longer serve and then canals were constructed directly from the end of an estero to a clump of trees.

What the clumps of trees may represent is not fully understood at present, but some clues are available. Mangrove trees are common along this coast where soil and other conditions permit their growth. Tidal inlets forming estuaries that show natural levee buildup usually are the hosts for mangroves. Sand and clay deposits slightly above the tidal water seem to form conditions that support the growth of the trees. Many of the canals are in tidal flat areas with no bar or ridge buildups and hence no trees; mangrove or other trees can only survive on rises of ground along this low alluvial coast. We have observed that the clumps of trees mentioned above are from 70 to 130 meters in diameter and have a mushroom shape, with low tree height at the edges and maximum growth at the center. We have also observed two instances in which the canals led to mounds denuded of trees (on one mound tree stumps were visible). The mounds were approximately the same shape and size as the nearby clumps of trees seen from the air, suggesting that the latter represent natural or artificial mounds. On one occasion we saw a mound, barren of trees, that had been extensively excavated. Archaeological looting would

Figure 10.6. Canals joining clump of trees (site?) to the seashore on the northern Campeche coast.

seem to be the only reason for excavation in a mound on this mud-flat coast. This particular mound may be the site listed as El Cuyo by Florencia Muller (1960:32). It is located approximately fifteen kilometers north of Isla de Jaina, the famous island site that yielded large numbers of figurines from burials.

Isla de Jaina appears to be linked to the mainland by artificial cuts which are joined to esteros. From the air can be seen what appear to be channels leading to the island from three different directions. These features may be fortuitous, as no on-the-ground investigations have yet been made.

E. B. Sisson (personal communication, 1976) suggests that William Dampier's voyage to obtain logwood (*Haematoxylum campechianum*) in 1676 along the Campeche Coast (Dampier 1906) may explain some of the coastal constructions found there. Robert West (1957) and Jonathan Sauer (1967) verify the suggestion of Spanish logwood operations along the coast of the peninsula in the early seventeenth century and note that logwood no longer occurs in the area. In interpreting the canals along the northern coast of Campeche, then, it is necessary to consider the possibility that they were, at least in part, constructed by logwood cutters. Ground observations by Hauck, however, indicate that at least one canal is associated with a pre-Columbian archaeological site. Other canals may also have pre-Columbian associations.

The Hydraulic System at Edzna

In the Edzna Valley annual precipitation ranges from 1,000 to 1,350 millimeters. There is no surface water other than that which accumulates in *aguadas.* Usually these are dry by March, although there are reports from the local Maya that water is found in a few deep *aguadas* of the Pic (a savanna located 12 kilometers south of the site) after that time. The rainy season begins approximately at the end of May and lasts until the end of December. A short remission of rainfall begins about the last week of August and lasts for two weeks, but in some years it does not occur. Maximum groundwater accumulation occurs approximately in mid October, although rainfall reaches its maximum intensity in September. From October to December rainfall diminishes, and scarcely any precipitation occurs from December to June.

Subterranean water at Edzna was found at a depth of nearly 20 meters. That the ancient Maya had the technical capability to dig wells to this depth is attested by the ancient wells at Dzibilnocac, a site about fifty kilometers to the south of Edzna. Our excavations at Dzibilnocac indicated that the wells had depths up to 13.4 meters or more. Our work at Edzna, however, produced no evidence of wells. Furthermore, we located only 12 chultunes at Edzna, indicating that this method of obtaining water was not important at the site. *Aguadas* are the only source of water in the Edzna Valley, and it is with these features that the ancient Maya worked.

Our surveys showed that *aguadas* occurred (and still do in places) over the flat valley floor in sufficient numbers to hold considerable water. No doubt man was attracted to this concentration of *aguadas;* he could have found them by the distinctive vegetation that grows around them. A strong Middle Preclassic manifestation at Edzna has been determined from over 150 test excavations. The Middle Preclassic occupation must be interpreted as a settlement of a permanent nature. Joseph W. Ball (personal communication) aptly calls the Middle Preclassic peoples the pioneer settlers of the Yucatan Peninsula. One of the problems they faced was the location of a dependable water source. It is posited that the pioneers modified *aguadas* to catch and maintain water over much of the dry season; otherwise significant numbers of people could not have lived at Edzna. Absolute dates for the Middle Preclassic occupation at Edzna are lacking, and so we must rely upon cross dating of ceramic materials. Radiocarbon dates for the Middle Preclassic occupation at Dzibilnocac (Nelson 1973) suggest a date of 600 B.C.

By Late Preclassic times a hydraulic system involving several canals and reservoirs had been conceived and constructed at Edzna. A 12-kilometer-long canal, connected with a moated structure that I call a fortress, was probably built in the Late Preclassic period. I assume on the basis of the overall site integration that the long canal was part of a grand scheme to create a hydraulic system in which canals aligned precisely with the physical layout of the site. The largest canal averages 50 meters' width and, where tested by excavation, about 1.5 meters' depth, holding approximately 900,000 cubic meters of water when full. Connected to the main canal is a moat system around the fortress that adds over 200,000 cubic meters of water to that of the canal. Several reservoirs and small canals, and a large canal over one kilometer in length, join the main canal-moat in a system that once held approximately 1.5×10^6 cubic meters of water (fig. 10.7).

The above figures represent an appreciable quantity of water storage in an area of the site where there are few residential mounds and only a few public buildings. The original excavation of the moat probably utilized one or more *aguadas.* This suggestion is supported by the identification of *Isoetes* sp. (a water plant) in buried soils on the moat banks, indicating that an *aguada* had

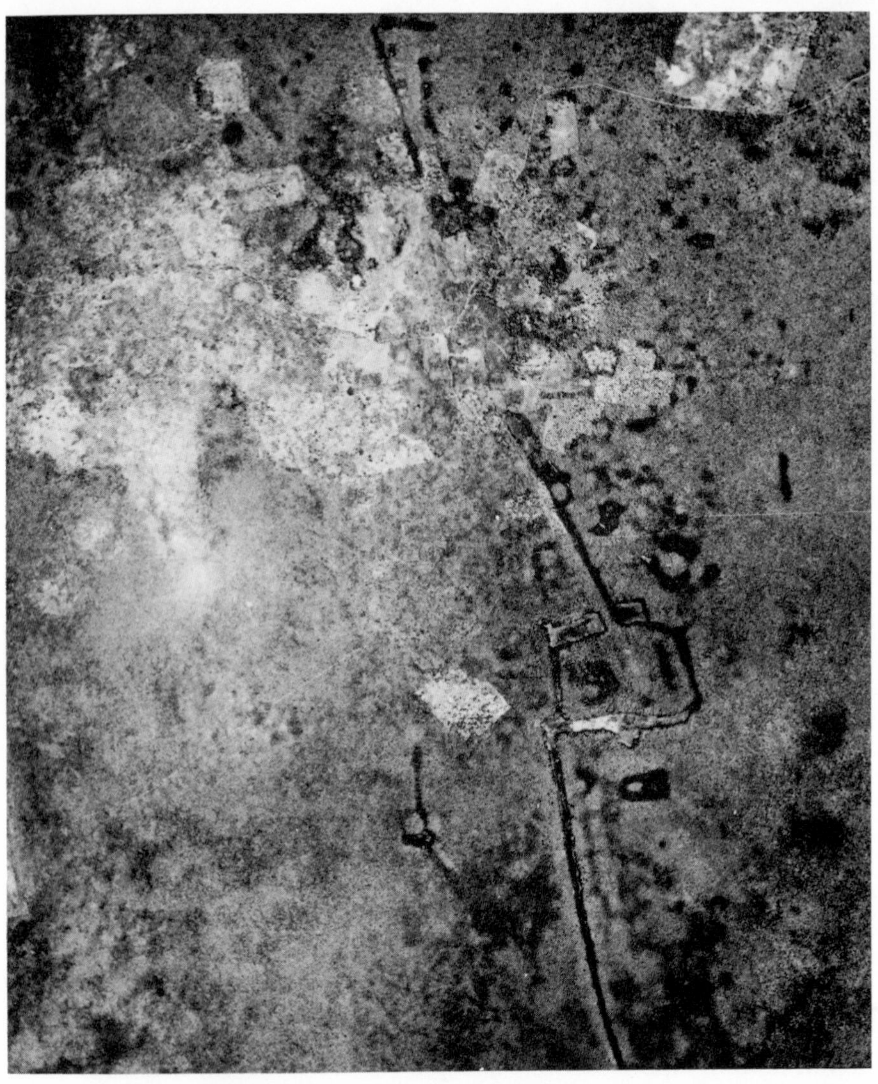

Figure 10.7. Aerial photograph of Edzna illustrating canals and reservoirs, which appeai as dark lines and patches.

originally existed there. It is postulated that the moat was dug for defensive purposes and that the main canal was dug to ensure a continuing supply of water for the moat. Once the crisis situation that stimulated construction of a fortress had passed, the water supply was probably seen as valuable, prompting the maintenance of the moat and canal.

The fortress and large canal were not afterthoughts of a population under stress but were clearly part of a grand scheme of original city planning. The main canal is in precise alignment with the geographic and ceremonial center of the city, and the fortress-moat system merges with another canal, also in precise alignment with the same area. Although an *aguada* may have been utilized originally in the fortress construction, it was worked into a plan compatible with the symmetry that probably formed an important conceptualization in the minds of the planners.

Twelve canals at Edzna form an extraordinary pattern of alignments. They lead to the central part of the site, which is considered to be the civic and ceremonial center. The canals stop short of actually converging, but if lines are extended from the end of each canal, they converge or nearly converge (fig. 10.8). The canals, in effect, form a radiating pattern, rather like the spokes of a wheel, with the center of the city as the hub. Obviously such a system was carefully planned.

The execution of the plan was even more remarkable. The alignments of the excavations were maintained everywhere except at about the 5-kilometer station of the main canal. At that point the 12-kilometer-long canal begins to deviate from its perfect alignment to the city center. Other canals maintain their alignments up to 3.5 kilometers from the focal point. Some canals miss the theoretically constructed focal point, but only by a few meters. Several canals are detectable only by remnant traces in a highly disturbed landscape, but even these traces show the faithful alignment toward the center of the site. One canal that was never completed (located approximately 3 kilometers southwest of the civic center) shows a plotted orientation that, if maintained, would have converged with that of the other canals.

Probable Purpose of the Canals at Edzna

The canals were designed to collect and store rainwater. Technically some of the canals should be classified as reservoirs, since they probably did not move water from one place to another. Most canals did, however, collect water from the soil in which they were dug and transfer this water to a slightly lower reservoir. The canals also served to drain inundated soils during the height of the rainy season and conserved this water for future use. An intricate system comprising reservoirs, feeder canals, holding tanks, and

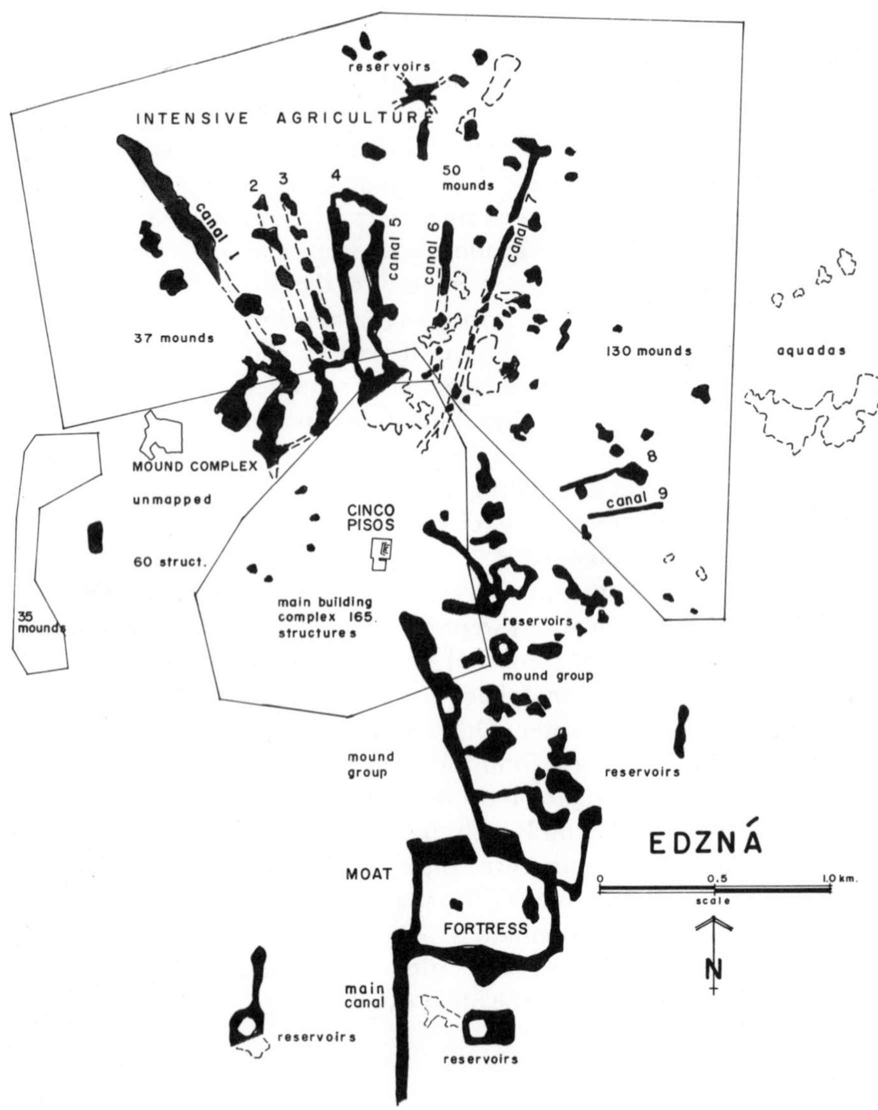

Figure 10.8. The major water structures, and concentrations of mounds and buildings, at Edzna, Campeche.

large canals was capable of sustaining a city in an otherwise groundwaterless valley.

Water in various parts of the system must have served different purposes. For instance, the main canal, which averages 50 meters in width and about 1.5 meters in depth, is of sufficient size and probably contained sufficient water to have maintained canoe or raft transportation. This canal, the fortress moat, and the causeway canal that led to the civic center could have provided a 13-kilometer course for traffic.

Hauck (1973) notes evidence of tanks in the hydraulic system that were probably utilized to clean the water collected in the northern canals. Many house sites are located along and between these canals in a zone that was probably a primary sustaining area. If farming was practiced in this zone, soil disturbances would probably have silted the reservoirs and canals, necessitating constant upkeep. From the holding (and cleaning) tanks, water was directed to other holding tanks, presumably for consumption in drinking and cooking.

The northern canals fan out over what I have considered prime agricultural soil. Over 200 house mounds are associated with these canals, and it seems reasonable to conclude that the area was important in carrying on agricultural pursuits. Analysis indicates gleyed surface soils, a product of reduction and waterlogging. The soils are poor in nitrogen, phosphorus, and organic material—a predictable condition of the tropics (Cowgill and Hutchinson 1963). It is interesting to note, however, that the highest concentrations of nitrogen and phosphorus occur in the bottoms of the canals; these same elements are lower in concentration on the surface, between canals.

The soil is poor in organic matter because temperatures never go below 12°C; this warmth promotes bacterial growth. Even in the canal bottoms, organic material is sparse because of constant moisture and bacterial activity.

Modern swidden evidence suggests that fallow periods up to seven years are required to regenerate Edzna's soil nutrients after two years of cultivation. Recent activities of the Department of Agriculture of the Mexican government in the Edzna Valley show that heavy applications of nutrients are required for successful harvests of such domestic plants as sunflowers, peanuts, soybeans, and rice. The Department of Agriculture has also cut massive canals in the valley floor providing improved drainage during the wet season. Well irrigation is utilized in some parts of the valley and rainfall in other parts. Modern agricultural techniques have modified soil conditions greatly since pre-Columbian times.

Probably 80 percent of Edzna has been surveyed. The density of its population is reflected in 471 known house mounds and approximately 100 public buildings and platforms (see fig. 10.8). The city also had 31 canals, 84 reservoirs, a moated fortress, and 18 rock quarries. All of the structures cannot be considered as contemporary, but testing shows maximum activity during the Late Preclassic period. The problem at hand is to explain how a dense population sustained itself in the valley.

I have suggested elsewhere (Matheny 1976) that if the canals and reservoirs of Edzna were cleaned periodically, the muck could have been worked into adjacent soils for enrichment (also see Denevan 1970). This method of fertilization is common in indigenous raised-field and other cultivation associated with drainage canals (Denevan and Turner 1974) and has been suggested in the soil studies of Maya raised fields in Belize (Olson 1975). Furthermore, hydraulic-type cultivation throughout pre-Hispanic Mesoamerica, including the chinampa system, often utilized mulches and composts (Armillas 1971:654). Even extensive swidden farmers sometimes apply mulch to their fields (Drucker and Heizer 1960:40). I submit, then, that the potential for intensive farming at Edzna in pre-Hispanic times was great and that swidden type cultivation did not account for all the food production.

Today in the Edzna Valley a Maya family uses approximately 200 liters of water each day during the dry season (a family is laterally extended to include 12 persons).[2] The same family uses perhaps one-half that amount of water daily during the wet season. All adults take at least one bath each day, but small children are bathed two to three times each day to cool them. Water for washing clothes and for animals is excluded from the 200 liter estimate. Each family member, then, uses approximately 16.6 liters of water per day. Based on an average of wet and dry season requirements (or 150 liters per family per day throughout the year), a family of 12 would utilize about 54,750 liters of water each year; one thousand families, about 54,750,000 liters.

The 2-million-cubic-meter-plus water storage at Edzna theoretically could support 36,000 families for about a six-month period, given the estimated consumption rates and the 0.6 percent daily water loss that has been calculated for evapotranspiration, plant transpiration, and seepage. The canals and reservoirs of Edzna, then, held sufficient water to support the needs of a populace much larger than we have reason to believe existed at the site.

Our estimate of water loss is based on data from the long abandoned slumped-in and grass-choked channels. In ancient times, if water was stored for use, the canals and reservoirs would have been maintained. Deeper bodies of water free from water-consuming plants would probably tend to reduce water loss. Aquatic plants may have been used to retard water evaporation as well. For example, the water plant *lechuga* (*Pistia stratiotes*) that grows on the surface of water in the hydraulic features today was imported to Yucatan to retard water evaporation. Water-temperature readings in ponds where *lechuga* was growing make it clear that the presence of this plant on the water surface reduces water temperature by several degrees. In ancient times the Maya may have used the hyacinth and the water lily, which also now grow on the water's surface. It is possible that these plants were also utilized to retard water loss. In short, our estimates of potential water storage may be conservative.

Today, water remains until March in the deepest channels and the combination of plant use, ground absorption, and evaporation rate will not allow storage through the dry season. Stephens (1843: fig. 9, 144–50), however, describes chultunes and wells in the bottom of an *aguada* at the Rancho Jalal, just north of Macoba. Although no wells or chultunes were found in the bottoms of *aguadas* at Edzna, they may be present. A Maya workman's report that cut stones were found in Canal 10 led me to believe that a construction similar to that illustrated by Stephens may exist at Edzna.

It is possible that portions of the canals may have been occupied by chinampas. Such relic fields may account for the generally obscure appearance of the canals. A type of raised-field (chinampa) farming may have been practiced along the Champoton River, where circular, low, mound constructions are found in wide, meandering bends. Aerial photographs show bananas growing on the mounds, which are about 60 meters in diameter and perhaps a meter or two in height. It is possible that the mounds were constructed from the silty deposits surrounding them, as they are located on mud flats of the river. The possibility that this form of agriculture was practiced along the Champoton River suggests that the Maya of Edzna could have been aware of it.

Some of the canals at Edzna may have been used in agriculture. An alternative assumption is that water in the canals was used for watering small kitchen gardens by hand. The careful placement of the canals may have had other functions of a nonpragmatic nature which are now lost to understanding. Robert L. Hall's stimulating article (1976) opens new possibilities for the design of the water system. At Fort Center, in the Ohio Valley, a Hopewell charnel platform containing the remains of 300 people was built within an artificial pond. Hall points out that certain historic Indians have believed that water formed a barrier to ghosts. He quotes J. N. B. Hewitt's 1894 remarks on the Iroquois: "It is a common belief that these skeleton ghosts dare not wade through cold water, preventing them from crossing in this manner fordable streams. This knowledge, it is claimed, often enabled persons to escape from these skeleton ghosts, by seeking shelter on an island or on a rock surrounded by water." A number of other ethnographic examples provided by Hall open a new possibility for the use of water and may relate to the use of reflecting ponds in Mesoamerica (Deanne Gurr, personal communication). Regardless of what we finally learn about water usage in the Maya lowlands, the overriding necessity of having sufficient water to sustain life remains.

THE LOWLAND MAYA CONSIDERED AS A HYDRAULIC SOCIETY

Karl Wittfogel (1957:3) attempts to distinguish between "hydraulic society" and "hydraulic civilization" on the basis of small-scale irrigation and large-scale, government-managed irrigation works and flood control. Wittfogel is interested in the "agromanagerial" and "agrobureaucratic" character of civilization as these concepts apply to the development of the state. He speaks of the "Hydraulic Revolution" (1956:152) as a phenomenon preceding the "Urban Revolution" described by Childe and argues that large-scale hydroagricultural enterprises were centrally managed by governments that "monopolized political powers and societal leadership" which "dominated their country's economy" (1956:153).

Julian Steward similarly argued (1949) for centralized control over coordinate labor in building public irrigation works that eventually led to highly structured political organization. Subsequently Steward (1970:212–16) retreated by suggesting that irrigation was only one of a number of possible causative factors in the development of civilization.

William P. Mitchell (1973) has summed up the critical hydraulic hypotheses concerning political and managerial developments of burgeoning states by reformulating the hypotheses. The new hypotheses seem more compatible with the Maya lowland situations where hydraulic works of considerable size were constructed, although the presence of states is questionable (Sanders and Price 1968:30–31).

If Wittfogel's terminology is acceptable, then a hydraulic society existed in the Maya lowlands at least from the Middle Preclassic period onward. Middle Preclassic manifestations are found at Becan, Dzibilchaltun, Santa Rosa Xtampak, Dzibilnocac, and Edzna, all on the Yucatan Peninsula, where the long dry season causes stress on plant and animal populations. The Middle Preclassic pioneers settled in an area where surface water is rare or nonexistent and had to develop a means of collecting and storing water if their settlements were to endure.[3]

The site of Santa Rosa Xtampak may be taken as an example. It is located in a valley, difficult to discern because of poorly developed drainage channels, that lacks definable karst formations. The site was built on a rock outcrop approximately twenty meters above the alluvial valley floor. One *aguada* lies within two kilometers of the site, but exposed bedrock there does not permit water storage over a few weeks at a time. No other surface water exists in the vicinity of the site. John L. Stephens (1843: vol. 2) and George Brainerd (1958) suffered there for lack of water, and I have had the same experience. The pioneers may have settled there because of rich soil found within one kilometer of the site. Water was undoubtedly an important concern, and the settlers must have devised a satisfactory method of meeting that need.

Evan I. DeBloois (1970) investigated chultunes at Santa Rosa Xtampak that were the principal means of water storage and collection. He found convincing evidence that the chultun was in use by the Late Preclassic period. (It may have been an earlier innovation but evidence is lacking.) The 67 chultunes at Santa Rosa Xtampak provided the last inhabitants with approximately 2,300 cubic meters of water storage—used conservatively, enough for drinking and culinary purposes for about 700 people using 8.3 liters each per day.[4] The chultunes may be replenished by the "northers" (northwest storms) that occur from February to April (E. W. Andrews V, personal communication).

The chultun is an efficient means of storing water. It is made by excavating into limestone bedrock, filling cracks in the rock with masonry, stuccoing with lime cement, and in some cases painting the stucco with a red pigment (DeBloois 1970:47). Pavements surrounded chultunes to serve as catchment areas for rainwater; E. H. Thompson (1897:77) describes such a pavement at Labna. Most chultunes were located in plazas or courts next to buildings where pavement and walls joined together. Rainwater descending from roofs and walls drained into a plaza, then directly into the mouth of a chultun. A stone plug was placed in the mouth to seal the chultun from animals and dirt.

The inhabitants of Santa Rosa Xtampak had few alternatives for water storage development. The lack of *aguadas* and of clay suitable to line reservoirs, and the fact that the water is deep under the surface, prohibiting excavation of wells, indicate that chultunes were a logical choice. There appears to have been only enough water from the chultunes for drinking and cooking and perhaps for the care of small gardens. Also, water was required for construction and maintenance of buildings, pavements, chultunes, and for processing of vegetal fibers as well as a host of other uses. Other chultunes that have not yet been discovered may exist at Santa Rosa Xtampak.

Planning, construction, and management of the water systems appears to have required minimal central authority. Each complex of buildings with its chultunes was largely independent of others. The architects probably constructed one complex at a time, designing water catchment plazas and chultunes to take care of the water needs of those who would use the buildings. Maintenance of buildings, pavements and chultunes probably was the concern of the users. One can conceive of strict control of construction, maintenance, and use of water from the chultunes, but central authority was not a necessity for such small concerns. Many small sites appear to have small, independently built and maintained hydraulic works.

Edzna, where hydraulic concerns were great, offers an excellent contrast to Santa Rosa Xtampak. There, only 12 chultunes have been noted in surveys of over 17 square kilometers of the site. Surface water was confined to *aguadas,* and wells would have been difficult to excavate with the water table at more than 20 meters below the surface. Development of existing *aguadas* was a practical alternative for water storage. Clay, lying one meter under the topsoil, is of the montmorillonite type that is impervious and makes a natural basin in which to store water. The elaborately laid out canals, interconnecting feeder ditches, and reservoirs constitute a planned system that may have related to world view. This hydraulic system appears not only to solve the problem of water storage, but also to satisfy other needs, which we do not clearly understand at this time.

The hydraulic system of Edzna was apparently a functioning complex, designed to collect, store, and distribute water to a city, rather than the simple sort of system found at Santa Rosa Xtampak. Planning, execution, maintenance, and additions to the Edzna hydraulic system called for much forethought and coordination of peoples. It is easy to conceptualize a central authority on the city level responsible for this type of activity. Further, I believe that the hydraulic system contributed significantly to food production through pot watering, possibly through soil enrichment when the system was cleaned out, and possibly in limited raised-field farming that may have encouraged the city's growth and maintenance. The large canals may have provided not only water for drinking and farming, but also additional protein, in the form of fish, and transportation of goods by canoe or raft. It is known that at one time part of the water system was used to fill a huge moat surrounding a fortress equal in size to the ditched fortress town of Becan (Webster 1976).

It is difficult to imagine how the fortress, moat, 12-kilometer-long canal, and other canal and reservoir networks at Edzna, involving about 1,107,000 cubic meters of excavation, could have been built without some centralized political authority. These features of the city are as large and complex as any found at Teotihuacan, Tikal, or any other large Mesoamerican center.

Another intricately constructed, large-volume hydraulic system is found at Uxmal. C. E. Brasseur de Bourbourg (1865) elaborated upon Stephens's 1843 account of the system of reservoirs and canals at this city. I have flown over the ruins of Uxmal during the height of the rainy season, when the ancient channels are filled with water, satisfying myself that such a system did exist. Brasseur's map (1865:255) of Uxmal shows six reservoirs, feeder and collection canals, and a moated fortress. In addition, the site has many chultunes and Morley (1958:77) shows that rain falling on buildings and plazas could have supplied the needs of several thousand people. Uxmal and Edzna represent sites of a category that involved large public hydraulic works.

I believe that many hydraulic systems will be discovered throughout the Maya lowlands as scholars begin to look for them. Each settlement had to have a water supply. Development of water systems was pragmatic but in some instances may have contained an element of the esoteric; this element may have been more important than is currently realized. Some hydraulic systems were simple and probably required little formal organizational planning or control. Others, far more complex, probably required careful engineering and the organization of extensive labor forces for construction and maintenance.

This brief introduction to some hydraulic features of the northern Maya lowlands shows, I believe, that we should consider hydraulic hypotheses important guides in attempting to understand the development of the civilization. In this respect, the Maya may be termed a hydraulic society by, perhaps, the Preclassic period. Further fieldwork may suggest that a higher-level hydraulic classification is needed.

NOTES

1. Canals were measured from Siemens and Puleston's data, and the assumption was made that their drawing was of correct scale.

2. The family includes eight small children, ages 11 years to four months, and four adults. At the time of our work at Edzna only three families were living at the site, each laterally extended by adult males to increase the labor force for milpa and hunting activities. Although the size of the family is unusual, water consumption per person should be valid in making estimates for water requirements.

3. This, of course, assumes that no significant changes in climate patterns have occurred and that rainfall in the past was about the same as it is presently.

4. Variables such as contemporaneity of the chultunes, state of repair of the catchment basins, ability of the Maya to fill the chultunes, and rates of loss through seepage are not taken into account.

11

DAVID T. VLCEK
Department of Anthropology, Northern Illinois University

SYLVIA GARZA DE GONZÁLEZ
Centro Regional del Sureste, INAH, Mérida, Yucatan, Mexico

EDWARD B. KURJACK
Department of Sociology and Anthropology, Western Illinois University

Contemporary Farming and Ancient Maya Settlements: Some Disconcerting Evidence[1]

Agricultural considerations are believed to have been the most important determinant of lowland Maya settlement and community systems; substantial data support this position. Contemporary Yucatecan farmers insist that the best soils are near ancient sites, and agronomists tend to agree. Control of small, scattered plots of high-quality intrazonal soils, for example, was probably instrumental in forming the pattern of site distribution near Labna. It is easy to explain the absence of large sites along the north and west shores of the peninsula, for a twenty-kilometer-wide band of swamp and savanna separates the beaches from any farmable lands. Prime soil, sufficient precipitation, and farm productivity are indeed keys to understanding the colonization and subsequent growth of pre-Columbian settlements.

The loci and proportions of some sites cannot be adequately

explained by these factors alone, since several pre-Columbian communities did thrive under conditions less than optimal for farming. Dzibilchaltun and Tzeme, for example, developed in dry areas with sparse soil, dense surface stone, and outcropping bedrock. Chunchucmil, a site covering between 10 and 20 square kilometers near the swamp and savanna that border the western Yucatan coast (see fig. 11.1), is another example of population concentration in an area marginal for agriculture.

Chunchucmil (lat. 20° 38.5′ N; long. 90° 11.5′ W) lies approximately seventy kilometers southwest of Mérida, and twenty-five kilometers inland. The famous saltworks near Celestun are thirty kilometers northwest, and the northern limits of the Puuc Hills (Sierrita de Ticul) at Maxcanu stand about twenty kilometers southeast.

The principal architectural complexes at Chunchucmil are not exceptionally large, but enough construction is present for the site to be considered a major center. Most of the architecture, at least from surface indications, dates from Late Classic times or earlier. Vestiges of collapsed vaults, representing both true masonry of the Early period and concrete-veneer techniques of the Florescent period (see Andrews IV 1965), can be observed in many places. No vaulted architecture remains standing.

Approximately 2,000 surface sherds from the site were examined by Eduardo Toro of the Instituto Nacional de Antropología e Historia (INAH) Centro Regional del Sureste, in Mérida. Most of the material consisted of the slatewares and unslipped pottery characteristic of Dzibilchaltun's Copo phase (Terminal Classic or Late Early period and Pure Florescent; see Ball and Andrews V 1975). A sizable number of Chicanel-like Late Formative wares were also present. Toro, who is thoroughly familiar with the Mayapan ceramics, found no Postclassic sherds in the collections.

Aerial photographs of large fields that had been cleared for pasture facilitate study of Chunchumil's dimensions and layout. Prominent architectural complexes containing high pyramidal structures, extensive terraces or plazas, and causeways between groups of buildings stand out in the imagery. Smaller mounds surrounded by low boundary walls fill low oblique shots of the adjacent areas. Isolated ruins can be distinguished in aerial views of more distant locations.

A central group of stately pyramids dominated by a mound that

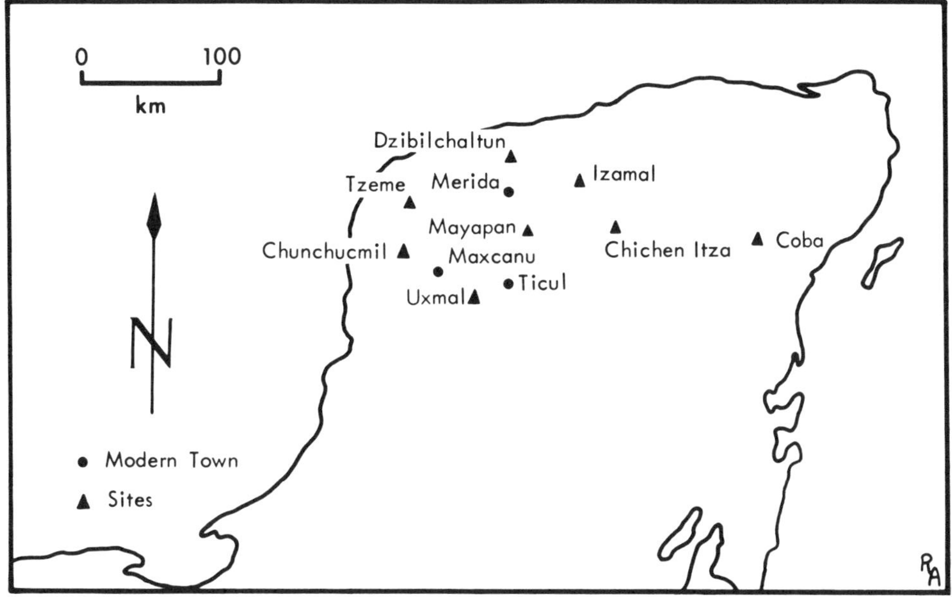

Figure 11.1. Map of the Yucatan Peninsula showing locations of sites mentioned in the text.

stands 18.5 meters above the surface must have been the focus of social activity at Chunchucmil (see fig. 11.2). Eleven structures in this central group are between 8 and 15 meters high; most of these pyramids are situated in quadrilateral building complexes averaging one-half a hectare each in extent. Raised causeways (*sacbeob*), constructed of limestone slabs retaining smaller-sized fill, connect the complexes (fig. 11.3). A low wall superimposed over the causeways encloses most of the larger ruins. The central group, then, is an aggregate that clearly contrasts with the remainder of the site. This nucleus covers an irregularly shaped area occupying slightly less than a square kilometer.

Six square kilometers surrounding the central group contain smaller ruins in such concentration that little vacant terrain can be found between closely spaced mounds and terraces (see fig. 11.4). Low boundary walls, reminiscent of the dry masonry *albarradas* bordering house lots in modern Yucatecan towns, delineate areas associated with complexes of presumably domestic architecture. Narrow walkways, between two and three and one-half meters wide, were frequently left between the walls. One distinctive corridor forms a straight line half a kilometer long; in some places the sides are limestone slabs one and one-half meters high. The

Figure 11.2. A low, oblique photograph of the central group of ruins at Chunchucmil, Mexico. Camera points northeast; the north-south road crossing the photograph diagonally is 1.2. kilometers long. Large plazas and tall pyramids in this view contrast with more densely packed structures within the surrounding residential zone (see fig. 11.4). Note the low wall enclosing much of the central group.

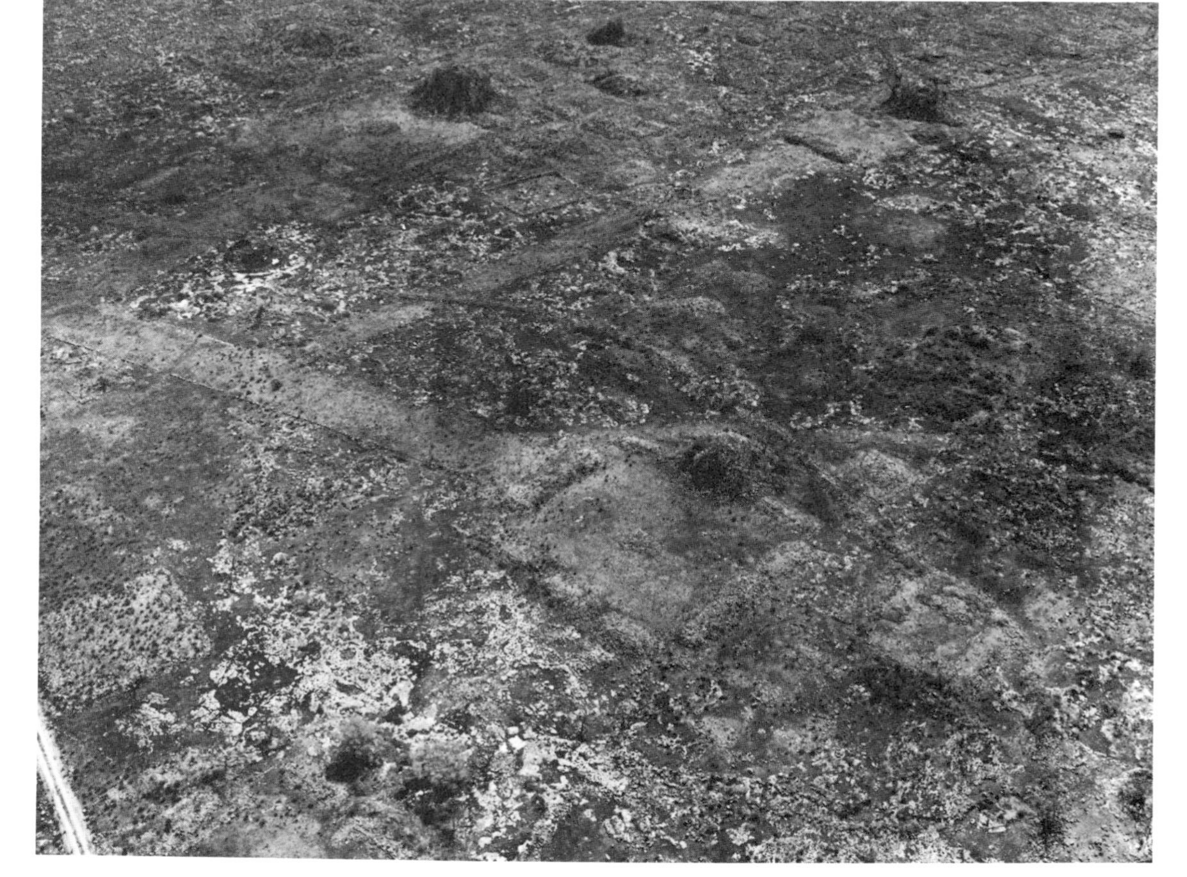

Figure 11.3. Large architectural complexes connected by causeways (*sacbeob*) within the central group of ruins at Chunchucmil, Yucatan, Mexico.

Figure 11.4. A low oblique scene illustrating distribution of smaller ruins within the zone of contiguous domestic architecture surrounding the central group at Chunchucmil. The area within the field shown in this view covers less than a quarter of a square kilometer. Camera points east; the right (south) edge of the photograph is approximately a kilometer north of the largest pyramid in the central group. Boundary walls surround dwelling complexes; narrow walkways between walls are the only vacant space. Six square kilometers of similar residential area are found at the site.

central group plus this zone of contiguous domestic architecture constitute the core of Chunchucmil.

Numerous architectural groups, some of them quite extensive, are found within the 13 square kilometers that surround the 7 square kilometers of ruins at the site's core. The groups consist of larger building complexes surrounded by smaller ones. The spacing of such groups, at least those visible on aerial photography, increased with distance from the center of the site. Chunchucmil's core and the large interface form a single demographic center contrasting in density of ruins with the surrounding environs.

Three concentric zones, then, formed the Late Classic community at Chunchucmil: (1) a one-square-kilometer central group with large groups of buildings containing tall pyramids and interconnected by at least 10 raised causeways; (2) a zone of domestic architecture covering 6 square kilometers, all of it carefully subdivided by boundary walls; and (3) some 13 square kilometers of heavily populated transitional space.

Limited mapping at Chunchucmil together with studies of aerial photographs show that larger domestic complexes outlined by boundary walls each occupy less than a quarter of a hectare. These complexes usually contain several structures. Some enclosed areas appear to have been partitioned several times; others are open on sides adjacent to larger architectural groupings that are central to several satellite groupings. These data may be considered evidence for variety in the size and composition of the residential kin groupings that utilized this architecture.

A population estimate for Chunchucmil can be attempted on the basis of a very conservative estimate of a minimum of 4 houses per hectare in the residential area surrounding the central group. Six square kilometers of such housing density would total 2,400 housing complexes. Multiplication by five individuals per household (see Kurjack 1974) yields a population of 12,000.

Even the austere 12,000 figure is surprising when compared with modern census data. The 1900 census of Mexico records the population of Mérida and Progreso at 43,630 and 5,125, respectively. Ticul, population 5,587, was the only other community with more than 5,000 inhabitants. Some twenty settlements contained over 2,000 inhabitants, and perhaps twenty-five others had populations between 1,000 and 2,000. Even the 1970 census lists only six communities with 12,000 or more residents.

Ticul must be similar to many pre-Columbian settlements. Approximately two-thirds of the Ticuleños farm, and a significant number make sandals and pottery. According to the 1970 census, 14,341 people inhabit 2,460 housing complexes in the community, whose area is approximately six square kilometers.

Neither the population estimate for Chunchucmil nor the data upon which it is based can be considered compatible with the general view of Maya settlement patterns found in the literature. Most Mayanists interpret the larger Classic sites as "ceremonial centers" rather than nucleated communities; this view is usually based on a combination of archaeological data and a series of assumptions about ancient farming practices.

Many scholars believe that Maya pyramids and palaces were not surrounded by clusters of smaller domestic architecture (Willey and Bullard 1965; Sanders and Price 1968). While it is usually allowed that some craftsmen may have lived with the social elite in these largely vacant settlements, most of the remaining population is thought to have been evenly dispersed in farming hamlets. These notions, clearly untenable in north Yucatan, appear to have been derived from early studies of swidden cultivation.

Concern with the Maya collapse rather than any attempts to understand contemporary life in lowland Mesoamerica aroused scientific curiosity to shifting agriculture. The Maya collapse, one of the oldest problems in anthropological studies of ecology, assumed importance when students of Maya writing discovered that erection of dated monuments ceased at southern lowland sites during the end of the ninth cycle in the Long Count calendar (cf. Culbert 1973). This observation was considered evidence for social disintegration and rapid abandonment of that area. A search for the causes leading to this apparent failure of Classic Maya civilization and subsequent population movements soon focused on the destructive aspects of swidden farming.

O. F. Cook (1921) is perhaps the pioneer student of swidden technology whose views have endured the longest; his explanation for the Maya collapse is still widely cited as an example of drastic environmental changes brought about through human action. Cook believed grass encroachment on swidden plots soon made them unusable. Wildfires from the annual burning of new fields swept through grass in fallowing plots, killing young trees and preventing rainforest regeneration. Land near a community was soon exhausted. Entire cities had to be abandoned as a ring of savanna that could not be farmed became wider.

Ralph Linton's (1940:32–40) arguments in *The Maya and Their Neighbors* are a good example of the exaggerated thinking that followed from Cook's thesis. Linton believed grass invasion of slash-and-burn fields to be so rapid that community locations had to be changed every few years. Shifting cultivation, therefore, was associated with small, widely dispersed temporary settlements. In another work, Linton (1955:100) even suggested that prefabricated homes that could be taken apart and reassembled were regular features of Southeast Asian highland life due to the frequent moves of shifting farmers. Such misleading statements demonstrate that their author had acquired a misleading impression of swidden cultivators.

In 1940, Linton proposed an interesting variation of the Cook hypothesis to explain the process by which ceremonial centers developed: as the ring of grass surrounding nucleated settlements expanded, farmers had to leave centers to cultivate more distant fields. Though the parent communities soon lost most of their populations, the functions as gathering places for social and ceremonial activity were retained. For this reason the size and extent of architectural complexes at Maya sites seems out of proportion to the small number of surrounding houses. Linton thought that the scattered Maya farmers must have lived in settlements smaller than villages.

George Brainerd (1956) endorsed ideas similar to those of Linton; he believed that fewer than 50 persons inhabited each dispersed farming settlement, or that perhaps nuclear families alone inhabited such settlements. He cites the general view of swidden cultivation as the source for this inference. A survey of 53 swidden societies in the New World by K. C. Chang (1958) overturned Brainerd's argument and suggested that the dispersed settlement pattern envisioned by many Mayanists is a very rare phenomenon.

The principle of least effort (Zipf 1949) underlies most of the proposed relationships between technology and settlement patterns. This maxim contends that humans are ordinarily economical creatures who organize their affairs in a manner calculated to expend as little energy as possible. Therefore societies evolve community sizes and distributions to facilitate efficient access to crucial facets of the natural and social environment. Such efficiency should involve both a measure of security and a minimum of travel in exploitation of the resources needed for survival. Many different resources are used by human groups, so the variables that enter into the complex equation for an optimum settlement pattern are also numerous. The single most important factor in the thinking of O. F. Cook, Linton, and Brainerd is energy used in travel between farmers' homes and fields. These scholars concluded that the ancient Maya must have established homes close to their dispersed agricultural plots, rather than spending time and effort walking to their milpas.

Sanders and Price (1968:195) also emphasize the need to minimize travel in their discussions of dispersed Maya settlement patterns. They hold that social integration of Yucatan's population in pre-Columbian times would have been particularly difficult because of the low population density that would result from shifting cultivation and the constant tendency to reduce effort by moving houses nearer swidden farms:

> Large macro-states and empires, and true cities did not evolve. Rather, the settlement pattern consisted of ceremonial centers or elite residence centers on the one hand, and scattered rural hamlets containing the bulk of the population, on the other. (Sanders and Price 1968:10)

Moreover, these authors maintain, transportation of staples over long distances was considered particularly uneconomical over much of Mesoamerica. Development of organic economies would remain limited under such conditions.

Data from Chunchucmil do not support the viewpoint of Sanders and Price. The site is far larger than one would expect from their conclusions. The locale is marginal for an agricultural settlement; better farms can be found a few kilometers farther east. Unless environmental conditions were very different in the past, it is difficult to understand how the population of the site could have been supported without importing food from the interior.

Low crop yields have long been characteristic of hacienda Chunchucmil, which was established near the archaeological ruins for the purpose of growing maize on a commercial scale. Harvests were so poor that the owners began to experiment with cattle raising. Soon this practice was abandoned in favor of henequen cultivation; today the plantation yields about half as much fiber as fields farther east. Recent government efforts to drill wells for watering citrus groves may end the long history of meager production.

Tzekel is a Maya word meaning Lithosols, or areas of very rocky soil. A cordon of *tzekeles* borders the coastal swamps; farther inland the soils are considered mixtures of Lithosols and Redzinas. Chunchucmil is near the transition between the two zones. Agriculture is almost impossible west of the site; satellite images show low scrub forest, savanna, and mangrove swamps between the site and the gulf shores.

While different environmental variables in the past may have made Chunchucmil more favorable for cultivation, today the area is very dry, with meager accumulations of soil. It is situated near the semidesert northwest corner of the peninsula, and annual precipitation measures a scant 850 to 1,000 millimeters. Considerably more rain falls a short distance farther east. The midsummer drought, so critical for Mesoamerican maize farming, is longer and worse here than in the interior. Moreover, annual variation in total precipitation, a factor considered crucial to the distribution of population over Mesoamerica, increases as one approaches the west coast (Trewartha 1961; UNAM 1970; Mosiño and García 1974).

Exploitation of coastal resources, especially salt, must have played an important role in supporting Chunchucmil's populace. These people dwelled in a large community near the salt-gathering places described in colonial documents (Roys 1957). The proximity to good sources for an essential trade item can hardly have been coincidental. Salt, rather than agricultural production, appears to have been the factor that determined the site's location.

Most scholars have emphasized continuity in the basic features of lowland adaptive systems, but the data from Chunchucmil and their interpretation pose obvious problems for this outlook. The estimate of 12,000 inhabitants in 6 square kilometers equals the population that today occupies the 2,000 square kilometers surrounding the site (Maxcanu and Celestun municipalities).

Two explanations for the difference between such interpretations of the archaeological record and the present demographic situation have been offered. Some scholars insist that only a few of the buildings at Maya sites were used simultaneously, but this argument carries less force where boundary walls attest to the scarcity of space near the center of a community. Others point to the Classic period's long duration, maintaining that lowland sites are deceptively large owing to accumulation of debris from centuries of occupation. While this fact must be evaluated more formally, the number of small Classic ruins at Maya sites contrasts with sparse remains at communities that have existed since the sixteenth century. We find neither argument useful in the case of Chunchucmil.

The utility of information from the living Maya for study of their past is obvious, but the discrepancy noted above indicates the need for more caution in the use of ethnographic analogy. Dramatic changes have taken place on the peninsula since the Classic temples were constructed. Steel tools, for example, were introduced by the Spanish; these are now an integral part of farming practices. The demographic situation has also been greatly modified, for the concentration of 200,000 people at Mérida was not a factor in the population distribution of Classic times. As more information concerning Maya settlement patterns becomes available, the model of an evolved Maya swidden society abstracted primarily from studies of contemporary farming rather than the archaeological record must undergo reexamination.

Evidence from Chunchucmil indicates that the ancient community there may have evolved beyond self-sufficiency in agricultural staples. Unless the environment of the site has changed dramatically since Classic times, food was probably imported to sustain the large population indicated by the archaeological remains. While this food need not have been carried from very distant locations, there must have been an organic relationship between Chunchucmil and the farms that sustained it.

Salt, rather than fertile soil and adequate rainfall, is the important resource in the vicinity of Chunchucmil. This commodity, known to have been extensively traded in protohistoric times, was probably the most valuable item produced at the site.

Interpretation of Chunchucmil in light of these data as a large community partly supported by commercial activity is incompatible with the rather simple view of Classic Maya economy and society that pervades the literature. A concentrated settlement, contrasting in function with agricultural zones that are the source of its food, is distinctly urban. The large transitional zone of diminishing population density at Chunchucmil served to integrate some food producers within the community, but preindustrial cities in many parts of the world also contained farmers. Chunchucmil's form and extent suggest that the complex social organization characteristic of early urbanism, with pronounced stratification, occupational specialization, and subcultural distinctions, was also present in the Maya country by Classic times.

NOTE

1. Reconnaissance at Chunchucmil is part of the ongoing Archaeological Atlas of Yucatan Project of the Centro Regional del Sureste, Instituto Nacional de Anthropología e Historia, coordinated by Sylvia Garza and Edward Kurjack. Our attention was drawn to Chunchucmil by Salvador Rodríguez L., director of the University of Yucatan's School of Anthropological Sciences; his sketch map was our first indication of the site's extent. We visited the site in 1975 when Kurjack and Vlcek were in Yucatan doing field exploration with financial assistance from the National Geographic Society. We are also grateful to E. W. Andrews V of Tulane University, Norberto Gonzales C. of INAH, and Richard Krause of the University of Alabama for assistance, advice, and encouragement.

12

DENNIS E. PULESTON
Department of Anthropology, University of Minnesota

Terracing, Raised Fields, and Tree Cropping in the Maya Lowlands: A New Perspective on the Geography of Power

The dissolution of the swidden thesis before a growing body of evidence for alternative means of food production is opening up entirely new perspectives on ancient Maya subsistence and many other aspects of the culture as well. The implications of the old model were enormous and deep-rooted, and it will undoubtedly be years before an integrated new perspective is fully achieved. Taking steps toward such an achievment, we can begin to examine the data with an eye to new insights and even tests for the explanatory potential of the new and still emerging model.

One of the most important ways in which the newly discovered subsistence systems of the Maya differed from swidden agriculture is that by all appearances they were production intensive; that is, yields per unit area were considerably greater over a long period of time. In this way at least three identified systems, characterized respectively by (1) terraces, (2) raised fields, and (3) kitchen-garden tree cropping, were similar to one another and differed from swidden techniques. They differed from one another in important ways, however. Most important for the present discussion, experimental studies in combination with ethnographic data show that the energy required to produce a given amount of food in each system was different—in one case enormously different. I shall suggest here that the geographic distribution of major dependence on each of these three systems was only partially overlapping and that the discontinuities can be directly linked to the differential distribution of major ceremonial centers in the southern Maya lowlands. Specificially, in northeast Peten, where kitchen-garden arboriculture appears to have been favored, I would suggest that a vast human-energy resource was a by-product of the comparatively greater energetic efficiency of this system. I see this available labor resource as instrumental in the rise and apparent predominance of the Peten core, a view which can explain one of the most basic and yet enigmatic observations about the overall distribution of ancient Maya settlements.

CORE PREDOMINANCE

The predominance of the lowland core area during Classic times is an important datum in this argument. Though generally accepted, it is still difficult to demonstrate quantitatively. Considerations of architectural mass, overall site size, extent and volume of long-distance trade, and iconographic and hieroglyphic evidence for political hegemony and military superiority are all potential sources of relevant insights. I wish only to acknowledge the importance of this problem here, since proper treatment would require lengthy discussion of poorly controlled data and complex arguments. Summarizing briefly, however, I think the best arguments for the assumption of core predominance, centered at Tikal, rest in (1) the overall density of sites in the core area (fig. 12.1), (2) the density of sites with greater total architectural mass in the core area, as determined by inspection of what are often incomplete site maps, (3) the presence of great temples at core sites, among them some of the tallest and most massive temple structures in the New World, (4) overall site size (the Tikal earthworks enclose an area of approximately 120 square kilometers), (5) the abundance of obsidian in household middens at Tikal and possibly other core sites, (6) the relative wealth and abundance of exotic materials in elite burials, (7) the consistency of ritual behavior as reflected in stelae and building caches, (8) the abundance of carved monuments with hieroglyphic texts, and (9) the dynastic importance of

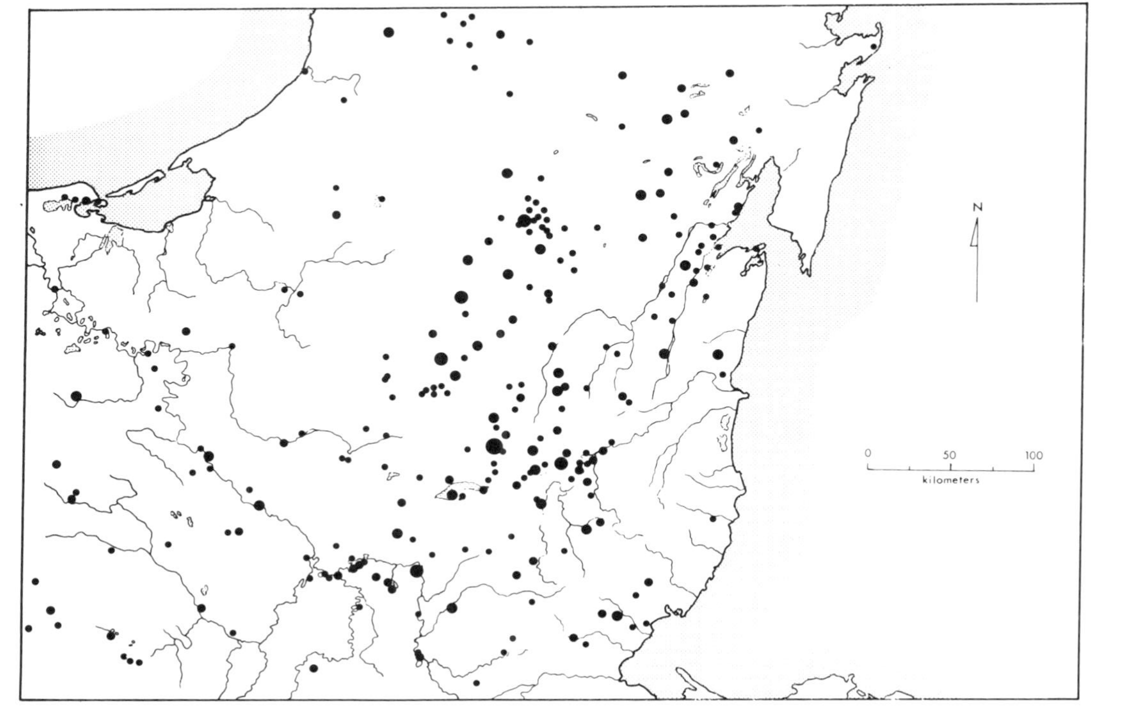

Figure 12.1. Site distribution map of the southern Maya lowlands. A higher density of major centers, as well as sites in general, seems to characterize the central southern lowlands, where utilization of kitchen-garden tree cropping is thought to have predominated. The system for rank ordering of the sites is based on and used with the permission of R. E. W. Adams as presented at a School of American Research Advanced Seminar on Lowland Maya settlement patterns, Santa Fe, 1977.

Tikal (Marcus 1973). This incomplete list serves only to point the way to a more comprehensive discussion in the future, when core predominance and relative grandeur can be demonstrated quantitatively.

From a historical standpoint it is important to note that the intrinsic discontinuity of the distribution of major Classic Maya centers has not gone unnoticed in the past. Rathje (1971) commented on the overall pattern and contrived an elaborate hypothesis using the seemingly paradoxical predominance of the core area to explain the rise and fall of Classic civilization. Briefly, he hypothesized that without any significant marketable natural resource and with a swidden subsistence base, the Maya in this focal core were forced to develop complex sociopolitical organization in order to obtain three trade commodities essential to the economy of every household. These commodities were metates, obsidian, and salt. Because suprahousehold organization was necessary to produce and distribute these nonlocal goods in the "resource redundant" lowlands, sociopolitical development occurred there before it did in surrounding "buffer" or highlands areas where resources were near enough to permit all necessary exchanges to take place at the household level (Rathje 1972:368).

From my standpoint there are at least three essential flaws in Rathje's argument, namely (1) his acceptance of the traditional view that Classic Maya subsistence economy was based on swidden agriculture, (2) his argument for the ecological redundance of the Maya lowlands, because they [core and buffer zones] "are part of the same biome and therefore contain the same resources" (Rathje 1972:372), and (3) his case for the essential role of metates, obsidian, and salt.

Since the arguments against the third point have already been mentioned by Sanders (1973:354), I will not pursue them in detail. Perhaps it will suffice to say that obsidian does not occur with any abundance in household middens at more than a few sites in the Maya lowlands, most notably Tikal. Elsewhere the Maya seem to have gotten along well with flint. The occurrence and apparent use of limestone metates all across the lowlands suggest that imported igneous metates were more an affordable luxury than a necessity. The same may be said for salt. When we were on survey around Tikal, experienced old chicleros on our crew showed us how food could be "salted" with ash of burned palm leaves. A small amount of ash included in the food can apparently meet the soluble salt requirements of most diets. Salt, especially as it is used today, is better considered a spice or condiment than a nutritional necessity.

Far more basic to Rathje's model are the first two flaws, and, as in the case of the third flaw, his failure to assess them correctly has a good deal to do with the traditional absence of and difficulties involved in a systematic approach to investigations of both the ecology and archaeology of the Maya lowlands. Archaeology in this region, for obvious reasons, has always suffered from the inordinately heavy bias toward "major ceremonial centers," their tombs, monuments, and architecture. A balanced ecological perspective has been similarly hamstrung by the unquestioning acceptance of the primacy of the milpa in subsistence models. For this reason, those ecological studies that have been carried out have emphasized swidden agriculture. The basic assumption was left unquestioned and unexamined.

Doubts regarding the assumption of the swidden maize cultivation model came initially from several angles. Bennet Bronson dealt the first blow with his paper on root crops (1966), which, though it did not question the primacy of the milpa as a cultivation system, questioned the assumption that the "holy trinity" of corn, beans, and squash were necessarily the caloric heavyweights in that system. An argument from another angle, resulting from the Tikal house-mound project, was proposed by Haviland (1963:528), who recognized the inadequacy of space for milpa cultivation around Tikal *plazuela* groups, and postulated the existence of a "sustaining area" beyond the limits of the 16 square kilometers of the site that had been mapped. The search for this sustaining area began with my mapping of the 12-kilometer south survey strip in 1965. This survey was followed by the mapping of the east, west, and north strips in 1966, and stratified random sampling of *plazuela* groups for ceramics on the north and southern strips in 1967 (Fry 1969; Puleston 1973). Even before the ceramic testing was begun, informal measures indicated that overall density of Classic settlement was disturbingly in excess of expectations, even in the presumed sustaining area.

These survey results led us to begin casting about for possibly unrecognized food supplements. As a beginning, in 1967, we initiated a survey of ramon trees (D. E. Puleston and P. O. Puleston in press), which yielded a startling correlation between the distribution of this species and prehistoric settlement. This correlation, in combination with the productive potential, edibility, and high nutritional content of the fruit, led to the formulation of a hypothesis to the effect that ramon had served as a primary staple (Puleston 1968a, 1968b). A third blow to the milpa model came with the discovery in 1969 of floodplain raised-field systems (Siemens and Puleston 1972) which further expanded the breadth of rapidly accumulating alternatives to the traditional model summarized by Wilken (1971). More recently, B. L. Turner (1974a) has focused new attention on long-ignored terrace systems represented by newly discovered examples in Campeche as well as already reported ones in Belize. Before these advances, monolithic adherence to the milpa model has begun to disintegrate. The argument for economic and ecological redundancy is going with it.

NONMILPA SUBSISTENCE MODES

Three basic subsistence modes are emerging from these new data, characterized respectively by terraces, raised fields, and tree cropping. To understand their impact on ancient Maya cultural development, it is necessary to discuss them as separate systems.

Terracing

Terraces, as mentioned above, seem to occur at various localities in the Maya lowlands, notably in the Rio Bec region (Turner 1974a; P. Thomas 1974) and in western Belize (Joyce 1926; Joyce, Clark, and Thompson 1927:315; J. E. S. Thompson 1931:228; H. H. Bartlett 1936:14; Lundell 1940:9; Wright et al. 1959:111–13; Saxe and Wright 1966). Turner (1974a) also has located a terraced site beside the road east of Flores, but apart from this report terraces seem comparatively elusive in central Peten. Negative evidence, despite its limitations, suggests a discontinuous distribution for terracing. J. H. Kempton (quoted in Hester 1954:95) refers specifically to the lack of evidence for terraces in northern Yucatan. Farther south, in the Peten, the Ricketsons found no evidence for them at Uaxactun (Ricketson and Ricketson 1937:12). They were not found anywhere on the more than 25 square kilometers of closely mapped terrain around Tikal (Puleston 1973:209). They were not found around Seibal (Willey et al. 1975: fig. 3) nor have they been reported elsewhere along the Usumacinta, in southern Peten, or in the Belize River Valley. Though a number of linear ridges running perpendicular and at angles across hillslopes were recorded in Rio Hondo Project surveys in northwest Belize, there were no more than a few possible "terraces" in the form of barely discernible horizontal lines of stones. Clearly even these possibilities did not occur with anything like the predominance and frequency found at Becan and in the Maya Mountains of western Belize. Given these suggestions for variability in the distribution of terraces, we may turn to questions regarding their function and origin.

In view of the paucity of controlled excavation, the dating of terraces must be tentative. Arthur Saxe's (Saxe and Wright 1966) excavation of a terrace at Cubetas Viejas produced possible Preclassic Mars Orange ceramics, but for the most part ceramics were undiagnostic. Similarly, B. L. Turner's excavations in the vicinity of Becan have not resolved the problem. The excavation of mounds attached to the terraces did produce datable ceramics, but the exact nature of the temporal association between the mounds and terrace walls is not precise enough to establish a firm date for the terraces. Their dating must be tentative with little more to go on than associated occupations that may considerably precede terrace construction. On this basis, terraces in the Rio Bec area are unlikely to have been constructed before the Late Pre-Classic period (Ball 1974:113). It is probably safe to guess that utilization was principally during the Classic period and may or may not have extended into Postclassic times.

Terraces in the Maya lowlands were almost certainly used in some form of food production. The possibility that some of them also served a residential function, however, as in the case of the linear terraces that encircle Monte Alban, should be examined. Assuming that terraces were for food production, it is unlikely that they were utilized for tree cropping as opposed to some form of open-field agriculture that would expose the soil to erosion. Wright (Wright et al. 1959:112), who believes that they served for permanent, intensive maize cultivation, outlines an evolutionary scheme for their development. He begins with the milpa. As a step toward intensification, he invokes the shifting of rocks during weeding to field edges for the creation of low, linear field walls. Some of these inevitably ran parallel to hillslopes and soon demonstrated on their own the principle of the silt trap. With refinements in wall construction (fig. 12.2), the Maya were able to make erosion an ally and at the same time utilize the greater fertility of hill soils. Grass fallowing or perhaps even continuous multi-cropping would have been possible, barring droughts, as suggested by Wright et al. (1959:113) and Turner (1974a).

Pollen analysis probably offers the best opportunity for determining at least some of the crops that may have been involved. A potentially informative attempt was made by Herbert Wright, John Bradbury, and William Watts, who took a sediment core from the Becan *aguada,* but fossil pollen were too degraded by the occasional drying out of the sediments to be identifiable. Without these data we are probably safe in assuming that maize was a principal crop, but let us remember that this is an assumption. Judging by the distribution of terraces and structures around Becan, where some three square kilometers of land outside the site have been mapped by Prentice Thomas (1974), an intensive infield agriculture (Wolf 1966) may have been in operation.

In view of the greater investment of time and effort necessary for the construction and maintenance of terraces (Wilken 1971:434) as compared to milpa fields, we may suspect that yields per unit area over a period of time were proportionately higher. Unfortunately the experimental reconstruction, cultivation, and monitoring of terraces, so strongly advocated by Wright et al. (1959:113), have not yet been carried out, so any estimate of productivity of agricultural systems must be based on ethnographic analogies. Bronson has reviewed the productivity of agricultural labor ranging from extensive root cropping in Africa to intensive irrigation in Southeast Asia (1966: table 8.1). His data show that semiintensive maize cultivation in Guatemala can achieve a calculated productivity of 1.07 bushels per man-day. Productivity increases proportionately with labor-time investment, so intensive cultivation of terraces was probably more productive than modern maize cultivation, although it is doubtful that it approached the levels given for intensive rice irrigation. Clearly what we need are some good experimental data. For the time being, I think it is safe to assume that effective maintenance required a labor commitment substantially higher than that necessary for a milpa of

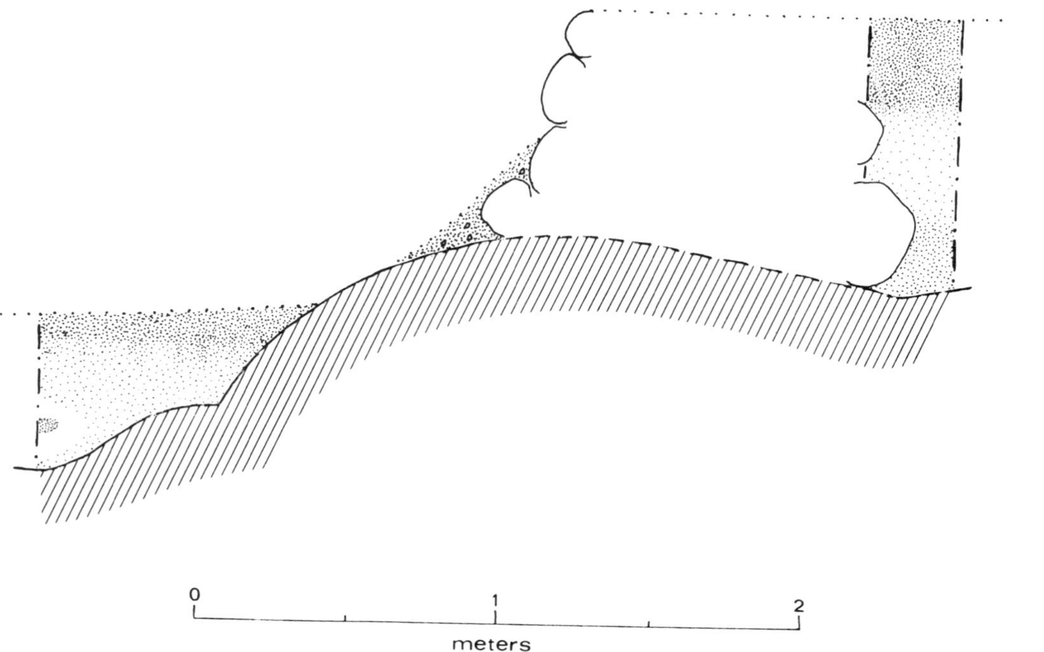

Figure 12.2. Cross section of excavated terrace at Cubetas Viejas, Belize. Prepared from Saxe's (1966) figure by Eileen Flory.

average productivity, with productivity falling somewhere in the range of 1.00–1.20 using Bronson's formula.

Raised Fields

The distribution of raised fields is still uncertain, as will be indicated below. Though these features have now been reported and even hypothesized for many parts of the Maya lowlands, actual excavations sufficient to confirm their identification as human artifacts have been carried out at only two locations—across the river from the settlement at El Tigre on the Candelaria River (Siemens and Puleston 1972) and at San Antonio, on the Hondo River in Belize. In all other areas where the fields have been reported, their identification is based on aerial inspection and aerial photographs alone, including Harrison's (1975) identification of nearly twenty-five hundred square kilometers of potential fields in Quintana Roo as well as a suggestion for the presence of fields in interior *bajos* of northeast Peten. The latter has been followed up with further aerial investigations carried out by Siemens and Dahlin in March 1976 (Dahlin 1976b).

In my opinion, the case for the presence of raised fields in the *bajos* of northeast Peten is extremely weak, and certainly even the most prominent features in Quintana Roo are going to require careful examination on the ground and excavation in order to demonstrate conclusively their human origin. The call for caution comes from the great similarity of raised fields to the natural rectangular, circular, and linear features, first described for Australia by J. A. Prescott (1931), called *gilgai* (fig. 12.3). These features, extremely similar in appearance and origin to surface patterns formed in cold climates by frost action (Washburn 1956), have been described for warm climates and have a formidable nomenclature (Hallsworth, Robertson, and Gibbons 1955). Out of six main types—(1) normal or round gilgai, (2) lattice gilgai, (3) wavy gilgai, (4) tank gilgai, (5) stony gilgai, and (6) melon-hole gilgai— at least three (normal, lattice, and tank gilgai) appear to be likely alternative identifications for features assumed to be raised fields in northern Belize, Quintana Roo, and Peten. Typically these features occur in montmorillonitic clays that can absorb a great deal of water and swell from 15 to 60 percent when they are

Figure 12.3 The vegetation lines marking natural gilgai in this aerial photo are located in the Red River Valley of northwestern Minnesota. Formed on montmorillonitic clay soils like those in Maya lowland *bajos,* they reveal the insufficiency of aerial reconnaissance alone for the identification of artificial raised fields. (Source: U.S. Dept. of Agriculture survey, 1948, BXW-1E-121)

wet but contract to leave deep open cracks when they are dry. Material washing or falling into the bottoms of these cracks produces lateral and upward pressure when the clays reabsorb water during the rainy season. This process ultimately results in raised surfaces ("puffs") separated by lower areas ("shelves") which, depending on local conditions, can manifest great variety in overall configuration, shape, and size. Olson (1969:17, 40) noted evidence of gilgai action in the *escoba bajo* along the south side of the Tikal airstrip, as indicated by undulating topography and deep vertical cracks filled with dark soil in the test-pit section. Having reviewed this material, examined the Tikal gilgai, and looked for raised fields in the Santa Fe *bajo* on the ground in October 1975, I am now very reluctant to accept aerial photographs alone as evidence for the presence of raised fields. Any case for raised fields based on aerial photographs alone will be particularly weak when the presumed fields occur on known montmorillonitic clays, where the seasonal alteration between wetting and drying is extreme and unrelieved by connections to more permanent water supplies. In many cases surface inspection will be insufficient. I am sure that certain features we have identified as raised fields in our 1973–74 surveys of northern Belize are indistinguishable, without excavation, from tank gilgai. The possibility that the *bajos* had much more water in them during Classic times than they do today and could provide permanent moisture seems very unlikely in light of Cowgill and Hutchinson's detailed examination of Santa Fe *bajo* sediments near Tikal. Without evidence of littoral deposits and the occurrence of dead root casts throughout the five-meter section, they were led to "conclude unequivocally that there had not been open water in the Bajo de Santa Fe at the site of the pit for the past eleven and a half millennia" (Cowgill and Hutchinson 1963b:39). Recently Dahlin (personal communication) has argued that since Cowgill's pit was not located at the lowest point on the *bajo* floor she may have missed evidence for a more limited body of water at its center. Granting such a possibility for the sake of argument, the overall flatness of the *bajo* and the consequent shallowness of the water, in combination with evapotranspiration and variations in rainfall, would seemingly make this limited body of water extremely variable in size and permanence. The lack of permanent water, of course, does not mean that swidden agriculture could not have been carried out on natural gilgai, but clearly such a system would be very different from riverine canal–raised field systems and would not have the same advantages.

We may now turn briefly to the question of the distribution of raised field utilization in time. Radiocarbon dating of worked timber found in canals on the Hondo River (Puleston 1977) may take them back to at least 1110 ± 230 B.C. Pollen data indicate the possibility of an even earlier date of 1800 B.C. (Bradbury and Puleston 1974). Perhaps with considerable variation in their relative importance, the use of raised fields evidently continued right through the Classic and Postclassic periods into the mid sixteenth century in the lowlands.

The function of raised fields as planting surfaces for maize and cotton is demonstrated by ethnohistoric accounts and by the identification of the fossil pollen of these cultigens in canal sediments (Puleston 1977). Excavation suggests that the fields were initially built up out of floodplain sediments (fig. 12.4, stage 1) and that at some later date they were converted to laboriously constructed limestone marl platforms (fig. 12.4, stage 2). The limestone was brought from still extant quarries on the uplands. How widespread this earlier phase was, and when the transition to marl platforms took place, are questions which require further archaeological work.

Experimental reconstruction of a raised field on the Hondo River has confirmed J. E. S. Thompson's (1974) case for the potential of fish protein production in the canals. Cultivation experiments show that squash, beans, tomatoes, and cotton grow well in the fields. A maize crop has not yet been successfully harvested because of difficulties with birds, flying insects, leaf-cutter ants, and coatimundis. All indications are, however, that, given proper protection, the crop should do well. As in the case of terracing, the rationale for the substantial labor input was the increased productivity of a field on which permanent cultivation could be carried out. Water, available through bucket irrigation from the surrounding canals, eliminated the risk of drought, always a threat to harvests on upland terraces. Perhaps the higher and presumably better drained limestone marl platforms reduced the opposite risk of too much water produced by excessive rain or flooding.

The calculation of productivity is hampered by the preliminary nature of the experiments carried out to date. In comparison to

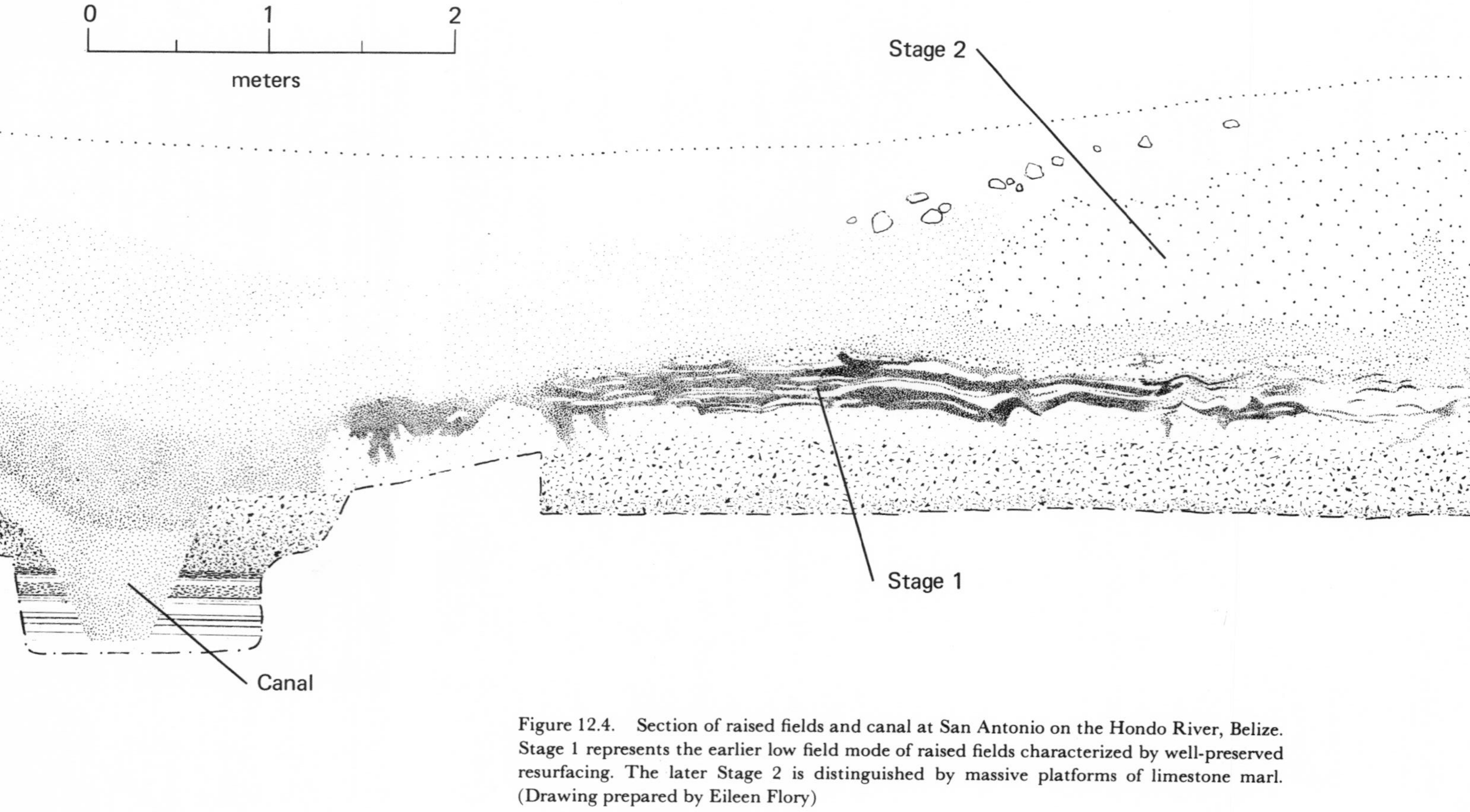

Figure 12.4. Section of raised fields and canal at San Antonio on the Hondo River, Belize. Stage 1 represents the earlier low field mode of raised fields characterized by well-preserved resurfacing. The later Stage 2 is distinguished by massive platforms of limestone marl. (Drawing prepared by Eileen Flory)

terracing, however, it seems probable that the labor investment required for initial construction was greater. The transport of approximately eighty-six tons of limestone marl from a quarry to the experimental field required 34.5 man-days of work and resulted in a minimal 10–15 centimeter cap on an area of about 620 square meters (Puleston 1974a). Topsoil built up from the excavation of the canals required additional work. Once constructed, the experimental field has required maintenance by weeding with a heavy digging stick; occasional dredging of the canals in combination with resurfacing the field; mulching; and repairs on the fence built to keep out pigs from the nearby village. Even without the supplementary fish protein from the canals, it seems probable that reduced risk and the potential for continuous cultivation would have given raised fields a higher productivity than terracing. The apparent absence of significant terracing on hillslopes along the rivers where raised fields occur suggests to me the possibility that both terraces and raised fields were used for the cultivation of maize, and that where raised fields were possible, the presumably less productive terraces were not necessary. With maize production shifted to the floodplain, the uplands may have been kept under the cover of shady and comparatively permanent orchards and kitchen gardens, which would have protected the soil from erosion. Raised-field productivity probably fell in the range of 1.00–1.50 bushels/man-day, with the higher end of this range favored if the production of fish protein were somehow included. (Bronson's productivity table might be usefully supplemented with calculation of productivity in terms of protein production per man-day.)

Ramon-Tree Kitchen Gardening

The case for the importance of ramon-tree cropping has been presented in my M.A. and Ph.D. theses (Puleston 1968a, 1973). Rather than reargue it here, I shall refer to relevant points as they arise. The distribution of chambered chultunes (fig. 12.5), apparently used for ramon-seed storage (Puleston 1971), seems to offer the best spatial indicator for utilization of ramon trees in Classic times. Subterranean chultunes are found over much of the Maya lowlands. We found them associated with residential

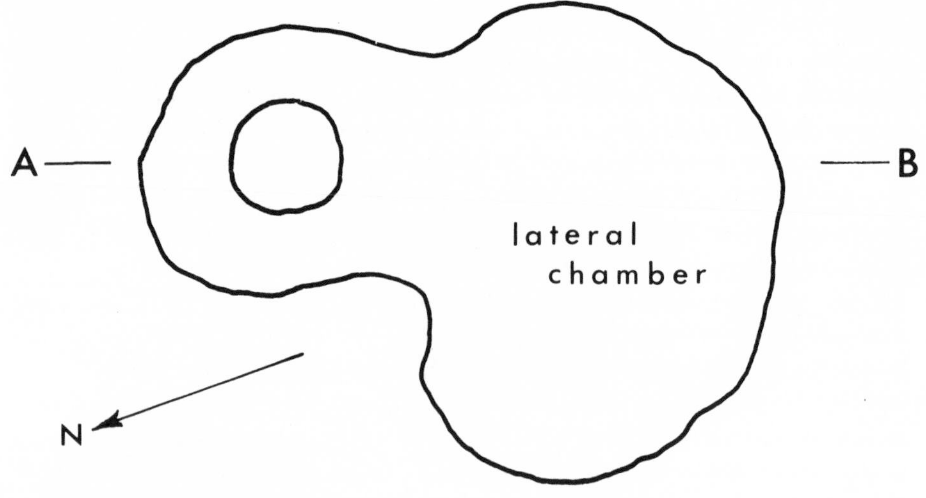

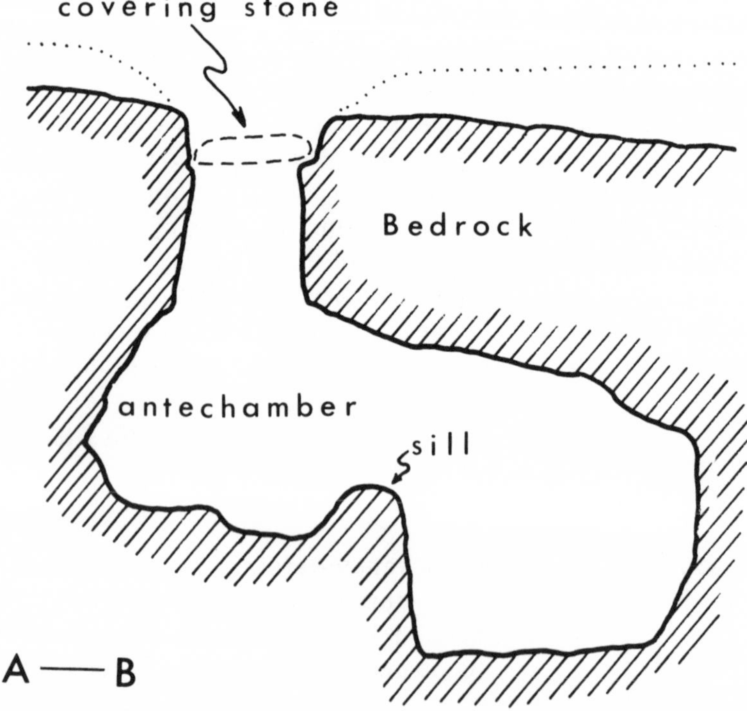

Figure 12.5. Section and plan of Chultun 5C-1, Tikal. Though one of the smaller chambered chultunes at Tikal, it is otherwise typical and displays all characteristics adaptive for ramon seed storage.

settlement along the Candelaria in Campeche, to the west, and along the Hondo in Belize, to the east. They occur as far south as Ixkun and Seibal in Peten and north up into the Chenes Zone, with one example recorded for Mayapan. Despite this broad distribution, however, chultunes are really abundant only in northeast Peten. Prentice Thomas (1974:143) notes, for instance, that "only five chultuns have been found in the environs of Becan." On a total of almost 3.5 square kilometers of carefully surveyed ground, this means an average of 1.4 chultunes per square kilometer. At Tikal the four survey strips in combination with the central 9 square kilometers have yielded approximately 480 chultunes on a total of 18 square kilometers for an average of 26.7 chultunes per square kilometer. Thus there are roughly 19 times more chultunes per unit area around Tikal than around Becan.

Chultunes date back to the Late Preclassic and possibly the Middle Preclassic. The construction and use of chambered chultunes for ramon-seed storage seems to have terminated with the end of the Classic period. Despite this time depth, a disproportionately large number of chultunes seem to have been constructed at the beginning of Late Classic times, when Tikal's overall population reached its peak (Puleston 1973: table 22). The relative abundance of chultunes even during Late Preclassic and Early Classic times combines with the lack of evidence for terracing and field demarcation to suggest that open-field agriculture was not a predominant subsistence mode around Tikal even during earlier times. Nor is there much evidence for a system in which infield ramon-tree orchard gardens would be balanced by outfield maize cultivation. The latter system is a possibility I have discussed elsewhere (Puleston 1968a:114, 1973:160, 229, 1974b:209) on the basis of the greater availability of cultivable land in intersite areas. A comparison of the ratio of chultunes to structures close to Tikal with that outside the earthworks system might be expected to show a significant difference if an infield-outfield system had been present, but it shows no decline in chultunes toward the periphery of Tikal. Evidently ramon-tree cropping was just as important in outlying areas as it was nearer the center—perhaps even more important, as the proportion of "discovered" chultunes is probably greater in the site area, where they are more likely to be found by archaeologists and workmen.

Assuming that the seed of the ramon was as important as maize has been in modern times, let us turn to the question of productivity. Typically a modern Maya family consumes 2,400–3,800 pounds of maize per year (Stadelman 1940:103; Steggerda 1941:103; Hester 1954:106; Cowgill 1962:277; Reina 1967:106). Weighing of fresh ramon seed at Tikal in 1973 revealed that a measured bushel held 48.2 pounds. If we round off the figure for annual carbohydrate consumption to 3,000 pounds, an equivalent year's supply of ramon can be calculated to be 62.2 bushels.

The labor required to obtain one year's supply of food is minimal. Obviously tree cropping requires no clearing, hoeing, planting, weeding, or mulching. The seeds of the ramon ripen on the tree and fall to the ground when they are ready to be eaten. Since individual trees are quite variable in yield, a specific grove has been used to calculate average annual production by collecting fallen seed from a randomly selected series of squares on a grid. Four years of data yield an average of 2,406.6 pounds per acre, or 2.7 metric tons per hectare.

In a separate experiment an estimate of productivity was obtained in the following manner. On August 7, 1973, a Maya woman, Marcela Quixchan de Contreras, and three of her daughters, Aida Henerlita (aged 16), Sonia Esmeralda (13), and Ali Amina (7), were engaged to collect ramon seed at Tikal. Working for one and one-half hours, not including a break of an hour and ten minutes for Marcela to breastfeed her baby, they collected a total of 72 pounds, 11 ounces (33 kilograms). Counting them as a unit of 3.5 people, a total of 5.25 "man"-hours was required to collect this amount. At this rate of 13.9 pounds per man-hour, 3,000 pounds of seed could be collected over a period of weeks during the fruiting season with a total labor investment of 215.8 man-hours. This figure is rounded off to 225 hours to allow for the additional time required to transport the harvest to a family chultun. This works out to 22.5 man-days on the basis of a 10-hour workday. With Bronson's bushels/man-day formula, a 62.2-bushel harvest collected in this amount of time yields a calculated productivity of 2.76. No agricultural system in the world approaches even remotely this astounding figure.

The implications of the productive efficiency of ramon-tree cropping for Maya history would appear to be significant. In northeast Peten, where this form of subsistence apparently predominated, a staggeringly large and otherwise uncommited all-male labor resource would have been in the hands of anyone who could control it. We may now look more closely at the evidence for an expected surplus of human energy in the Central Peten, where chultunes are most abundant.

At Tikal the utilization of an abundance of human energy is clearly implied by the Late Classic building craze of the megalomaniacal Ruler B. During his 34-year reign (A.D. 734–68), Temple I was completed, a "twin-pyramid" group was built that has been dated to 9.16.0.0.0 (A.D. 751), Temple IV was constructed and dedicated, and work on Temple VI was initiated (Jones 1977).

The power and influence commanded by Ruler B and his impressive predecessor and presumed sire, Ruler A, who reigned from A.D. 631 to 733 (9.12.9.17.6–9.15.2.2.0+), is very possibly also linked to a period of militarism. Clemency Coggins (1975:406) finds that between 9.12.0.0.0 (A.D. 672) and 9.14.0.0.0. (A.D. 711) the ceramics of Tikal changed completely in character "from curving, rounded graceful forms . . . to an emphatic, virile and simplified vocabulary of forms with a radically reduced iconography, executed in intense color. . . . the new order emphasized weapons and death in its personal emblemata, and the new ceramic aesthetic seeks clarity and simple visual solutions in military fashion."

Apart from such leads provided by iconography, an increase in the importance of warfare at this time is suggested by the presence of Tikal's 40–50-kilometer defensive earthworks. A midden associated with a moat causeway excavated in 1966 (Puleston and Callender 1967:43, 45) suggests use and possibly construction during early Late Classic times, though an earlier construction date cannot be ruled out. It is suggested here that the realization of the labor commitment necessary to create such a barrier and the maintenance of the human military support required to defend it effectively were facilitated by the efficiency of the tree-cropping subsistence mode.

Trade is one more aspect of ancient Maya culture that would have placed heavy demands on the energetic potential of an ancient Maya center. Without beasts of burden or wheeled land vehicles, the size of the human labor resource available to serve as porters would have been a critical variable in determining the magnitude and effectiveness of trading operations. As the summaries of Rathje (1971), Tourtellot and Sabloff (1972), and many others have suggested, trade was probably of considerable importance to the ancient Maya. Tourtellot and Sabloff have argued that the bulk of this trade at regional and areal levels principally involved nonutilitarian, ceremonial, and luxury goods without significant movement of basic, particularly subsistence, resources. As in Rathje's (1971) model, discussed above, the argument derives a great deal of its strength from the assumption of resource redundancy and the relatively low productivity of swidden agriculture. Clearly, arguments based on these assumptions deserve reexamination. With a large available labor resource and what I would argue was a low per-capita production of maize, northeast Peten may well have imported substantial quantities of maize over relatively long distances. While it is probable that only the elite actually enjoyed any substantial proportion of maize in their diets, it is possible that the general population had access to limited and probably variable quantities of maize to mix with their ramon seed, even as modern populations do (Puleston 1968a:71, 73). The Rio Bec region and other terraced inland localities may have been a source for this hypothetical trade maize, but, given the likelihood that productivity was higher on raised fields, I suggest we look to the riverine floodplains for evidence of major commitments to interregional movements of both maize and cotton.

Preliminary assessments of the still scanty data available suggest the existence of ties between Tikal and the east coast of Yucatan during Preclassic times. Marine materials that appear in Preclassic tombs were important early elements in Peten Maya symbolism (Coggins 1975:56) and must have come from this region. Pendergast (1968) has described two vessels from San Antonio, on the Hondo, that are almost identical to Cauac vessels found at Tikal. Whatever ties existed during this time were apparently broken off during the Protoclassic. Tikal seems to have entered a period of relative isolation that was maintained until the Early Classic. Under a strong new "Teotihuacan influence," Tikal renewed its connections to the Yucatan coast (Coggins 1975:155), and I suspect a flow of maize, cotton, and other subsistence resources from the riverine floodplains was resumed. Assuming this model does not violate the available evidence, we may shift to consideration of the Late Classic, when major changes occur. Following the hiatus of 9.5.0.0.0–9.9.0.0.0 (A.D. 534–613), Tikal seems largely to have relinquished its relationships to the east in favor of ties to the west, specifically to the major sites of the Usumacinta Drainage. There is no evidence of extensive raised fields here (Siemens and Puleston 1972: fig. 1) apart from those of the Candelaria Basin to the north, and it is possible that intersite movement of subsistence goods declined. The increase in chultun construction in Tikal at the beginning of the Late Classic may be evidence of such a decline; at the very least, it seems to suggest a shift to greater utilization of the ramon.

Greater reliance on the ramon would have reduced the energetic commitment to the transport of maize. It may well have been economies of this nature, engineered by the new order of Ruler A, that fostered the Late Classic renaissance of Tikal.

With all this going on in the core area, what was happening in the peripheries, where we find evidence of major commitments to raised fields, canals, and terraces? By all appearances and despite tentative evidence for an equivalence of local population densities (Turner 1976b; Dahlin 1974), proportionately less effort was going into the construction of major architectural monuments. In northern Belize, where the maintenance of raised fields presumably consumed even more energy than open-field terracing, major sites appear to be correspondingly less elaborate and less massive.

In conclusion, then, a direct relationship between the energetic requirements of major intensive subsistence modes and the nonsubsistence achievements of distinct lowland Maya regions is hypothesized. The explanatory potential of our new subsistence data appears at first glance to be considerable, but at this point we are still working with only the most rudimentary of concrete data. If the vague patterns visible from the air in the vast Peten *bajos* turn out to be Classic-period raised fields rather than gilgai, then clearly a great deal of the model discussed above will have to be rejected. If it is found that chultunes were not for ramon storage, or that terraces were nonagricultural, it will similarly be subject to major overhaul or complete rejection. Be that as it may, our new perspective on the complexities of pre-Hispanic Maya subsistence cannot fail to catalyze reassessment and new discoveries on a broad front.

13

PETER D. HARRISON
Middle American Research Institute

Bajos Revisited: Visual Evidence for One System of Agriculture

A regional survey conducted in southern Quintana Roo, Mexico, in 1974 revealed a pattern of settlement and a feature of vegetational patterning that pose some provocative questions. Some features of the settlement pattern have been described elsewhere (Harrison 1975, 1977). Briefly, it reveals that site distribution in southern Quintana Roo is closely linked to the incidence of *bajos* from at least as early as the Late Preclassic period. The pattern of correlation indicates that *bajo* edges were a preferred site location.

The vegetal pattern has also been described in the same sources, but an expanded discussion of its nature is appropriate here. This pattern occurs in the *bajos* in question and has been observed by Harrison on aerial photographs, by Siemens (see above, fig. 6.11), and by Turner directly from the air (1974a:121). It constitutes a grid of varying sharpness and clarity extending over vast tracts of *bajo* terrain (fig. 13.1).

Confirmation on the ground of the presence and nature of the components of the grid pattern seen from the air has not yet been made. For this reason, the fullest possible explanation of why they are interpreted as artificial is important now. The components are the lines of the grid and the blocks outlined by these lines. The lines are so straight on the aerial photos that a ruler can be laid

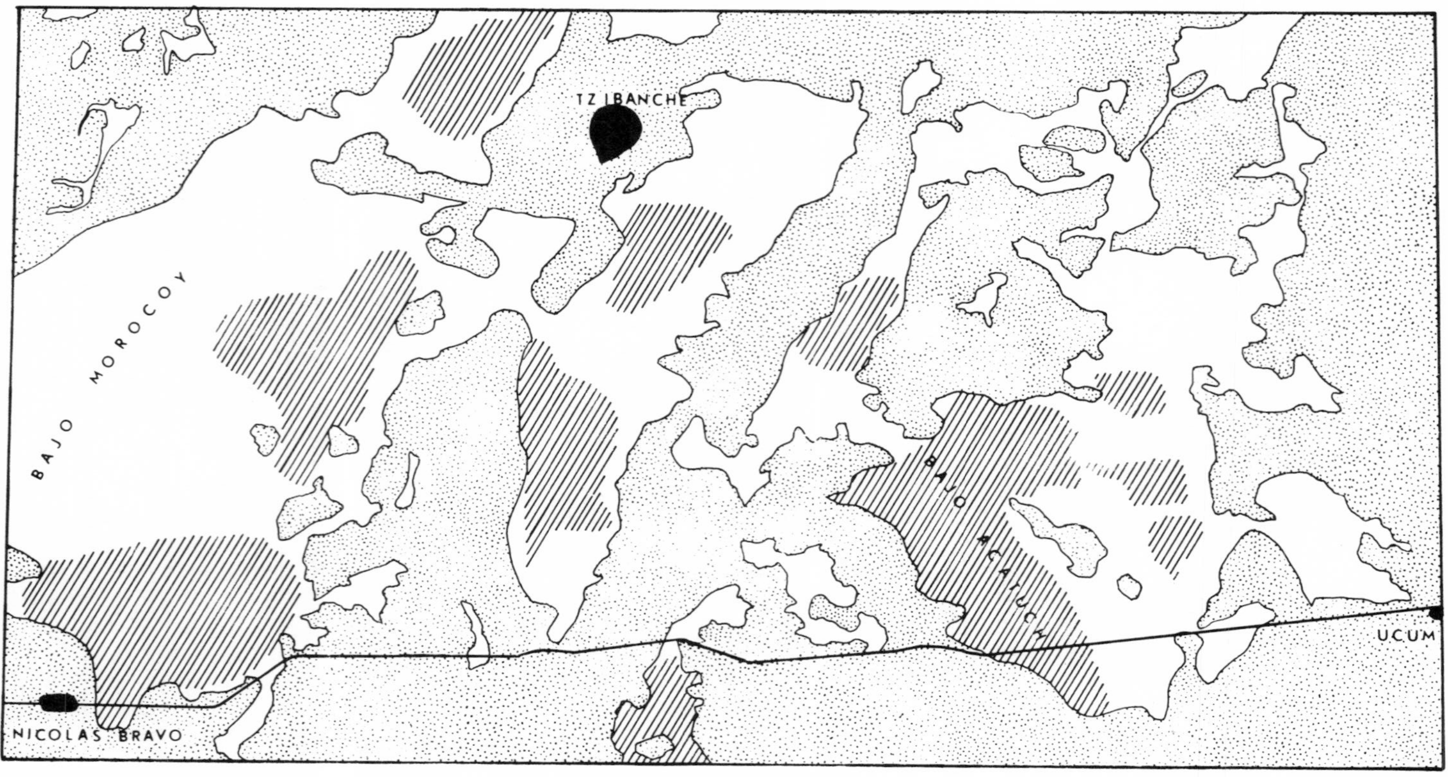

Figure 13.1. Map of a portion of southern Quintana Roo, showing distribution of vegetal patterning in *bajo* terrain.

along them with little deviation. Furthermore, these lines intersect at an angle near—but not exactly—90°. The variations from a right angle are indeed an interesting feature. A slight element of uncertainty of the location of magnetic north is present on the aerial photographs, so it is best to describe the alignments of north-south versus east-west in terms of the angle formed at their intersection. Preliminary tests of angles formed by these grids show that the angle does vary a little from one *bajo* to the next, but very little within each *bajo*. Some sample angles are the following: near Ucum (eastern zone of sample area), 95°, 95°, 95.5°, 95°; near Acatuch (central zone of sample area), 94.5°, 94° (see fig. 13.2); near Francisco Bravo (western zone of sample area), 89.5°, 91°, 92.5°, and 92°. The localized variation in angle within each *bajo* is quite small, indicating a degree of regularity not expected from natural causes but found in man-made features.

In the absence of ground verification, the interpretation of the meaning of these lines derives from the published work of Siemens and Puleston (1972) on the identification of "ridged" (raised) fields in the Candelaria Basin, and from similar work accomplished by William Denevan (1970) and James Parsons (1969) in South America. The similarity to these latter examples of raised fields seen from the air encourages the interpretation that we are seeing the same phenomenon in Quintana Roo. In the latter location, the visual lines of the grid would be drainage canals, and the blocks formed by the lines, relic raised fields. In fact, what we actually see is merely a pattern of differential vegetation, and these features could be very difficult to locate and identify on the ground. The raised fields do not necessarily have any vertical dimension today as did those fields investigated by Siemens and Puleston. On the contrary, centuries of erosion and sedimentation may well have leveled the fields and filled the canals, leaving only patterns of soil and moisture retention that in turn are reflected by differential growth patterns.

In view of the present lack of ground verification, we are faced with questions. How much importance should be ascribed to the *bajo* patterns of southern Quintana Roo? To what extent is speculative interpretation justified? Even if these patterns do represent a distinct system of intensive agriculture, as contended here, how much attention does it warrant? This last question can be answered in part by some concrete figures on distribution and

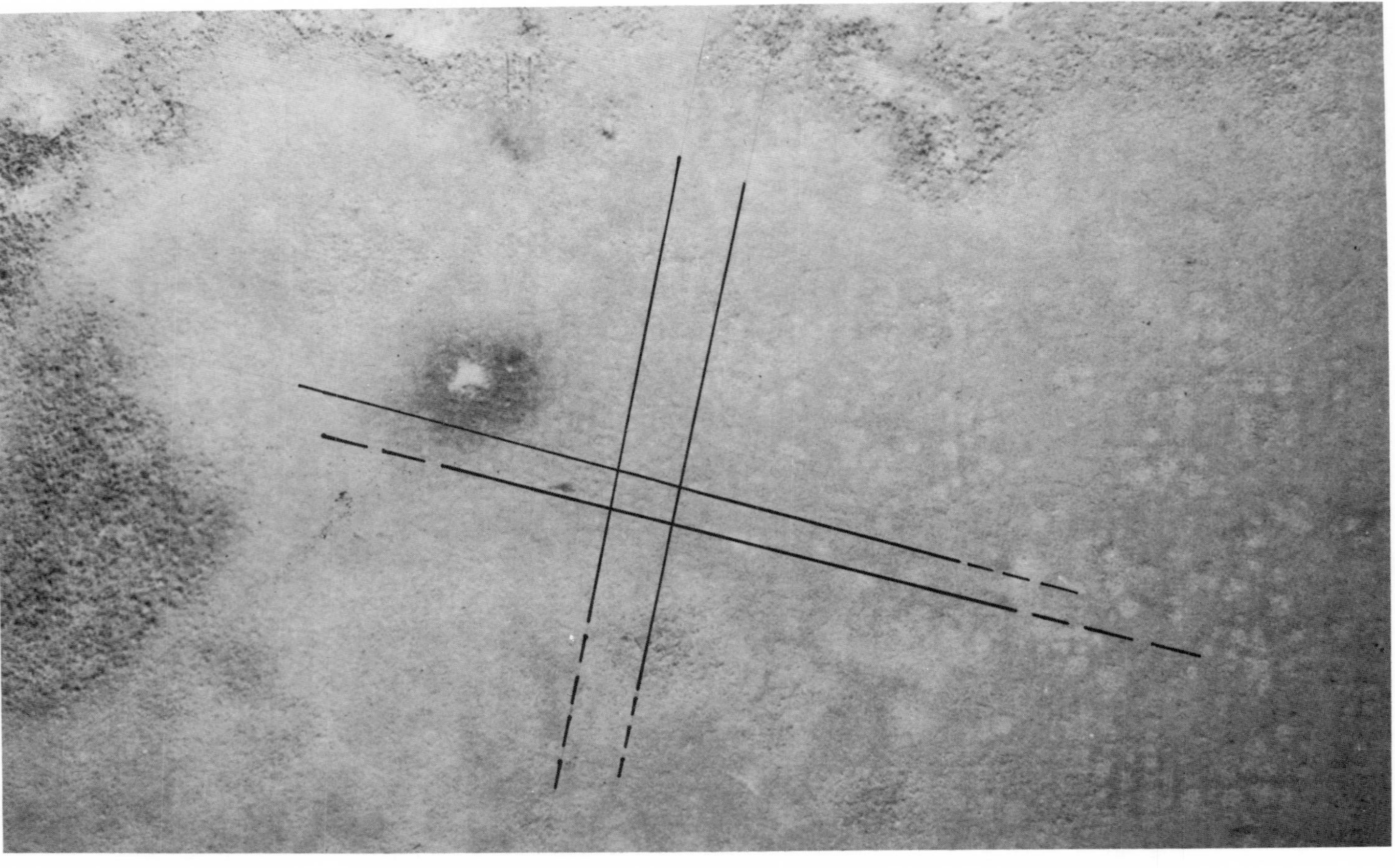

Figure 13.2. Aerial view of a portion of Bajo Acatuch, showing vegetal patterning and superimposed alignments.

scale. The sharpest and clearest "blocks" of patterning occur on a grand scale (fig. 13.1). When proven man-made, their sheer extent, regardless of date or specific functions, will warrant very close attention indeed. So far 2,460 square kilometers of patterning have been traced in an area covering 10,700 square kilometers between Ucum and Nicolas Bravo alone. The large site of Tzibanche is central to this region, located on a "peninsula" of high ground and surrounded by patterned *bajos.*

There are various possible explanations of the function of raised fields in *bajos* (Denevan and Turner 1974). Water control by canals as well as soil aeration of raised fields on the scale indicated would represent a highly organized and highly productive form of intensive agriculture. Questions of whether these "canals" contained seasonal or permanent water must await concrete field data for a definitive answer. Despite these questions, however, the implications for population sizes, political organization, and settlement patterns are enormous.

The visual evidence of vegetal patterning is clearest in southern Quintana Roo. Similar vegetal patterning has, however, been noted in other parts of the Maya lowlands, also located in *bajo* terrain. These other cases are less clear both on aerial photos and by inspection from a plane. They could represent functionally different systems of agriculture, possibly systems of *bajo* drainage designed to prolong the season of productive usefulness of the land.

Outside of Quintana Roo the patterns are less regular, less extensive according to present knowledge, and nearly impossible to reproduce photographically. If these other examples of *bajo* patterning also represent a system of *bajo* agriculture through water control or soil aeration, then their relative lack of clarity could be explained in terms of age, environment, and function. They could simply be older than those seen in Quintana Roo—more eroded and retaining less soil and moisture differentiation to be reflected in the visible vegetation. Alternatively, the functions represented by these other patterns may be different—less complex and less technologically advanced than those in Quintana Roo. At any rate it is worth documenting the known examples of such recognized patterns outside of Quintana Roo.

1. Linear configurations of vegetation, occurring in both roughly east-west and north-south orientations, have been reported in the Bajo de Santa Fe, east of Tikal in central Peten. These lines are

ephemeral, difficult to locate, and not detectable on aerial photographs. The pattern does not form a clear grid since only the lines in one orientation are visible at one time. Similar but somewhat clearer alignments are visible in a small *bajo* on the west side of Tikal. These patterns were reported by Harrison (1975, 1977), and have also been visually confirmed by Dahlin (1976b) and by Siemens (chap. 6, above). Owing to the difficulty of reproducing this pattern photographically, its meaning and value have been met with skepticism (Puleston 1977 and chap. 12 above).

2. Dahlin (1976b) has reported a similar set of ephemeral lines visible in a *bajo* near the banks of the Rio Holmul, to the west of the site of Nakum.

3. J. M. Keshishian has photographed a clearer group of vegetal patterns in the immediate vicinity of the site of Mirador (in Stuart 1975:785). This example is comparable to the grid patterns in southern Quintana Roo for its clarity, but similar to examples 1 and 2 above in that only the lines of one orientation can be seen at one time. The east-west alignments appear to lie at a near right angle to the great causeway extending southward from this northern Peten site. These lines can be seen in the published photograph. The causeway in question crosses a large *bajo.*

4. In various locations between and adjacent to the New and Hondo rivers in Belize, the patterning of raised fields has been reported in *bajos* by both David Friedel and Dennis Puleston (personal communications, 1977). In all cases the patterns have nonriverine locations, although the flooding of *bajos* may be linked to river levels in this region. Recently Puleston has plotted and mapped the distribution of such raised field patterns in the upper zone of this drainage system.

5. Four locations of visible "ridged" fields outside of the Candelaria Basin were reported by Siemens and Puleston (1972: fig. 1, p. 231). The locations are briefly described:

> Individual, areally limited instances of linear patterns, *somewhat different in form from those around the Candelaria* [italics mine], were found to the south, near the La Mar and Budsilha sites just opposite the western extremity of Guatemala's Peten, as well as around the northern end of Lake Santa Clara and in several other locations between there and Bonampak, but not in the immediate proximity of that site.

Excepting those at the edge of Lake Santa Clara, there is no indication whether these examples are located in *bajo* terrain, or on river levees. The difference in form from those in the Candelaria Basin suggests that the latter is not the case. If the three examples cited are indeed located in *bajo* terrain, then this list totals eight reported cases of vegetal patterning in the Peten, Chiapas, and Belize. None of these cases are ground verified to date, but the mounting evidence from so many different pairs of eyes indicates that something of considerable significance exists in the *bajos.*

This discussion deals with still unconfirmed evidence for a system of agriculture—a system that would be intensive and apparently discontinuous in its distribution in the lowlands. Discussion of it at this time may be a trifle premature. The ephemeral vegetation lines that identify its presence have been noted in almost every *bajo* that has been specifically observed with this kind of evidence as an objective, but unfortunately very few *bajos* have been searched in this fashion.

It is presumed that the system of intensive agriculture that is represented by this category of visual evidence is a system that resembles chinampa agriculture in some cases, and a system of water control of lesser sophistication in others. Extremely early dates have been reported for raised fields located on river edges (Puleston 1977; Hammond 1976a, chap. 3 above). It would seem unlikely, however, that such early dates would apply to similar systems in *bajos,* given their broader distribution and association with large sites having a strong Classic component.

It should be emphasized that this particular category of visual evidence represents only one type of intensive agriculture for which there is evidence in the lowlands. The urgent need for ground verification is obvious.

14

BENNET BRONSON
Field Museum of Natural History

Angkor, Anuradhapura, Prambanan, Tikal: Maya Subsistence in an Asian Perspective

INTRODUCTION: THE MAYA IN CONTEXT

In recent years the old problem of the subsistence of complex tropical societies has found new solutions. The issue once was simple in many specialists' and laymen's minds. Tropical forests are poor and difficult environments. Most have to be farmed through shifting methods of cultivation, food-producing regimes that provide no stimulus to political or economic growth and that are only capable of supporting a small number of people. Thus, the accepted thesis ran, tropical areas have rarely produced civilizations, and when they have those civilizations were doomed to poverty and a rapid decline. The prime example for many theorists was that of the ancient Maya, who were unquestionably shifting cultivators and who just as unquestionably, although perhaps not with ideal rapidity, declined. Hence there is great importance in the breakthroughs detailed elsewhere in this book.

A consensus is developing to the effect that the Maya were not just swiddeners and that their tropical environment offered them a wide range of techniques for gaining a livelihood, some of these highly efficient in terms of the number of people a given plot of land could support, and some capable of producing massive surpluses with a minimum input of labor. While not all of these options can be shown to have been picked up, some can. And so the old questions have largely lost their meaning. We may no longer deny, somewhat unrealistically, that the Maya *could* have succeeded or propose that their environment was so inimical and their adaptive capacity so limited that they were bound to fail. Interest now has shifted to questions of "how" rather than "whether": which among the vast array of solutions open to them did the Maya actually select, and what were the likely social and economic effects of these?

It is in this regard that the study of other tropical forest civilizations assumes importance not just for general theory but for Mayanist research. For the Maya were by no means alone in coping successfully with their humid forest environments. Some of the others who succeeded, like the various Central American chiefdoms, might not be thought comparable since they did not attain as high a degree of sociopolitical organization. Some, like the highly organized kingdoms of West Africa, may seem too late or too uninterested in such touchstones of civilization as large stone monuments to impress theorists as truly comparable to the Maya. In Asia, however, there are several ancient societies that bear striking similarities to the Maya in most important respects: in gross environmental setting, in societal and political complexity, and even in partiality to monuments. The parallels have long been recognized. Yet these Asian cases have only occasionally been brought into discussions of Maya subsistence.

The most serious recent attempt to make such comparisons is a seminal paper by Michael Coe (1961), where the Cambodian site of Angkor is compared in some detail with the larger sites of Peten. Coe indicates the various similarities between the two regions, emphasizes the undifferentiated nature of their environments by comparison with Mesopotamia and Central Mexico, and concludes that, because of a lack of microenvironmentally reinforced economic integration, both the Maya and the Khmer failed to develop true complexly specialized and integrated urban societies.

The present paper will touch only in passing on the questions of whether the Maya and the Khmer had real cities (see Wheatley 1963; Blanton 1976:253–54) and whether the economies of either were actually less specialized and complex than the economies of more environmentally variable regions. (For an example of astonishing specialization within a uniform tropical environment, see Gourou 1955.) But in spite of differences in focus, the overall approach of this paper is quite similar to that of Coe's. Comparing the Maya with Old World civilizations is here considered possible and meaningful, even when the comparison is expanded to include groups other than the Maya and Khmer. One incidental benefit of using a larger sample will be to help the reader judge the truth of Coe's (1961:69) contention, "Unquestionably, the Khmer Empire and the Classic Maya civilization were the highest cultures ever developed in the tropics."

The sample examined here includes four rather than two early tropical societies: the Maya, Khmer, Javanese, and Sinhalese. All were situated within areas whose natural vegetation was dense forest and whose climates were indisputably tropical, and were presumably subject to whatever limitations inhere in environments of that kind. All nevertheless achieved substantial success; they had large populations and complex governments, lasted for at least several centuries, and were notably creative in several fields, including the construction of large stone buildings. Indeed, one of the four (the Khmer) may surpass all other ancient civilizations, temperate or tropical, in per-capita production of cubic meters of carved stone.

In order to treat these societies compactly, I propose to focus on a single site belonging to each: Angkor in Cambodia, Tikal in Guatemala, Prambanan in Java, and Anuradhapura in Sri Lanka. Each site has claims to be the chief political and ritual center of its region and should therefore exemplify the mechanisms through which tropical urban or quasi-urban societies are organized and sustained. A further reason for choosing these is that I have visited all of them and, having participated in excavations at sites contemporary with and related to all four, feel passably familiar with the relevant archaeological data.

After a short review of the main features of the sites, the discussion will move on to ecological topics. The environmental settings of the four will be sketched. What is known and can be inferred about their agricultural systems will be set out. And lastly, a number of tentative conclusions will be suggested. The Maya were almost as capable as their Asian counterparts at feeding a larger urban population. Yet they clearly were more vulnerable in some respects, especially in logistic capacity and in protein supply.

THE SITES

A full archaeological description need not be attempted here. The sites to be discussed are famous; each has had more written about it than any similar site in its region. Certain archaeological details, however, are important to the central argument.

Dates and History

The histories of the four centers, as far as these are known, follow interesting similar courses. Each rises from an obscure but by no means primitive "Preclassic" background sometime in the early or mid first millennium A.D. The "Classic" periods of all four last an appreciable length of time and are characterized in the popular mind by a sudden and spectacular flowering of monumental art. Their subsequent declines are rapid and comparatively complete. Tikal and Angkor were empty and overgrown when first seen by Europeans. Anuradhapura and Prambanan, though in still-populated countrysides, were no more than rural villages.

The precise chronologies of all four sites are controversial. Table 14.1 represents what I take to be the approximate consensus of current research; I will not try to defend its details here.

Table 14.1. Florescence of the Sites

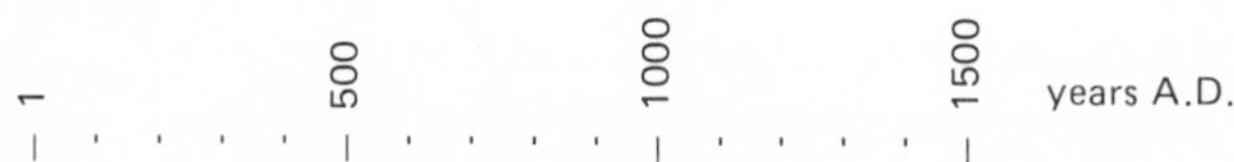

Tikal	XXXXXXXXXXXX
Angkor	XXXXXXXXXXXXX
Anuradhapura	XXXXXXXXXXXXX
Prambanan	XXXXXXX

The declines of the sites and the societies of which they were capitals have been ascribed to a wide variety of political and natural causes. Concerted attacks by outside groups can be demonstrated or inferred in three cases: by Mexicans on the Maya, by Thai on the Khmer, and by Tamils on the Sinhalese. Internal struggles have been postulated as contributing causes in the decline of the Maya, the Khmer, and the Javanese. Among natural causes, only in the case of the Maya has the intrinsic unmanageability of the environment proved a popular explanation of decline. Numerous other natural explanations have been proposed, however, of which several are still current: encephalitis and certain other diseases in the Maya area, malaria in Sri Lanka (Nicholls 1921), and volcanic eruptions in Java (van Bemmelen 1956; Boechari 1973).

Physical Size

At the height of their power, the four sites covered the areas listed in table 14.2—Tikal during the Late Classic, Angkor in the twelfth century, Anuradhapura in the seventh through tenth centuries, and Prambanan in the ninth through tenth centuries.

Only Angkor possesses a physical boundary, the moat dug by Suryavarman II, that can reasonably be interpreted as an approximate limit to the area of denser settlement. Otherwise, the areas of the sites have been considered to coincide with the distribution of large public structures as shown on various available plans: for Tikal, Carr and Hazard (1961); for Angkor, Lunet de Lajonquière (1911) and Groslier and Arthaud (1968); for Anuradhapura, Hocart (1924) and Paranavitana (1936); and for Prambanan, van Goor (1919), Verbeek (1891), and unpublished archival data from Suaka 1, Dep. P. dan K., Prambanan.

Population

It should not be imagined that any of the sites was built over solidly within these spatial limits. Substantial gardens, fields, and other open spaces probably accounted for a very large proportion of the total area in each case. Tikal is in fact the only one of the four at which there is direct archaeological evidence for the existence of any residences at all, partly because early excavators at the Asian sites were not interested in such matters and partly because only the Maya seem to have utilized permanent materials, in the form of stone and earth foundation platforms, when constructing nonceremonial buildings. At Prabanan and Angkor,

Table 14.2. Areas of the Sites (in hectares)

Tikal	ca. 1200 (excluding *bajos*)
Angkor	ca. 3200 (moated area 2020)
Anuradhapura	ca 400+ (walled area 110)
Prambanan	ca 1200 (area between Candi Sewu and Ratu Boko)

even kings lived in wooden palaces; neither site has produced a single indisputably secular structure since research began there in the nineteenth century.

On the other hand, no grounds exist for supposing that any of the Asian sites consisted exclusively of sacred monuments and elite residences, as Coe (1961:72–73) suggests with regard to Angkor. The chief historical source on Angkor, the fourteenth-century Chinese traveler Chou Ta-kuan (Pelliot 1951), called the Khmer capital a city without hesitation; coming as he did from a normally urbanized society, Chou (and other Chinese sources like Chao Ju-kua [Hirth and Rockhill 1966]) would surely have thought it worth remarking if Angkor had been populated solely or even largely by priests, administrators, and servants. Furthermore, we possess abundant information from European accounts of South and Southeast Asian cities in the sixteenth and seventeenth centuries, a time well before the spread of imposed Western patterns of urbanization. None of these sources describes a single political and religious capital that did not contain numerous merchants, artisans, laborers, farmers, and so forth; a center devoted entirely to ritual and administration, such as is often supposed to have existed in the Maya area, would have appeared as aberrant and noteworthy to these European travelers as to their Chinese predecessors. Unless we suppose that great changes occurred in tropical Asia between the middle of the first millennium and the time of Chau Ju-kua and Chou Ta-kuan, we must conclude that the vacant ceremonial center model is inappropriate for the Asian sites. It is remotely possible that a major regional capital in the New World might have been empty of people, despite the lack of any historically documented instance of such a settlement. In the Old World it seems certain that all such centers would have had normal complements of nonelite inhabitants.

How large and dense these urban populations were is at present an unanswerable question. My own impression, based on personal observation of the density of sherds and other residential debris at these and related sites, is that none were as closely settled as the average early city in the Middle East or the Valley of Mexico. All of them, on the other hand (with the possible exception of Prambanan, which seems unusually artifact-poor), show substantial levels of refuse density: ten or twenty sherds on each square meter of bare earth and much higher densities in certain spots. Both Angkor and Anuradhapura are, if anything, more artifact-rich than Tikal. No reason exists for doubting that they achieved or surpassed the minimum density of habitation suggested by the housemound surveys at Tikal (Haviland 1968:111, 1972): at least two single-family dwellings per hectare.

In terms of overall population, each of the sites must have had several tens of thousands of inhabitants. Any economic and agricultural system believed to have existed there must have been able to feed a concentration of people of that size.

ENVIRONMENTS

A necessary preliminary to comparing the agricultural systems of the four areas is to describe the main outlines of the natural environments with which those systems had to contend. Although varied, these environments seem to have had more in common that would four randomly selected locations within the tropics.

Climate

The climatic situation is summarized in the four charts included here (fig. 14.1), taken from Walter and Leith's (1967) monumental *Klimadiagramm-Weltatlas.* The charts are drawn so as to show the relationship between temperature and rainfall in terms of the surplus or deficit of the latter at given values of the former. The upper line represents mean monthly rainfall while the lower one represents mean noontime temperatures; stippled areas, where the rainfall line dips below the temperature line, indicate periods of significant moisture deficit. The digits in the upper right give mean annual rainfall in millimeters and noontime temperature in degrees Celsius; those in the upper left show the number of years for which trustworthy temperature and rainfall data are available from that recording station.

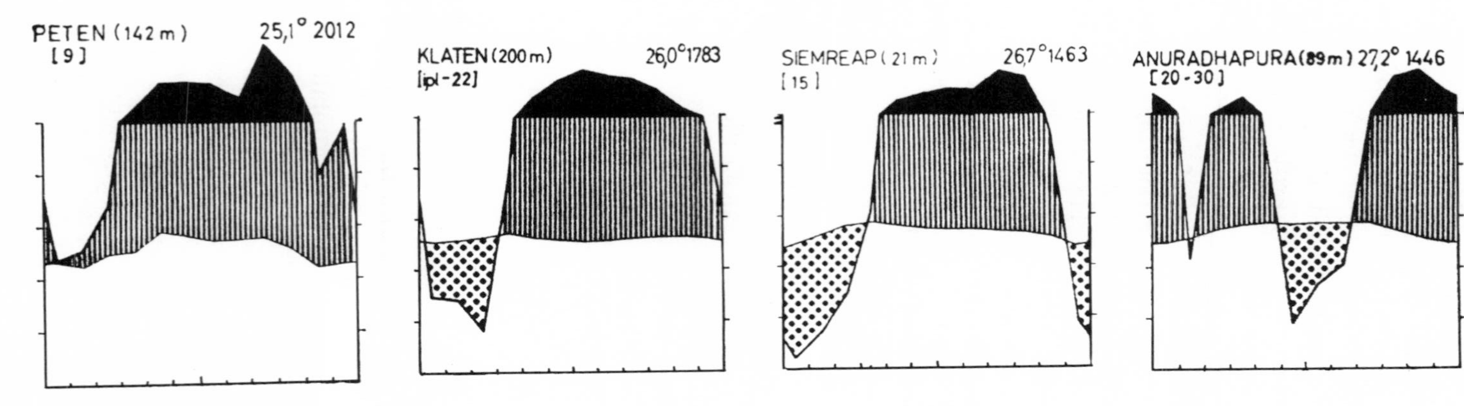

Figure 14.1. Climate at Peten (Flores, 50 km from Tikal), Klaten (11 km from Prambanan), Siemreap (2 km from Angkor), and Anuradhapura.

It will be observed that the four climatic charts are roughly similar, with moderate, constant temperatures and rainfall so distributed as to produce an annual time of water surplus and a shorter season of drought. The yearly dry period at Flores appears to be minimal; that at Tikal, although probably somewhat longer than at Flores, should be the least severe of the four areas. The annual drought at Klaten-Prambanan is of short duration. The one at Anuradhapura is more serious; when the minor rains of February and March fail, it can last as long as six months. Ordinarily, however, it is Angkor that suffers most from lack of rainfall; a drought of five months is normal.

In sum, while far from desertlike, all four areas are on the dry side for locations within the forested tropics. Enough rainfall exists for the raising of one crop without irrigation. Yet none of the sites is so well watered as to preclude an interest in canals, dams, and reservoirs.

Vegetation

The original plant cover of all four sites lay somewhere on the spectrum between partially canopied semievergreen forest and low, largely deciduous forest; none lay either in high evergreen forest or in the thorny deciduous scrub typical of such areas as northern Yucatan and the northwestern coast of Sri Lanka.

Flora that approaches a climax condition survives only at Tikal and, in a very patchy form, at Angkor. Both forests are 15–20 meters high with many emergents that reach 25–30 meters (Lundell 1937; Legris and Blasco 1972). High emergents are now very rare in the neighborhood of Anuradhapura, where continuing swidden cultivation and perhaps climatic factors limit the forest to a height of 9–19 meters, sometimes with a thorny underlayer (Gaussen et al. 1964, 1965:27–43). Not even this much survives at Prambanan, where the extraordinarily dense central Javanese population has long since swept the landscape of everything that is not deliberately planned and planted. According to Steenis (1965:16–35), the natural vegetation of most of lowland Java was a single-story monsoon forest, apparently quite similar to the semideciduous forests of Cambodia and Sri Lanka.

We may presume that in ancient times the forests of all four areas produced a sufficient variety of the usual tropical forest products: structural hardwood, fibrous vines, poisons, resins, fruit, and tubers.

A few important differences existed, however, between the forests of the Old World and New World tropics, and some of these may have had cultural and economic consequences.

The Mesoamerican forest is largely lacking in bamboo, a material of almost incalculable importance to Sri Lankans, Cambodians, and Javanese. Neither Sri Lanka nor Mesoamerica produces rattan, which to Southeast Asians is nearly as fundamental as bamboo and which, together with bamboo, forms the basis for a lightweight structural technology that has no real New World counterpart. The Javanese and Cambodians could erect scaffolding, bridges, and aqueducts more quickly and with less labor than could any ancient people of the New World.

On the other hand, the Asian forests had no wild tree with the capabilities of the Maya ramon for large-scale and labor-free food production (Puleston 1968a). South and Southeast Asia do have their tree staples—jackfruit, breadfruit, banana, coconut, sago—but these all are unproductive in their wild or feral versions with the exception of sago, and the various sago-producing palms require an inordinate amount of labor to extract the edible starch from their trunks.

A last difference should be mentioned even though it has no direct bearing on physical subsistence. The Old and New World tropics are astonishly dissimilar in the number of psychotropic drug-producing plants they are known to contain. La Barre (1970) quotes Schultes to the effect that the New World contains upwards of forty, while Eurasia has no more than three or four. As the Paleotropics contain at least as great a number of plant species as do the Neotropics, the difference may be due to variation in cultural interest and not to an uneven natural distribution of alkaloids. But whatever the explanation, the druglessness of the Asian tropical cultures is one of their most anomalous characteristics when viewed from a New World perspective.

Soils

The quality of the available pedological data is unsatisfactory, partly because extensive survey work has not been done but also because some existing information is restricted for political reasons.

The paucity of data and the incompatibility of the terms used by soil specialists trained in different schools makes it impossible for now to impose a uniform nomenclature along the lines suggested by the U.S. Soil Conservation Service (1960) and utilized, for instance, by Turner (1976a) in his discussion of the physiographic divisions of the Maya lowlands. One therefore cannot easily compare the soils in terms of structural and chemical composition. However, enough data do exist to make a rough evaluation of them from the standpoint of agricultural possibility.

Soils at Tikal

In some areas, like central Java, the ultimate proof of soil quality is its present capacity to support a large rural population. The situation is quite the opposite in central Peten. The very scattered populace that now inhabits the Yaxha, Jolja, and Chalcate clays of Tikal's hinterland currently does so little farming, and that so nonintensive, as to make evaluation of the soils a largely speculative exercise.

The two existing professional surveys, those of the Instituto Agropecuario de Guatemala (Simmons, Tarano, and Pinto 1959:571–88) and the British Honduras Land Use Survey team (Wright et al. 1959:182–95), are distinctly unenthusiastic about the usefulness of the clay lands of Peten in "developing an economic and rational agriculture." Anthropologists and geographers have tended to be less pessimistic. Even though Cowgill's tests (Cowgill and Hutchinson 1963b) of the low-lying *bajo* soils at Tikal revealed a gleyed alluvium which was very unpromising (indeed, almost sterile), Maya specialists have kept in mind the fact that a substantial population was once supported by the hill soils of the region. Turner (1976a) represents the consensus: the mollisols or rendzinas on the hills and better-drained flatlands are fertile but thin and in need of careful management. The acid entisols and vertisols of the *bajos* are not at all fertile and can only be cultivated through laborious techniques such as ridging, deep subsoil draining, and applying large amounts of lime and fertilizer.

It should be said, however, that these *bajo* soils resemble the typical rice soils of several parts of tropical Asia. Although equally infertile and poorly structured, the Asian alluvial clays have proved to be adequately productive under the peculiar self-contained rules of wet-rice farming, where virtually all nutrients can be provided from the water and the microorganisms in it, while the soil itself functions mainly as a support for the roots of the crop. Maya agriculture sorely needed a rice substitute. Perhaps one of the hydrophytic root crops—*Xanthosoma, Maranta,* or *Canna* —will be shown to have fitted the requirements.

Soils at Angkor

The small soil map reproduced by Legris and Blasco (1972), based on earlier work by C. D. Crocker, indicates that a complex set of soils exists in and around Angkor: red-yellow podzolic soils north of the site, a belt of hydromorphic soils immediately south of it, and waterlogged lacustrine deposits farther south along the edge of the Great Lake, all of these mingled with smaller patches of acid lithosols and lateritic clay.

The general opinion, represented by such general works as Gourou (1940) and Dudal and Moorman (1964), by Legris and Blasco's own comments, and by the few available reports of field trials (T. L. Ho 1961), is that the better soils of Cambodia lie far to the southeast in the general vicinity of modern Phnom Penh. No one thinks the soils of Angkor are fertile. The red-yellow podzols, the lateritic clays, and the acid lithosols range in quality from poor to very poor (Legris and Blasco 1972:40–47). The lacustrine deposits are too liable to deep flooding to be cultivable by ordinary methods, although some can be planted with the so-called floating rice. Even the hydromorphic soils, undoubtedly in the past the mainstay of the local agricultural economy, are nothing special in terms of quality. Ho (1961) strikes a markedly pessimistic note when describing the results of experimental rice plots laid out within the boundaries of the ancient site itself.

Soils at Anuradhapura

Even at the detailed scale at which the Soil Survey of Sri Lanka is currently working, the soils in the neighborhood of Anuradhapura appear quite uniform. The most recent version of the Ceylon General Soil Map (Panabokke 1967a) assigns 80 percent of the soils within a 50-kilometer radius of the site to one group, the Reddish

Brown Earths. The remaining 20 percent are upland lithosols of little agricultural value.

The Reddish Brown Earths seem to be a rather distinctive (Panabokke 1967b:68–69) variety of ultisol: nonlateritic, moderately high in clay content, and not easy to cultivate when wet (Panabokke 1967b:84). The unirrigable upland phases of the group are said to be adequately fertile, suffering only from an irregular supply of moisture. The low-lying, poorly drained phases, mostly clays with a low humic content, are "the most productive rice growing soils of Ceylon" (Panabokke 1976b:85). This judgment is confirmed by Senewiratne and Appadurai (1966:7–13), who point out that rice fields in the Anuradhapura district regularly yield almost 2,000 kilograms per hectare, which is high by South and Southeast Asian standards. On the other hand, we may infer that these irrigable gleyed phases of the Reddish Brown Earths are none too abundant. The 1949 land-use map of the region (Survey Department 1949) indicates that less than 5 percent of the area around Anuradhapura is covered by rice paddies.

Soils at Prambanan

In this case, as I said earlier, soil quality is easy to evaluate. The Prambanan area now supports more than 500 persons per square kilometer of culitvated land and has done so for many decades with little input of chemical fertilizer or animal manure (the Javanese do not dress their fields with nightsoil). We cannot doubt that the soils of the southern Javanese lowlands are extraordinarily fertile, a judgment that is supported by specialist reports and indeed by any casual stroll through the local countryside.

According to the available maps (Ned. Aardrijkskundig Genootschap 1938: pl. 16; Direktorat Landuse 1969–70) the wide bottomlands of the Dengkeng-Otak Drainage are composed of immature soils: colluvium from the nearby volcano, Merapi, on the north side, and alluvium on the south side. The southern edge of the alluvium, where it borders the limestone hills that underlie the volcanic massif of Lawu, appears to contain some marl and much montmorillonite and may therefore be subject to some of the minor problems for irrigation detailed in Eysvoogel (1951). The rest of the alluvium, however, along with the more southerly portions of the colluvium, is structurally suited to rice growing and of immense natural fertility. As Mohr (1945) emphasizes, young basic volcanic deposits like these are by far the most productive soils in the Asian tropics.

Hydrology

The distribution of surface and near-surface water has, naturally, an important effect on farming and on the possibilities for water transportation of farm products. For the moment I am concerned only with these possibilities, not with ancient practice. Whether boats were actually used and irrigation was carried out will be discussed at a later point.

Hydrology of Tikal

It is a familiar fact, if one too infrequently emphasized, that most of the interior of the central and northern Maya lowlands have no surface water for much of the year and no flowing streams at any time. Water movement is confined to underground aquifers several tens of hundreds of meters beneath the karstic surface. In this respect Tikal and its neighbors are almost unique among ancient urban centers. Conditioned to images of civilizations that grew up on the shores of rivers, lakes, and sheltered seas, a non-Mayanist may find it difficult to envision a city whose economy involved no direction of surface water for agricultural purposes and no watercourses along which goods could come and go. There are indeed hints that this nonhydraulic condition may not have been absolute. Harrison (1977) and Siemens (1976) have plausibly revived the old idea that the *bajos* may once have been navigable to some degree during the rainy season, and evidence to be sketched later shows that the Maya took some interest in irrigation. But still, the situation is extraordinary. The economy of Tikal suffered from highly unusual hydrologic constraints.

Hydrology of Angkor

In spite of its massive water control and storage facilities, Angkor would have little irrigable land were it not for the proximity of the floodplain of the Great Lake. As will shortly be shown, the Siemreap River was elaborately dammed and diverted into canals but cannot have carried enough water to irrigate more than a small suburban area. On the other hand, the Great Lake, through its deep-water connections with the Mekong and the sea, provided Angkor with better long-distance communications than were enjoyed by the other sites. Angkor was the only one of the four to have easy access to what was effectively a seaport for even the largest of ancient ships.

Hydrology of Anuradhapura

The Dry Zone of Sri Lanka may be the driest of the four areas if we take into consideration both annual precipitation and the availability of water derived from distant watersheds. Domros (1974:203–11) cites data on total yearly runoff within the three river basins, the Malwatu, the Kala, and the Moderagama, which drain the hinterland of Anuradhapura. In none of these does sufficient water exist to irrigate more than 29 percent of the otherwise irrigable land during the rainy season; during the dry season, there is not enough to irrigate more than 2 or 3 percent. The wet-season total is still respectably large: the indicated 100,000 hectares could, if planted in wet rice, feed a sizable population. Yet water is by no means abundant, and Anuradhapura, unlike Angkor, lacked a system of waterways that would have made it easy to bring in foodstuffs from distant areas. The double-cropped rice fields of the Wet Zone, where annual runoff exceeds that of the Dry Zone by a factor of four or five, were more than a hundred kilometers distant by the overland route, and Anuradhapura was separated from the sea by fifty kilometers of unnavigable river.

Hydrology of Prambanan

Prambanan is better supplied with irrigation water than the other three sites. Direct rainfall together with runoff from nearby mountain slopes is sufficient to provide for wet- and dry-season cropping of most of the flat, arable land in the area. Irrigation is possible during the dry season without large reservoirs. Even though the watersheds of the local streams are small, they receive enough water to keep canals full for much of the year.

As far as transportation goes, however, Prambanan is not in a much better position than Anuradhapura. Neither the Otak nor the Dengkeng is navigable, and the nearby southern coast of Java is too dangerous to be often used either by traditional or modern shipping. The Dengkeng flows into the Solo near Surakarta, some thirty kilometers to the east. Ships of modest size can reach this point from the Java Sea, yet the trip is so long by that route that it seems likely that in antiquity, just as in modern times, most commerce went overland to the north coast of the island. In spite of their insular locations, and even though both were closely involved in long-distance trade, neither Anuradhapura nor Prambanan was less landlocked than Tikal.

Environmental Summary

The data presented above may be summarized as follows (see table 14.3). It will be observed that the environments of the four sites are similar enough to dispel serious doubts about the validity of comparing them. The general sameness of settings naturally does not dictate close similarities in agronomic response. Available crops may differ, as may needs, preferences, perceptions, technologies, and labor and capital resources. The rest of this paper describes the subsistence strategies adopted by the four centers, as far as these can be reconstructed. There appear to be important differences.

AGRICULTURAL SYSTEMS

Direct evidence of ancient agriculture is scanty at all four of the sites under consideration; in three of them (Anuradhapura is the exception) there even are serious defects in the information available on modern farming. The situation is far from hopeless, however. By using modern data cautiously, with due allowance for recent changes in crops grown and techniques used, and by combining these with environmental information and with existing archaeological, historical, and botanical-zoological evidence, it is possible to arrive at a plausible estimate of the nature and

Table 14.3. Summary of Environmental Features

	Angkor	*Anuradhapura*	*Prambanan*	*Tikal*
Latitude	13° N	6° N	7° S	18° N
Altitude	30 m	89 m	200 m	150 m
Annual Mean Temp.	26.7° C	27.2° C	26.0° C	25.1° C
Dry Season Length	5 mos	4 mos	2.5 mos	3 mos
Annual Rainfall	1,463 mm	1,446 mm	1,786 mm	(2021 mm)*
Variability of Rain	moderate†	moderate†	moderate†	moderate†
Natural Vegetation	moist/dry semidecid	moist/dry semidecid	moist semi-deciduous	moist semi-deciduous
Soil Quality	fair/poor	fair	good	fair
Irrigation Water	some	some	much	little
Water for Transport	yes	no	no	no

*Data for Flores; Tikal probably 100–200 mm less.

†Available records do not permit accurate estimates of long-term variability; droughts do occur but not as often or as severely as in places like northern India and West Africa.

capabilities of the subsistence systems of the early Maya, Khmer, Sinhalese, and Javanese.

The treatment that follows is necessarily unbalanced. Although data have been compressed as much as possible, certain topics have been brushed past rapidly: tools used, nonagricultural subsistence, exchange, and the role of domesticated animals. That these are slighted does not imply a lack of importance; as the conclusion shows, some (for example, the great commercial and fishing resources of the Khmer) may have been decisive for the overall subsistence capacities of the economies in question.

I have sought, on the other hand, to avoid excessive simplification. Theorists have already spent too much time with reductionist contrasts between agricultural systems classified on a single axis, according to relative permanence of fields, type of tools used, employment of seed or vegetative reproduction, and so forth. The subsistence of any real village, not to mention that of any real regional center of the status of a Tikal or an Angkor, depends on a large assortment of microenvironments, crops, techniques, and strategies (see, for instance, those sketched by Harris 1969, 1977a; Netting 1977; Terra 1958). Many of these can, in principle, be critical to the success or failure of an economy. All must be controlled before one can state confidently that the subsistence system reconstructed for center *X* was more efficient, adapted, or advanced than the reconstructed system of center *Y*.

This is why I have made no attempt to treat in detail statistics for yield and efficiency or for theoretical carrying capacities. In the areas under discussion environments are too complex and quantified subsistence data too inaccurately reported and too dependent on postindustrial inputs to be meaningfully extrapolated backward a thousand years or outward over ten thousand square kilometers. It suffices to say that none of the environments or major field systems described here was incapable of attaining a reasonable efficiency in terms of land and labor use. As I have argued elsewhere (Bronson 1972, 1975), a wide variety of agricultural regimes have proved to be flexible and intensifiable. Many have surpassed in land- and labor-using efficiency that cynosure of earlier agricultural evolutionists, traditional European mixed stock and grain farming.

Availability of Crops and Livestock

The most important change in subsistence known to have occcurred since the four centers were abandoned, and hence the most troublesome problem in evaluating their preabandonment farm economies, is the pantropical diaspora of domesticates that took place during the sixteenth and seventeenth centuries. In present-day Java, for instance, three of the four most important carbohydrate staples—manioc, maize, and sweet potato—are of New World origin. In much of Mesoamerica, three Eurasian staples—wheat, rice, and banana—have come to be of primary importance, and the entire region derives the bulk of its animal protein from Old World chickens, cows, and pigs. It also seems likely that much intrahemispheric diffusion occurred simultaneously with the more famous transoceanic movements of plants and animals. An effort clearly must be made to separate post-European introductions from the foodstuffs which were available to ancient farmers in each of the four areas.

Crops and Livestock at Tikal

With regard to the Maya area, much of the work has already been done. In spite of continuing disagreement over certain aspects of the Maya plant and animal economy (e.g., the importance of manioc—see Cowgill 1971 and Renvoize 1972), a broad censensus has now been reached among specialists (Lundell 1938; Netting 1977; Pickersgill and Heiser 1977). The lowland Maya possessed maize, manioc, ramon, sweet potato, *Xanthosoma, Phaseolus,* and a variety of other plants (like *Canna edulis,* the corozo palm, and several amaranths and chenopods) that are not known to have been widely utilized but that were capable of development into productive staple crops. On the other hand, the Maya were rather less well supplied with domesticated sources of animal protein. Their only farm animals were the stingless bee, the dog, and possibly the ocellated turkey. Otherwise, they were forced to depend on fishing in the coastal areas (Lange 1971) and on the not-inconsiderable returns from hunting (Pohl 1974).

Old World Crops and Livestock

Research along similar lines is much less advanced in Old World tropical regions. On the next few pages I have attempted a preliminary sketch of the situation. Not all possible sources have been used, however. Inscriptions and monumental reliefs contain many data that have still to be gathered and collated. Historical linguists are now making substantial progress in isolating plant and animal names that date to the breakup of the various major language groups of South and Southeast Asia (for Austronesian, see Blust 1976; for Austroasiatic, see Zide and Zide 1972). And there are paleobotanical and osteological data that I have not seen, although none from sites as late as Anuradhapura, Angkor, and Prambanan. The archaeologists who have traditionally worked on South and Southeast Asian sites of the historic period have rarely concerned themselves with burned seeds and animal bones.

The lists presented here are therefore somewhat conjectural, with many omissions. On the other hand, we may at least be confident that most of the listed plants and animals are true domesticates. At sites of earlier periods the Southeast and South Asian paleoecologist is plagued by the absence of comparative collections, and so by the impossibility of distinguishing between wild and domestic species, but this particular problem disappears when dealing with sites of the late first and early second millennia A.D. In the literate capitals of the great regional empires, we may validly assume that most of the important food species already had several thousand years of cultivation behind them.

Crops and Livestock at Angkor

Rice was the staple carbohydrate crop of the Khmer. Domesticated *Oryza sativa,* or at least a large-grained and semidomesticated *Oryza* species, was present in the northern part of Northeast Thailand as early as the fourth millennium B.C. (Gorman and Pisit 1976:17–20). A fully domesticated variety appears at several sites close to the Cambodian border in the early first millennium A.D.; at least one of these sites evidences later occupation by Khmer of the Angkorean period (Higham 1973b). Khmer plastic art of the eleventh through thirteenth centuries depicts a grain that is probably rice. And the eyewitness account of Chou Ta-kuan (Pelliot 1951:25) makes it clear that much rice was grown at Angkor, including the highly specialized variety known as "floating rice."

Several species of *Dioscorea,* including the extremely productive *D. alata,* are thought (Burkill 1951; Coursey 1972) to have been domesticated originally somewhere on the Southeast Asian mainland. While of little current importance in Cambodia, the relative drought resistance of yams and their high yields under swidden conditions make them possible staples for the dry and unirrigable forest region that stretches north of Angkor.

Millets (*Setaria italica* and perhaps *Panicum mileaceum*) appear in northern China as early as 4000 B.C. (P.-T. Ho 1977); they are still staples in the hilly regions of southern China (Li 1970) and northern Thailand and Laos (J. E. Spencer 1966:118). Ma Tuan-lin (1883:477) quotes the *History of Sui* as recording that a millet of some kind, possibly *Setaria,* was being grown in Cambodia during the seventh century. Maize and dry rice are now the chief unirrigated staple grains of the country. In earlier times, millets may well have occupied the place of maize; while less high-yielding, they can withstand drier conditions and have a much higher protein content (Gopalan, Rama Sastra, and Balasubramian 1971:139–40).

Taro, *Alocasia* and *Colocasia,* is often seen growing in gardens in present-day Siemreap. Its function seems as much decorative as dietary, and the situation may not have been greatly different during the Angkorean period.

Sago, preeminently a crop of brackish swamplands in southern Southeast Asia, would be out of the question if not for a definite statement by Chou Ta-kuan (Pelliot 1951:11, 129–32) that he saw sago palms (*Metroxylon* spp.?) growing on the moat-surrounded ramparts of Angkor. As the region is abundantly furnished with swamp, it is not impossible that sago, a remarkably productive if labor-demanding starchy staple, might have been important in the ancient Khmer economy.

The situation with regard to ancient Cambodian legumes is unclear. Several Old World varieties—*Pisum, Lens, Cicer, Glycine,* and *Phaseolus mungo*—are now sold in Cambodian markets alongside New World legumes like *Hypogaea* and *Phaseolus vulgaris.* Some must have been extensively utilized in pre-European times, although it is possible that the centrally important *Glycine,* the soybean, is a late introduction from China.

As for sources of animal protein, Higham (1973a: table 3) reports domestic *Bos, Sus,* and *Canis* at Non Nok Tha in Northeast Thailand in strata dating to the third millennium B.C. All three species, together with chickens, horses, and geese, appear in art of the Angkorean period. Modern Cambodia is said to have a comparatively high density of livestock including some that, extraordinarily, are herded in a transhumant pattern (Dumont 1957:128). No matter how large this animal population once was, however, it can have been but a supplement to the 100,000 metric tons of fish harvestable annually from the waters of the Great Lake (Chevey and Le Poulain 1940:47).

Crops and Livestock at Anuradhapura

As in the case of Angkor, there is little doubt that rice was the main irrigated crop and the main carbohydrate food source at Anuradhapura. While *Oryza sativa* has not yet been found anywhere in South Asia at sites much earlier than 2000 B.C. (Vishnu-Mittre 1977), it had unquestionably penetrated to the part of India closest to Sri Lanka well before the beginning of the Christian era. It occurs at Iron Age sites in Tamilnadu (Allchin 1969:325), where it is associated with black-on-red pottery similar to that found in the deepest strata at Gedige in Anuradhapura (Deraniyagala 1972).

Millets are currently the second most important carbohydrate crop of Sri Lanka and the most important to be grown in swiddens or chena fields. *Eleusine coracana* dominates the wet-season chenas of the Anuradhapura area and *Panicum mileaceum* the dry-season chenas; five other millet species are also grown (Senewiratne and

Appadurai 1966:125–44). *Eleusine* occurs at Hallur in central southern India in strata dated 3800—3500 B.P. (Vishnu-Mittre 1977) and was observed growing near Anuradhapura by Knox (1966:313) in the seventeenth century.

Yams, *Dioscorea alata* and *D. esculenta,* are at present eaten in Sri Lanka as curries rather than as bulk starch foods. Nonetheless, they exist there in great variety (Senewiratne and Appadurai 1966 list more than forty), grow in all parts of the island, and would seem on this evidence to be old. Their importance may have been much greater before the introduction of competing root crops like manioc, sweet potato, and white potato.

Coconuts are now a major cash crop of the coastal plain of the Wet Zone and are eaten in one form or another by all Sri Lankans. However, Tennent (1859:436) thought in his day that they were a recent introduction. If the ancient Anuradhapurans had no coconuts, they would have had to depend for fats on sesame (a common swidden crop in Sri Lanka) and butter.

Major field legumes, all eaten in dhal-like preparations, include *Vigna catiang, Cajanus cajan, Glycine max, Phaseolus mungo, P. aureus, Cicer arietinum,* and *Lens esculentum,* as well as several others (*Pisum, Dolichos, Vicia, Lathyrus*) of lesser popularity. All of these except *Glycine* were probably available to early farmers in the Anuradhapura area. About half of them were originally domesticated in South Asia, which possesses the largest and most environmentally diversified inventory of leguminous crops of any comparably sized part of the world.

Cattle and water buffalo appear quite often in art of the Anuradhapura period. To orthodox Hindus and many Buddhists these would be important mainly for traction and for dairy products. However, it is not certain that all Anuradhapurans were so orthodox. An archaeological team of which I was a member found numerous animal bones, many showing marks of cutting and burning, in Rouletted Ware–period strata at Kantarodai at the far northern end of Sri Lanka. These utilized species include bovids (probably both cattle and buffalo), a goat- or deer-sized ruminant, and many pigs. Because Deraniyagala (1972) found a closely related ceramic assemblage at Anuradhapura in strata just predating the major constructional phases there, it seems quite possible that some early Anuradhapurans shared the carnivorous habits of their contemporaries at Kantarodai.

Crops and Livestock at Prambanan

So dominant is rice in the modern Central Javanese landscape that its presence during the eighth and ninth centuries would be unquestioned but for the apparent fact that the frontier between wet rice and the Melanesian root-crop complex has been moving steadily eastward through Indonesia for many centuries. On this basis, J. E. Spencer (1963) has argued that rice is recent even in western Indonesia, perhaps too recent to have been a major staple for the Javenese of the Classical period. This thesis is contradicted, however, by the inscriptional evidence, where words referring to rice and rice paddies appear frequently (J. Wisseman, personal communication). Moreover, rice-chaff impressions have been found in bricks from Ratu Boko and Candi Perot, eighth- to ninth-century sites on the southern edge of the Prambanan complex.

That millet was an important crop during the heyday of Prambanan is a tradition among Java specialists based apparently on representations of a foodstuff (perhaps a grain) composed of spherical, seedlike units on reliefs at Borobudur and Loro Jonggrang, and on an etymology that derives the name *Java* from a word meaning *millet.* Hard evidence is scarce, however. A millet of some kind, probably *Setaria, Panicum,* or *Eleusine,* is still seen growing in small quantities in several parts of Java and Sumatra and was until recently called *jagung,* a name now used exclusively for maize. In premaize times any of several millets may have been grown in permanent and shifting dry fields. *Coix lachrymajobi* is a particularly interesting possibility in this regard. Grown throughout Southeast Asia for the ornamental uses of its seeds, it is a possible local domesticate (Jain and Banerjee 1974) and is thought once to have had some dietary importance (Burkill 1966:638–39).

Several yams (*Dioscorea alata, D. bulbifera, D. esculenta,* and *D. pentaphylla*) are cultivated in moderate quantities in modern Java. Their great importance in Melanesia and New Guinea suggests that they may have played a greater role in Javanese agriculture before the introduction of the New World roots. The terms *uwi* and *mūlaphala,* not uncommon in Old Javanese inscriptions (J. Wisseman, personal communication), probably both refer to *Dioscorea* species.

Taros (*Colocasia* and the introduced *Xanthosoma*) are omnipresent in the contemporary Javanese landscape, growing in gardens, banana groves, marshy patches, and along the bunds of rice paddies. *Colocasia* appears in inscriptions under the names *tales* and *keladi* (J. Wisseman, personal communication), and is often planted as an irrigated field crop in Melanesia and Polynesia. Several authorities have suggested that the paddy method of irrigation was originally developed for the growing of taro and only later adapted to rice.

Sago is not now grown in southern Central Java, but extensive areas of suitably marshy soils formerly existed near Demak on the north coast. Sago palms are said to grow wild in dense stands within the forest reserve at the western extremity of the island.

Several other starchy tree crops are raised near Prambanan and are thought to be old there, including jackfruit (*Artocarpus communis*), breadfruit (*A. integra*), coconut, banana, and canary nut (*Kanarium spp.*). All are productive, serving as staple carbohydrate food sources elsewhere in Indonesia and the Pacific.

Little information exists on legumes in ancient Java. A bewildering variety are eaten there nowadays, and some are certainly old. The epigraphers know of two ancient terms which refer to legumes, the generic *kacang* and *hartak,* perhaps *Phaseolus aureus* (J. Wisseman, personal communication). On the other hand, neither of the two main protein staples of the modern Javanese diet, the peanut and the soybean, were available there in antiquity.

Cattle, buffalo, chickens, pigs, and horses all appear in reliefs on monuments of the Central Javanese period, while contemporary inscriptions add goats and ducks to the list. A distinctive subspecies of modern cow, the humpless type with white leggings characteristic of Bali and eastern Java, appears to have been locally domesticated from the wild banteng, *Bos "sondaicus."* The extraordinary dates being obtained for the presence of pigs in New Guinea (Bulmer 1975) indicate that pig tamers, if not pig breeders, were passing through Indonesia as early as 10,000 B.C.

Irrigation

All three Asian sites are at present furnished with elaborate systems of reservoirs, canals, sluices, and irrigated fields. In this they differ markedly from most sites in the Maya area.

Irrigation at Tikal

That the Maya knew about true irrigation, the provision of an artificial water supply for fields, is no longer open to serious question. Modern Chorti do a good deal of irrigating (Wisdom 1940:53–54); given the apparent suitability of their environment for irrigation, we need not assume that this is entirely a Hispanic innovation. Matheny (1976, chap. 10 above) has recently discovered a moderately extensive system involving water distribution (rather than simple drainage) at Edzna in Campeche. And portions of at least one minor distribution network, utilizing a deepened natural gully, a diversion sluice of complex design, and several channels spreading out in a downslope direction, have been found at Tikal itself (in 1966—Bronson, unpublished Tikal Project field notes). On the other hand, no evidence has as yet appeared for any Maya system of water control so large as to require state management. While the ridged and raised fields of Campeche, Quintana Roo, and perhaps of the central Peten (Harrison 1975) covered large areas of land, central coordination of such drainage systems as these seems unnecessary and even improbable. Lacking focal reservoirs and dendritic canal layouts, the drainage systems had no key points that could be controlled by a despotically minded government, and their construction and management cannot have necessitated coordination beyond the local level.

Irrigation at Prambanan

Early Java must have been more dependent on hydraulic agriculture than the early Peten. About 75 percent of the nonresidential land near Prambanan is now under irrigation. The canals and small dams currently in use are not older than the late colonial period, having been built by the Dutch in an effort to facilitate the distribution of water to fields producing export crops. The precolonial system cannot, however, have been greatly different as regards scale; given the hydrology and topography of the Otak-Dengkeng plain, it is unnecessary and impractical to construct canals longer than a few kilometers or to coordinate water use over an area greater than a few hundred hectares. Inscriptions of the Central Javanese kingdom show little evidence of governmental interest in water works. That such interest would not have been needed can be inferred from the example of modern Bali, where nonstate *subak* irrigation societies (Geertz 1959:995) build and maintain systems a good deal larger than any that can have existed in the neighborhood of ancient Prambanan.

Irrigation at Angkor

By contrast, Angkorean irrigation was structurally centralized and involved the building of very large canals and reservoirs—in fact, the two biggest reservoirs at Angkor each covered an area greater than the 25 square kilometers included on the Carr and Hazard map of Tikal. The capacity of this system, however, is not altogether clear. Some authorities have suggested that it was very great (e.g., Goloubew 1941; Groslier 1958:107–21). D. G. E. Hall (1968:133–34) understands Groslier to say that the total irrigated area reached five million hectares, from which three or even four crops were harvested each year.

This is an exaggeration. The total usable capacity of the reservoirs at Angkor, vast though they are, comes to little more than 100 million cubic meters. If one sets the duty of water for a single dry-season crop at an economical 1.5 hectare meters (the Sri Lankan standard—see "Agricola" 1965:187) or 15,000 cubic meters per hectare, and if one assumes unrealistically that all of the stored water could be delivered to the fields without loss, one still finds that the total Angkorean system could irrigate only about 6,700 hecares for long enough to grow a single four-month crop. In order to irrigate one wet-season and two dry-season crops on five million hectares of paddies, Angkor would have required, at a minimum, two thousand times its actual water storage capacity. To need that much food, incidentally, Angkor would have had to have a population several times that of the whole of modern Cambodia.

The actual capabilities of the system were undoubtedly more modest. Triple- and quadruple-cropping (the datum derives from Chou Ta-kuan's account—Pelliot 1951:24), although technically feasible with very fast-growing rice varieties, cannot have been at all common and may have been confined to leafy vegetables and other market garden products. Moreover, even double-cropping must have been limited to farms very near the city. The 3,000-hectare area of central Angkor itself would have consumed much of the available water. The amount left over was not enough to accomplish more than to keep the transportation canals full and to irrigate some of the fields and gardens in the suburbs.

There is in fact reason to believe that the bulk of Angkor's rice supply came from fields irrigated by less capital-intensive methods, that is, by natural flooding and by direct rainfall. The ten-kilometer-wide strip of land separating the Angkor complex from the Great Lake is mostly floodplain, annually inundated by water backing up the Tonle Sap from the Himalaya-fed Mekong. The inner fringe of the lake floods deeply and is uncultivable, being covered with a mangrovelike freshwater swamp forest (Legris and Blasco 1972:132). The land several kilometers back from the edge, where the high-water level does not exceed two or three meters, is planted in floating rice (Division d'Agronomie 1972:5; for its ancient presence there see Pelliot 1951:25). Ordinary rice is grown in areas still farther back, sometimes protected from the crest of the flood by dikes and embankments. The total of flood-irrigated land seems at present to be much greater than the total of canal-irrigated land. In ancient times, it must have supplied a large proportion of the rice grown near Angkor.

We need not assume, however, that Angkor was fed entirely or even chiefly by ricefields in its immediate neighborhood. As indicated earlier, the areas around Battambang in the west and around Phnom Penh in the southeast are currently the granaries of the country, responsible for almost all of the rice which, until recently, formed Cambodia's chief export. According to Nuttonson (1963:38), the majority of the paddies in the latter area are still "irrigated" by the rainwater that falls directly into them. The productivity of these paddies seems to be due to a consistent use of labor-minimizing methods of wet rice growing, such as broadcasting (whose efficiency is detailed by Hanks 1972:58–64) rather than transplanting, and avoiding the construction of canals.

Needless to say, this "extensive" system of wet rice agriculture was available to the ancient Angkoreans. It would have enabled the government to increase enormously the output of food on short notice and with a minimal commitment of labor and capital.

Irrigation at Anuradhapura

Any city located in the Dry Zone of Sri Lanka would, in the abstract, seem likely to have been more dependent on large-scale irrigation than a center of similar size in central Java or central Cambodia. Nowhere near Anuradhapura are there water routes which, as at Angkor, could enable the city to subsist on provisions coming from other regions. And the Dry Zone environment made it difficult for Anuradhapura, unlike Prambanan, to depend on local farms for food unless a substantial investment was first made in water supply facilities.

The actual irrigation system fulfills these hypothetical expectations. It is larger than the system at Angkor and dwarfs whatever systems once existed at Prambanan and Tikal. A single reservoir in the ancient network, the Kala Wewa (data from Brohier 1934:4–17), was partially reconditioned in the 1890s by the British, who chose to limit the spillway heights to seven meters even though the surviving embankments of the reservoir are almost three times as high. In its present reduced condition the Kala Wewa covers an area of 1,700 hectares and contains about 60 million cubic meters of water—twice the capacity of the East Baray, the largest reservoir at Angkor. Sources quoted by Brohier (1934:6) estimate, incredibly, that the Kala Wewa once measured forty miles in circumference, meaning a capacity of several billion cubic meters. While such extreme guesses must be taken with several grains of salt, we cannot doubt that the ancient system was of great size and constructed with consummate skill. It is a famous fact that the Yodi-ela, the 87-kilometer-long canal that crosses a watershed in connecting the Kala Wewa with Anuradhapura, was laid out so carefully that its gradient, for the whole of its length, did not vary more than a few inches in each mile.

Even Anuradhapura, however, cannot have depended entirely on large-scale hydraulic farming. The limits imposed by scanty runoff have been discussed previously: no matter how massive and sophisticated the system, there was simply not enough water for it to have irrigated more than a few thousand hectares during the dry season. During the rainy season, of course, the total of irrigable land was much greater, but that was when the massive system was not all that necessary. An annual precipitation of 1,400–1,500 millimeters concentrated in the growing season is quite adequate for a single crop of wet rice, provided that the farmer has access to a very modest system of catchment reservoirs and distribution canals. Such, indeed, is the method used in several thousand villages scattered over the Dry Zone in present-day Sri Lanka.

The average village reservoir covers a few hectares and is maintained and regulated by the villagers themselves (see, e.g., Leach 1961).

It would seem, then, that the main purpose of the large-scale irrigation facilities at Anuradhapura was to ensure a steady supply of water to a relatively small area in the immediate neighborhood of the capital. This quantity of water made it possible to raise dry season crops on, at a maximum, 5,000 hectares of rice paddies. The extra food thus produced was sufficient for the needs of several tens of thousands of people and may well have been critical to the survival of Anuradhapura as an administrative and commercial center. It did not, on the other hand, greatly affect the carrying capacity of the rest of northern Sri Lanka. Most of the population of the hinterland of Anuradhapura undoubtedly subsisted, like their descendants in the same area, on a combination of small-scale irrigation, gardening, and shifting agriculture.

Swidden Cultivation

At none of the four sites was irrigated farming the only means of livelihood. As will presently be shown, all used a variety of intensive infield techniques. And all combined these intensive methods with the use of swiddens, of fallow-fertilized and often extensive outfields.

Swidden Cultivation at Tikal

The literature on Maya swiddening is large and need not be reviewed here, but several salient facts need underlining. First, no good, detailed studies exist of shifting cultivation by Mayas in places ecologically similar to Tikal. Second, many of the Maya agricultural regimes thus far studied belong to groups with low population densities and highly market-oriented economies. And third, no contemporary Maya regime shows nearly the level of land-use efficiency and environmental sophistication that is attained by some swiddeners in other tropical areas—for instance in Mindoro (Conklin 1957) and in New Guinea (Hogbin 1938). Several of the documented Maya systems are, in fact, unusually extensive in terms of the land farmed to obtain a single crop. As

Steggerda (1941:91–111) indicates, single-family fields in dry northern Yucatan often cover several hectares, are planted with a simple mixture of crops, and receive a very low input of labor per unit of planted area. Such a system is quite inappropriate for a well-populated moist environment like that of central Peten, which causes one to doubt that ancient swiddening at Tikal much resembled the modern swiddening of Yucatan.

Swidden Cultivation at Prambanan

Of the four areas under discussion, central Java may have been the one where shifting cultivation was least important. The Dengkeng-Otak plain has resources of fertile and easily irrigable land sufficient to have fed an ancient population of almost any size by means of the present combination of houseyard gardening and wet ricefields. One might, of course, argue that the earliest farmers in the area were swiddeners and that therefore shifting cultivation should have survived in the less populated parts of the plain until well after the time Prambanan declined. Such a contention would be based on the twin assumptions that swiddening is in general earlier than wet rice farming and that, as several specialists have contended (Boserup 1965), swiddening is usually preferred by farmers where populations are not yet so dense as to enforce a more labor-demanding mode of land use.

Wet rice, however, is not necessarily later than dry rice. Burkill (1966:1622) thought it was; Bartlett (1962) and Gorman (1974) have maintained that, to the contrary, the first rices taken into cultivation were those already adapted to marshy habitats. Moreover, few kinds of swiddening are more labor-efficient than wet-rice agriculture. I have presented evidence (Bronson 1972) showing that a wide variety of wet-rice systems are outstandingly efficient in terms of productivity per man-day. Comprehensive data collected by Hanks (1972:58–64) indicate that in central Thailand, even with equipment and other capital costs included, transplanted wet rice is half again as labor-efficient as swidden-grown dry rice; broadcast wet rice is more than twice as labor-efficient.

It would seem, then, that the inhabitants of Prambanan had little reason to abandon their irrigated fields and to begin swiddening in forested parts of the region. Ladang or shifting cultivation is rarely practiced in Java at present. In those portions of other Indonesian islands where wet rice is grown in the valleys and swiddens are cut on the hillsides, the latter are often planted in cash rather than subsistence crops: in coffee, cinnamon, rubber, pepper, or cloves. A similar pattern may have existed in early Java, where the moderately important class of land that the inscriptions call *gāga*—either shifting or permanent dry fields—seems to have produced market crops like pepper and cotton (Wisseman, personal communication). Whether the proprietors of these *gāga* fields subsisted on carbohydrate foods grown in them may have depended on their proximity to irrigable areas. Those in remote locations could have lived on dry-farmed rice, yams, and millets. Those close to irrigable places could have possessed both kinds of fields, growing wet rice and dry cash crops in the same fashion as many present-day Sumatrans and Sinhalese.

Swidden Cultivation at Angkor

In spite of its highly developed hydraulic system and its access to large areas where low-cost irrigation was possible, Angkor may have been more dependent on shifting cultivation than Prambanan. Fallow-fertilized dry-farming techniques seem the only possible way to grow food on the poor, unirrigable soils of the northern part of Cambodia. C. A. Fisher (1964:82) has suggested that as late as the fifteenth century shifting tillage provided much of the food consumed at Angkor. The forests of the northern half of Cambodia show evidence of extensive and long-continued disturbance in antiquity—just as concentrations of ramon (*Brosimum alicastrum*) seem to indicate foci of early Maya agricultural activity (Lundell 1938:38), so the presence of numerous wild litchi trees (*Nephelium litchi*) is thought to be a relic of extensive forest farming by the ancient Khmer (Legris and Blasco 1972:110–11).

A major difficulty in assessing the capabilities of early Khmer swiddening is the comparative rarity of the practice in modern Cambodia, where the population density is still far below the point where a shortage of rice land might drive large numbers of farmers into the forested regions. J. E. Spencer (1966:1974) estimates that the country contains no more than 2,000 families who live mainly by shifting cultivation, and one imagines that the majority of these live in the hilly high-rainfall areas to the southwest and in the mountains close to the Vietnamese-Cambodian border. The non-Khmer swiddeners of the latter area, judging by reports on related groups living on the Vietnamese side of the border (e.g., Condominas 1957), are not strikingly capable farmers. However, the border Montagnards should not be taken as models for the early farming groups that once inhabited the area north of Angkor. As stated earlier, the latter had a number of productive crops available to them. They may have produced a sufficient surplus of food so that some of it reached urban markets, or they may have concentrated on nonstaple export crops. The latter choice is suggested by a statement by Chou Ta-kuan (Pelliot 1951:20) that the "savages" in the hinterland of Angkor supplied its export markets with cardamom. The various cardamom-producing *Amomum* species are usually grown in swiddens.

Swidden Cultivation at Anuradhapura

The probable role of swiddening in early northern Sri Lanka can be reconstructed in greater detail. It was important, accounting for perhaps one-third of the carbohydrate food produced locally. But it was the exclusive occupation of only a handful of farmers.

Modern villagers in the Dry Zone regularly cultivate three kinds of land: wet ricefields, houseyard gardens, and swiddens or chena fields (Farmer 1957; Leach 1961). Few individuals lack access to a small expanse of rice paddy, and many can raise enough in their paddies and gardens to meet their basic nutritional needs. Nonetheless, most households clear chenas as well, for these provide cash income and an important reserve of food against times of scarcity. The millets which form the chief chena-grown carbohydrate crop are not considered palatable food by most urbanized Sri Lankans, suggesting that some farmers may choose to eat what they produce in their swiddens and to sell their paddy-grown rice on the market.

That a similar pattern of mixed regimes existed in ancient Sri Lanka seems highly probable. The presence of numerous small and widely dispersed ancient reservoirs (Sarkar 1957: fig. 3) indicates that early villages, like modern ones, were far enough apart to have ready access to a circle of forested land around each irrigated nucleus. Knox's (1966:294–329) description of the landscape near "Amoragdburro" confirms that swiddening (with fallow periods long enough to permit substantial forest regrowth) was commonly combined with wet rice farming during the seventeenth century; he even says that some of the swiddens were planted in "corracan" or *Eleusine.*

What this amounts to is an "infield-outfield" system, where the permanently cultivated core of each village is irrigated, rather than simply fertilized by household wastes and animal droppings as in the classic European infield-outfield regimes (McCourt 1955). In Conklin's (1957:2) terminology, the early Sri Lankans would have been "partial" rather than "integral" swiddeners, with few of them willing or able, unlike the peoples of remoter parts of tropical Asia, to subsist entirely from shifting, dry-farmed fields. Partial swiddening is in fact an expectable and even usual phenomenon in places where irrigable soil exists and where the farmers are within the economic and cultural sphere of one of the great lowland Asian civilizations. It was suggested earlier that a similar mixture of regimes may have existed near Prambanan and Angkor. One would not be surprised to find something of the sort at certain early New World sites.

Other Techniques and Field Systems

Whereas irrigation and shifting cultivation are both found as integral systems in some places, the methods reviewed in this section are intrinsically partial and supplementary. Some are techniques that serve to extend the capabilities of irrigation- or swidden-based systems. Some are independent complexes of techniques which, although they qualify as systems in their own right, are supplementary rather than dominant in the economies of the places where they are used.

Inter-cropping and Multi-cropping

The virtues of inter-cropping in tropical climates, usually expressed in terms of the protection afforded to the soil by a mixture of crops growing in a single field, have been too often discussed to need comment here. I might point out, however, that inter-cropped main fields which have such "tightly woven, dense botanical fabrics" that they constitute "miniature tropical forests" (Geertz 1963:24–25) are an ideal type rarely encountered except among small and isolated groups like the Hanunoo (Conklin 1957) and the Wogeo (Hogbin 1938). The great majority of the inter-cropped fields one sees tend to wear a much more open aspect, with numerous patches of soil exposed to the sun and rain.

This is true of most of the main-field inter-cropping done in the four areas under discussion: not even in Java and the Maya area, where farmers seem especially interested in inter-cropping, is one likely to mistake a producing main field for forest, and in many cases the mixed plantings seem no more protective of the soil then would a tighly spaced single crop. One suspects that the motives behind inter-cropping often have little to do with an appreciation of the virtues of soil conservation. Judging from personal observation in Java, many farmers choose to inter-crop because they expect some of the plants to be destroyed by drought or insects before harvest, or simply because they want to raise two kinds of food and have only one field. This is not to say that the practice is not desirable from an agronomic standpoint or that, when practiced on a restricted scale in houseyard gardens, it cannot form part of an immensely productive system. Yet very few farmers use it to its full potential, probably including the farmers under discussion here.

The reason why multi-cropping is rare has more to do with environmental possibility than failure, on the part of tax collectors at least, to appreciate its virtues. Java is at present the only one of the four areas where the majority of fields produce more than one crop annually and the only one where this can have been done regularly in antiquity; its soils and water supply are better than in the other areas, and with rice it possessed a suitably quick-maturing crop. Angkor and Anuradhapura were limited by their long dry seasons. As stated earlier, neither could manage to irrigate more than a small percentage of its fields during the dry parts of the year. More possibilities were open to Tikal from a climatic point of view. If it had possessed a staple crop that matured more rapidly than maize, it could undoubtedly have produced two crops each year in spots where the soils were sufficiently fertile, assuming that its farmers had the proper demographic or administrative incentive.

Raised Fields and Terraces

The distribution of raised fields in the New World has been traced by J. Parsons and Denevan (1967) and in the Old World by Denevan and Turner (1974). Agricultural terracing in Asia has been studied by J. E. Spencer and Hale (1961) and Spencer (1964) and in the Maya area by Guzmán (1962) and Turner (1974a). Although both can make a substantial contribution to the food-producing capacity of an area, terraces and raised fields are not so much systems as they are techniques for bringing certain kinds of difficult land temporarily or permanently into cultivation. Except when combined with retaining walls, heavy fertilizing, or complex methods of water control, neither is intrinsically labor-demanding. Constructing low mounds or cutting steps into a hillside with a heavy hoe, as is commonly done by farmers of all kinds in Asia, seems to this observer to be little more work than hoeing up a field of similar size on level, well-drained ground.

Wet rice farming automatically involves a certain amount of terracing, just as any attempt to raise ordinary crops in water-logged soils will involve mounding and field raising. To this extent we may be sure that the techniques were used by farmers in all three Asian areas. However, we cannot be certain that either they or the central Maya built field ridges or terraces on a truly large scale. The land near Prambanan and Anuradhapura is uneven enough to require terraces almost everywhere, but these cannot be compared to the vast stone-revetted mountain fields of southern China and the northern Philippines. Terraces in Java and Sri Lanka are simply steps, more or less shallow, cut into sloping land surfaces; modern farmers at Prambanan do not consider that making the terraces takes more than a small fraction of the time spent in raising a crop. The land around Angkor is nearly flat. At Tikal, agricultural terracing would appear to have been minimal.

Ridges systematically laid out in rice paddies are a common feature of low-lying areas in southern central Java; however, these are temporary and usually of minor importance, serving mainly as an expedient for growing small numbers of roots and other crops in flooded ricefields. In Sri Lanka and central Cambodia, the agricultural field raising one sees tends to be small and dispersed: casual earthpiles under fruit trees, ridges planted with bananas, turmeric, and taro, or complexly arranged networks of lands and channels in suburban market gardens. The floodplain at Angkor would seem to offer an opportunity for developing a major system of raised fields, but thus far no trace of one has been reported. Harrison (1977) and Dahlin (1976b) have reviewed the evidence for large systems of raised or ridged fields in the *bajos* near Tikal. The evidence is suggestive but not yet compelling. The *bajo* soils of the central Peten are less fertile than the soils of those places where Maya ridged fields are known to have been highly developed (e.g., Belize, Quintana Roo, and Campeche—see Siemens and Puleston 1972 and Harrison 1975). Without a "self-fertilizing" crop like rice or an abundant supply of animal manure, cultivating the Tikal *bajos* may have been too unproductive to be worth the trouble.

Infield Gardens

Small fields in and adjacent to settlements, fertilized by domestic refuse and thus permanently cultivable, constitute a distinct type of field system rather than a technique. They are widespread in the tropics (see, e.g., J. E. Spencer 1966:147–48) and are more likely than main fields to be so closely inter-cropped that they resemble natural forest. Trees are an almost universal component of such gardens, and a sufficient variety of low and shrubby crops is often planted to fill quite densely the vertical space between the ground and the tops of the trees.

By and large, infield gardens are supplementary to other field types, although as in modern Nigeria (Netting 1977) they may be expanded to provide the bulk of a family's nutritional needs. Terra (1954) cites data showing the great nutritional efficiency of infield gardens in Java: they produce half again as many calories per hectare as rice paddies. In the district studied by Terra, they provided one-third of the food each family consumed.

Comparable data for other areas are hard to obtain. From personal observation I would judge that the modern Khmer are more casual than the Javanese in their gardening. They grow a few tall trees, some bananas, some condiments, and a few leafy vegetables, but these cannot account for more than a small percentage of the average farmer's yearly diet. Near Anuradhapura, infield gardens are universal and midway in importance between those of Java and of Cambodia. Located where the soil is permanently moist from reservoir seepage, these *gamgoda* (Farmer

1957:26–27; Leach 1961:97–100) are devoted largely to shade-adapted ground crops such as taro, yams, and turmeric, and to tree crops, including jackfruit, coconut, and bananas. None of the gardens of the Anuradhapura area are as elaborate as the superb infield and market gardens of the Jaffna area at the northern tip of Sri Lanka, where dozens of crops are routinely inter-planted and where careful plant-by-plant irrigation makes continuous production possible in spite of an eight-month dry season.

Modern infield gardens are least important in the central Maya lowlands. Houses in the vicinity of Lake Peten often have only a scattering of useful plants growing near them. In Yucatan, gardens are more developed (Hester 1954:95) but still not comparable to those of Sri Lanka and Java. While I believe that some Maya groups in lowland Chiapas and Belize do a good deal of gardening, we clearly cannot use modern data to assess the potential importance of complexly planted infields to the economy of ancient Tikal. Netting (1977) suggests that a possible model can be found in the intricate gardens of Nicoya in Costa Rica. A system like that of the Nicoyans or the Javanese might have made a substantial contribution to the Maya diet. It might also have helped to buffer an early urban economy in times of scarcity when, as will presently be shown, centers like Tikal must have found it especially difficult to depend on provisions brought in from places where the shortage was less severe.

CONCLUSION: THE SUBSISTENCE OF TROPICAL CITIES

The Tropics and Ancient Urbanization

The introduction to this paper has already touched on the persistently popular notion that tropical soils and climates are intrinsically hostile to the development of urban society. Considered in the aggregate, tropical areas may indeed, as J.-H. Chang (1968) argues, be slightly inferior to higher latitudes in terms of several environmental factors that affect food production: net photosynthetic energy, for instance, or perhaps overall soil quality. However, the aggregate of all tropical environments is not to the point. Many parts of the humid tropics have environments that are less unmanageable than the environments of temperate and desert areas that formerly supported major ancient states and cities. No one who has visited both central Java and southern Mesopotamia will argue that the soils and climate of the latter are superior from the standpoint of intrinsic demographic capacity.

Without question, an appreciable difference in this respect exists among different parts of the tropics. Yet it is difficult to pin down any individual environmental factor in those places which was critical to early social and economic development. Mohr (1945) and Sanchez and Buol (1975) assert convincingly that the density of modern tropical populations is strongly correlated with soil fertility, but in the premodern period one finds few clear-cut illustrations of this rule. Of the centers in our sample, only Prambanan has soils that greatly exceed the average in terms of agricultural quality. Angkor, one of the largest and longest-lasting of all early tropical cities, has soils that are actually poor. Even if the inquiry is extended to include every tropical area that anciently supported cities or substantial populations, few can be found that have notably good soils, and few areas where soils are good (Kenya, northern Sumatra, Assam) can be shown to have been important centers of early socioeconomic development.

The relationship of tropical climate with population is less random but not much more useful if one wishes to explain ancient socioeconomic and demographic differences. All four of the centers under consideration are located in areas of deciduous monsoon forest with significantly long dry seasons and a total annual rainfall of 1,450–1,900 millimeters. Since most other early tropical states and cities grew up in similar climates (very few indeed existed in wet evergreen rain forests, while those in drier parts of the tropics tend to be considered "desert" rather than "tropical"), one is tempted to conclude that moist monsoonal climates were necessary to success in tropical state-building. The difficulty is, however, that most of the tropical world has this kind of climate. The association is real but lacks explanatory power.

Comparing the four sites yields another negative conclusion, one that is perhaps surprising: there seems to be no association at all between site location and the spatial distribution of nonagricultural subsistence resources. Angkor is the only one of the four to possess a major resource, the fisheries of the Great Lake, within its immediate hinterland. The others are situated quite far from the nearest concentration of the kinds of biological and geological commodities that are likely to have been important in ancient interlocal and interregional trade. Concentrations of such resources do exist in all four regions—conch and pearl fisheries and gem mines in Sri Lanka; spices, incenses, and resins in Indonesia; spices and metal ores in Thailand and Cambodia; cacao, shells, and obsidian in Mesoamerica—but these tend to be located on or even beyond the boundaries of the economic spheres of the capitals. Moreover, none of the sites is well positioned to control trade to and from these resource concentrations. Although, naturally enough, traders did come to the sites in the days when these were regional capitals, they were not following routes that had to pass that way for any geographical reason. The routes and the traders themselves disappeared from the neighborhoods of the sites as soon as these declined. By the time European observers appeared on the scene, none of the sites was within several days' travel of a major artery of interregional trade.

In short, one has difficulty finding any environmental or geographical attribute that seems to correlate closely with ancient tropical urbanization. The explanation is, I believe, simple. Cities, especially those that serve numerous central functions, are by their nature partly independent of local subsistence environments. Centers like the ones in the sample were foci of political and religious authority that extended over tens of thousands of square kilometers. They served as nuclei of economic networks that integrated even larger regions, often through commercial mechanisms that were highly organized, institutionalized, and even marketized (for early Java, see Wisseman 1977; for early Cambodia, see K. R. Hall 1975:320–23 and Pelliot 1951:27). The watersheds from which taxes, tithes, and commerce flowed were many times the size of the hinterlands of an ordinary settlement. The food supply of an Angkor or Anuradhapura could if necessary be brought in from great distances. Its quantity was limited less by environmental factors than by commercial efficiency and political will.

The history of tropical Asia contains a number of examples showing the virtual independence of such superordinate centers from their local environments. In Thailand, seventeenth-century Ayutthaya is thought on good evidence (Sternstein 1965:93–95, 1966:229) to have held upwards of two hundred thousand people, or between 5 and 10 percent of the entire thinly settled region under its control. The Thai government, then as now, was willing to mobilize the economy of an enormous area in order for its capital to survive. The Malayan city of Malacca in the fifteenth and sixteenth centuries represents an even more extreme case. According to contemporary sources (e.g., Duarte Barbosa, Ma Huan, and Tome Pirés—Dames 1921:2:178; Mills 1970:108–14; Cortesão 1944:2:107–9), Malacca had a population of several tens of thousands of people and had no local hinterland at all. For more than two centuries it was provisioned entirely by food imported from Burma, Thailand, and Java—places several hundred kilometers distant and outside its political control.

It stands to reason, then, that local soil types and crop yields will not play a great role in determining the location of major urban sites. Such factors will not even affect the continued survival of those sites unless they are assumed to be uniformly and drastically unfavorable over a very large area. Whether region-spanning environmental catastrophes actually did intervene in the histories of the sites under discussion must remain an open question. There is little evidence. And it seems certain that any of the sites, if its government and economy was powerful enough, could have survived in environments much more impoverished than those of the present day.

The Tropics and Maya Urbanization

Two possible a priori objections arise when one begins to make comparisons between the irrigating civilizations of the Asian tropics and the swidden-based society of the Maya. The latter, it might be claimed, is not validly comparable to the former either because it was mainly nonhydraulic or because it failed to advance beyond the "horticultural stage" of subsistence. The first objection implies a belief in the hypothesis that the primary impetus for true state formation was the need for regulation and capitalization involved in building large-scale irrigation systems, with the corollary that peoples practicing little or no irrigation are unlikely to have developed effective and centralized governments. The second objection stems from the idea that some sorts of agriculture are inherently superior to others and so more conducive to the development of civilization. Peoples who practice irrigation, raise grain, use plows, and keep large domestic animals have often been considered *ipso facto* more evolved than swiddeners, hoe or digging-stick cultivators, and tropical horticulturists.

Neither objection need keep us long. The hydraulic hypothesis of Wittfogel has been refuted in elaborate detail over the past three decades (Claessen 1973; Netting 1974:33–34). Moreover, as I have sought to show in the preceding pages, none of the three Asian societies in the sample appears to have been greatly dependent on large-scale irrigation, even though one of them possessed the most elaborate system of canals and reservoirs of any ancient tropical society. The Anuradhapuran kings took a strong interest in irrigation (Nicholls 1959) and undoubtedly used it as an instrument of political control where they could. However, few of their subjects could be thus controlled except those on the outskirts of the capital. The great majority of irrigating Sri Lankans, subsisting as they did on small-scale systems that they built and maintained themselves, could manage well enough without the royal engineers.

The idea that the Maya's main style of farming is inherently inferior seems little more than culture-centric prejudice. Tilling with tools other than plows is widespread in several regions where cultivation is admitted to be "advanced," including Java and China, while plows are dominant in some of the most unproductive farming systems on record—for instance, the dry wheat and barley farming of the Middle East. The northern European mixture of grain cultivating with the keeping of numerous large meat and draft animals is found only in places settled by North Europeans and cannot be considered a superior adaptation in most environments. Even in Europe itself the stock-grain system, except in its most concentrated and labor-consuming form, requires as much land per unit of output as the majority of tropical regimes. Grain crops are not necessarily superior to root and tree crops except in terms of cultural prestige (Bronson 1966). And regimes that depend on fallowing for fertilization are capable of impressively high levels of productivity, land-use efficiency, and environmental balance. Good farmers exist in the tropics as well as bad ones, and sweeping characterizations of them are inherently suspect. They often reveal a quite baseless pride in the plow-using, grain-growing, stock-breeding, and sometimes irrigating farm systems of the characterizers.

If such aprioristic problems as these are laid aside, we find that three main issues are raised by the comparison of urban subsistence systems in the Asian and Mesoamerican tropics: the possible superiority of wet rice over dry maize, the possible inferiority of the Maya system with regard to protein supply, and the probable effects of the limited capacity of the Maya for logistics.

Whether or not irrigation predisposes to despotism, it cannot be doubted that rice-based irrigation was desirable from the standpoint of the rulers of an ancient state. It rendered farmers immobile and easy to find when tax-collecting time arrived. And it was astonishingly efficient in terms of the land and labor needed to produce a given quantity of food—perhaps more efficient in these respects than any other preindustrial farming method (for example, see data cited in Bronson 1972:192–93). In terms of sheer long-term caloric productivity the ancient Maya had nothing to equal it.

My own inclination, however, is not to see this as a decisive disadvantage for the Maya vis-à-vis their Asian counterparts. Much of the food of the ancient Sri Lankans, and perhaps of the Khmer as well, came from fields other than rice paddies, just as the Maya possessed several field systems more productive than long-fallowed swiddens. And in dry farming the calorie-producing advantage was with the Maya. Maize has a higher per-acre yield than any of the dry grains formerly grown in the Asian tropics. Ramon is at least as efficient as any of the Old World tree crops and, like wet rice, has the advantage from a political standpoint of obliging those growing it to stay in the same place for substantial periods of time. Further, several of the Maya root crops, notably manioc but also sweet potato and *Xanthosoma,* seem superior to the comparable Asian domesticates. They have succeeded in displacing yams and taro over much of tropical Asia and Africa.

With regard to protein supply the Asian and American tropics are not so evenly matched. At Angkor, the Great Lake was by itself capable of supplying the minimum protein requirements of several million people, assuming a weekly intake of half a kilogram of fish per person and an annual production of 100,000 metric tons. The Javanese and Cambodians both are pisciculturists at present and must have raised at least some fish in special ponds and rice paddies in ancient times. The Javanese, Cambodians, and Sinhalese all kept between five and ten species of ruminant and omnivorous domestic animals, including several that did not have to be killed before they yielded food. All possessed grains that contain more and better-balanced amino acids than does maize. And all had access to a very large number of species of leguminous field crops.

The inland Maya, by contrast, were entirely dependent on one incompletely herbivorous domestic animal, on a protein-poor grain staple, on preserved fish carried in from the distant coast, on such wild animals as could coexist with a dense human population, and on one or possibly two species of legume. The more important of these legumes, *Phaseolus vulgaris,* can equal most of the Asian legumes in productivity and may exceed any in the number of varieties extant and so in the range of environments in which it can be grown. Yet the Maya had only one such species where the Sinhalese had ten. Their great dependence on that one species made them vulnerable. If a major pest or disease of *Phaseolus* had appeared, if this could not have been controlled through burning and dispersing the fields, and if no alternative leguminous crop existed, the interior of Peten might have been rendered uninhabitable.

In terms of logistic capabilities, perhaps the most essential factor of all in maintaining the well-being of cities, the comparison is especially unfavorable to the Maya. It is true that only Angkor among the Asian sites had water transport and thus the ability to draw bulk supplies from very great distances. However, Prambanan and Anuradhapura did both possess wheeled, animal-drawn vehicles, and these made it feasible for those cities to exploit a much larger area for their subsistence than could Tikal.

A striking illustration of what differences in mode of transportation mean with respect to subsistence potential can be obtained by examining the tables of preindustrial transport costs assembled by Clark and Haswell (1970:196–203), expressed not in monetary units but in kilograms of grain per ton-kilometer of transported goods. In table 14.4 these figures are used to calculate the maximum size of the food-supplying hinterlands of centers using three types of transport.

The figures for size of hinterland are calculated using the median per-kilometer costs cited by Clark and Haswell, under the assumption that a very high cost: load ratio, with nine units of food consumed in transit for each unit delivered, might have been acceptable to an ancient government faced with the necessity of feeding a hungry capital. These constants could plausibly be

Table 14.4. Transport Costs and Maximum Hinterland Size for Centers Using Boats, Carts, and Porters.

	Costs in Kg./Ton-Km.			*Hinterland Size at Median Cost Level*	
	max.	*med.*	*min.*	*radius**	*area*
Porter-supplied center	32.7	9.0	2.0	100 km.	31,000 km.^{2}
Cart-supplied center	16.4	3.4	1.2	265 km.	220,000 km.^{2}
Boat-supplied center	5.8	0.9	0.2	1,000 km.	3,100,000 km.^{2}

[* = distance from center to point where cost equals 90% of load]

revised upward or downward, however, without affecting the conclusion I wish to draw. What matters is not the absolute size of the hypothetical hinterlands but their relative size when mode of transport is made the chief variable. All else being equal, it seems safe to say that the exploitable hinterland of a water-supplied center can be expected to be one hundred times as large as the hinterland of a center all of whose provisions must come in on human backs.

Harrison's (1977) and Siemens's (1976) suggestion that the *bajos* of the Peten may once have been navigable is thus seen to have great potential importance. If the suggestion proves incorrect, and if Tikal and the other inland sites of the karstic region are shown to have had no water-borne transport at all, then we will have to conclude that numerous Maya centers operated under a severe and unusual disadvantage. The disadvantage might not have been insuperable given sufficient determination and organizing ability on the part of lcoal governments. Yet nonetheless, viewed from an Asian perspective, it seems the gravest of the subsistence problems that the ancient Maya may have faced.

POSTSCRIPT: FURTHER DATA ON ANCIENT JAVANESE SUBSISTENCE

Several important articles have come to my attention since the above was written. The editors have kindly allowed me to include data derived from these as a postscript.

Ancient Javanese Crops

An extensive list is given by A. Steinmann (1934, "De op de Boroboedoer afgebeelde plantenwereld," in *Tijdschrift van het Bataviaasch Genootschap 74*:581–612) of plants recognizable in reliefs on monuments of the Central Javanese period (seventh to tenth centuries A.D.). These include *Setaria* millet, most of the nonleguminous crops mentioned earlier, and two aroid root crops, *Alocasia* and *Cyrtosperma.* The absence of the third major aroid of the Old World tropics, *Colocasia,* is seen as surprising by Steinmann, especially in view of the frequency of inscriptional references to *tales,* or taro.

Steinmann is also surprised by the scarcity of clearly identifiable growing rice on the reliefs. In this connection it is worth pointing out that I. Glover (1977, "The Late Stone Age in Eastern Indonesia," *World Archaeology* 9:52) believes he has found rice, perhaps domestic, at Ulu Leang in Sulawesi at levels dating to the fourth or fifth millennium B.C.

Job's tear millet, *Coix lachryma-Jobi,* is not mentioned by Steinmann. Glover (1977:43) states, however, that it was found by him at Uai Bobo in Timor in contexts earlier than 5000 B.P. A. C. Kruyt (1934, "De Rijstbouw in Balantak," in *Tijdschrift 74*:125) observes that *Coix* was commonly used as food by the Torajas of central Sulawesi in the early 1900s.

Ancient Javanese Domestic Animals

Several species should be added to the list presented earlier: geese, goats, sheep (both fat-tailed and ordinary), dogs, cats, and perhaps doves and peacocks. These animals have been identified on reliefs in central Java by Steinmann (1934, "De dieren op de basreliefs van Boroboedoer," in *Tijdschrift 74*:101–22) and by S. Kadarsan et al. (1977, "Fauna Asing Pada Relief Candi-Candi di Pulau Jawa," *Majalah Ilmu-Ilmu Sastra Indonesia 7,* 2:1–12).

Ancient Javanese Irrigation

Although speculation exists about the connection between irrigation and the development of the early Javanese kingdoms, no definite reference to governmental involvement in hydraulic projects is known in the surviving inscriptions of the seventh to tenth centuries. Discounting an early Sanskrit inscription from West Java, the first such reference does not appear until the eleventh century and in a place, Kamalagyan, about 200 kilometers from Prambanan. The inscription refers to a dam and states that the farmers, as well as several other groups, were happy that it had been built by the king (see Riboet Darmasoetopo 1976/1977, *Repertoire Onomastique* [Jogjakarta: Lembaga Penelitian Universitas Gajah Mada], pp. 229–230).

Ridged Fields in Modern Java

A brief description of the ridges, or *surjan,* that the Javanese build in rice paddies for raising dry crops simultaneously with wet ones is given by Werner Roll (1974, "Wenig bekannte Formen agrarer Bodennutzung auf Java, Der Surdjan und Gundukan Bau," *Geographische Rundschau* 9:364–69).

15

DAVID R. HARRIS
Department of Geography, University College London

The Agricultural Foundations of Lowland Maya Civilization: A Critique

It is often assumed that Maya civilization is an exception to the rule that humid tropical lowlands were inimical to the rise of complex, urban societies. This assumption stems from a European view of world history that looks on the dry lands of Southwest Asia as the cradle of civilization. It also reflects a persistent misconception of tropical lowlands as monotonous, forested environments of low ecological diversity. Although even the most ardent adherents to the Eurocentric view have come to acknowledge the existence of ancient urban traditions in temperate northern China and in the highlands of Mexico and Peru, there is still a tendency to regard lowland Maya society as an aberrant form of civilization. The supposition that it was atypical also rests on the entrenched assumption that Maya society was supported solely, or principally, by long-fallow swidden cultivation, an assumption that I have previously criticized (Harris 1972:257–59) and one that the other contributors to this book effectively refute. Just as the claim that the Maya represent the world's only swidden-based civilization can now be rejected, so can the idea that civilizations failed to develop in humid tropical lowlands elsewhere. Bronson's deft comparison in this volume of three early urban centers in the Asian tropics with the Maya site of Tikal makes this point emphatically; and the existence of complex Yoruba societies focused on ceremonial centers in southwestern Nigeria (Wheatley 1971:238–40) extends the frame of reference to the African tropics.

To deny Maya civilization its claim to uniqueness means that the scholarly challenge is less to discover the idiosyncratic circumstances in which the ancient Maya created a civilization in the eastern lowlands of Mesoamerica than to look on the Maya experience as one—and currently the most fully investigated—example of a tropical lowland civilization. Specifically, it moves the study of Maya agriculture into a potentially fruitful comparative framework that can be expected to yield new understanding not only of civilizations in the Old World tropics, but, conversely, of how the Maya economy itself functioned.

In evaluating the present state of knowledge of pre-Hispanic Maya agriculture, as represented in this book, my aim is not to give a comprehensive summary but to examine three themes: environmental diversity in the Maya lowlands; Maya systems of food procurement; and the relationship between intensive agriculture and Maya civilization.

ENVIRONMENTAL DIVERSITY IN THE MAYA LOWLANDS

Although geographers, soil scientists, and others have published detailed accounts of the geomorphological and edaphic diversity of the Yucatan Peninsula (for example West 1964:70–73, 93–95, 298–305), only recently have students of lowland Maya civilization begun to pay close attention to environmental variability. The realization that beneath the cloak of forest and scrub vegetation that swathes most of the area lie diverse sets of soils and small-scale relief features that affect agricultural potential has helped to undermine the mistaken impression of environmental uniformity. So has closer attention to the structure and composition of the plant cover itself, although this too had long since been described (for example by Lundell 1934, 1937). Variations in the climate and hydrology of the area are also taking on new significance in studies of Maya subsistence and settlement.

All these trends are represented in the individual contributions to this book. Several authors rightly stress the relationship between spatial variations in soil quality and patterns of settlement, and there is general agreement that there is a close distributional correlation between pre-Hispanic sites and the more fertile soils. Interesting exceptions to this generalization exist, especially in the drier northern third of the Yucatan Peninsula. Here such centers as Dzibilchaltun, Tzeme, and Chunchucmil developed in areas where thin soils and lack of surface water make agriculture so difficult that, as Vlcek, Garza, and Kurjack (chap. 11) show, a site as large as Chunchucmil, with a conservatively estimated Late Classic population of 12,000 strategically located for the exploitation of salt and other coastal resources, was probably sustained by imports of food from more favored farming areas to the east. In his regional reconstruction of agricultural land use in the southern Maya lowlands during the Late Classic period, Turner (chap. 9) adopts the broader analytical framework of physiographic zones. These incorporate characteristics of slope, drainage, and vegetation, as well as of soils, and provide a clear environmental context in which to discuss the evidence for agricultural modifications of the landscape, such as terraces on hill slopes, stone walls on flatlands, and raised fields and canals in valleys and *bajos.*

The question of what former economic role was played by the enclosed, seasonally flooded depressions or *bajos* that are such a prominent feature of the limestone terrain of the southern lowlands is discussed by several contributors. Siemens (chap. 6) provides the essential physiographic dimension for this discussion in his analysis of karstic hydrology and geomorphology, thus helping to fill a conspicuous gap in our appreciation of environmental diversity in the lowlands. His demonstration of the positive relationship that exists between karstic rivers such as the Candelaria, Hondo, and New, with their relatively regular interseasonal flows, and the vestiges of pre-Hispanic canals and raised fields has predictive as well as explanatory value; and his close examination of the topography, hydrology, and vegetation of the *bajos* themselves provides the physical background necessary for informed speculation about their former use. Thus he stresses the importance of natural *aguadas* at low points on the *bajo* floors, some of which were created or extended artificially to provide a water supply that would last through the dry season, as at Uaxactun. The commonly observed concentration of settlement sites at the edges of *bajos* may imply that artificial *aguadas* lined with clay to make them impervious were part of a regular pattern of *bajo* exploitation. Alternatively, as Harrison hypothesizes (1977), many of the *bajos* may, in the Classic period, have been shallow lakes in which intensive agriculture was carried out on raised fields.

This hypothesis, which suffers at present from a lack of positive field evidence, focuses attention on another controversial aspect of the *bajos* to which Puleston and Siemens refer. This is the reported presence in a *bajo* near Tikal of gilgai, or areas of uneven ground with deep cracks caused by seasonal shrinkage and subsidence in the clay soil of the *bajo* floor. Gilgai patterns seen in other parts of the world are sometimes picked out by lines and patches of denser vegetation where more moisture is available along the cracks, and Puleston (chap. 12) argues that the vegetation patterns observed aerially in *bajos* in southern Quintana Roo and northeastern Peten by Harrison, Dahlin, and Siemens may be the result of natural gilgai rather than the relics of ancient raised fields and/or canals. Siemens allows that some of the vegetation patterns that appear on vertical air photographs of Peten *bajos* may be the result of gilgai formation, but until more detailed and extensive field investigation is undertaken, the widespread occurrence of gilgai in the *bajos* cannot be assumed. Indeed, such investigation must be an integral part of the search for improved understanding of the role that the *bajos* played in ancient Maya subsistence.

The significance of variation in the plant communities of the Yucatan Peninsula is acknowledged, implicitly or explicitly, by most contributors. Turner's classification of physiographic zones associates ridge and flank lands with seasonal forest, alluvial valleys and *bajos* with scrub forest and herbaceous vegetation, savannas with grasses on level terrain and trees on low hills, and the ridges of the Maya Mountains in the southeast of the peninsula with a cover of pine, oak, and grass. This classification has the merit of undermining any lingering misconception of the Maya lowlands as covered by undifferentiated tropical forest, but it is, as Turner acknowledges, too general to reveal the high degree of economically significant vegetational diversity that exists on the ground. Wiseman's (chap. 5) description of ten types of vegetation found today near Lake Peten Itza better demonstrates this diversity, even though it excludes riparian and *bajo* communities. Furthermore, by comparing habitat variability in the Maya lowlands and the Sonora desert, he makes the fundamental point that the supposed contrast in ecological diversity—and in resource potential—between the Mesoamerican highlands and the tropical lowlands that is assumed in Rathje's (1971) and Sanders's (1973) models of Maya subsistence is illusory. It could be argued that much of the variation in plant communities observable in the lowlands today is the result of many centuries of human disturbance of the vegetation. This probably has led to the replacement of forest by savannas over extensive areas, and to the creation of other unstable communities of pioneer and weedy species, but there is no reason to think that in the past the drier and cooler highlands were exempt from comparable human pressures on plant and animal life.

Mention of man's impact on the plant cover raises the related question of whether it is misleading to base inferences about ancient Maya subsistence on analysis of the present physical environment. Some contributors, such as Turner and Rice, explicitly assume that environmental conditions in the lowlands today are essentially comparable to those that existed during the Classic period, even though these authors are well aware that there are as yet insufficient paleoenvironmental data with which to test this assumption. In my view the merits of making the assumption as a working premise outweigh the obvious drawbacks. To do so allows ecologically based hypotheses of Maya subsistence to be formulated that can then be refined or rejected as more data become available. Wiseman attempts to do just this, using palynological evidence from Lakes Petenxil and Eckixil to test his simulation model of agricultural evolution from Preclassic to Postclassic times. The agricultural sequence that he derives from a comparison of the results of simulation and palynology is the most specific reconstruction of long-term land-use change offered in the book. It demonstrates the potential of a model-building and -testing approach to prehistoric subsistence, although clearly its validation depends on the independent acquisition of more paleoecological data.

Only one contributor, Covich (chap. 7), specifically addresses the question of the nature of preagricultural ecosystems in the Maya lowlands. He rightly emphasizes that recent theoretical work in ecology has thrown doubt on the established view that the biotically and structurally complex ecosystems of the tropics tend to be more stable—in the sense of being less prone to perturbations in their constituent populations—than less complex ecosystems. If such complex ecosystems as tropical forests, lakes, and rivers undergo relatively large or abrupt changes in species composition and population numbers independently of human influence—as a consequence, for example, of climatic changes—then the difficulties of distinguishing between natural and culturally induced ecological disturbance are accentuated.

Referring mainly to paleolimnological evidence, Covich stresses the problems of interpretation that arise when attempts are made to distinguish between natural ecosystems that have a long history of stability and those that have undergone major changes. Until more is known of the *natural* history of plant and animal communities in the Maya lowlands, attempts to assess the impact on them of early agricultural activities must remain highly speculative. For example, as Covich points out, if the preagricultural ecosystems of the lowlands were relatively uniform and adapted to minor changes only in such environmental factors as rainfall, nutrient cycling, and the incidence of fire, then the onset of extensive swidden cultivation would probably have devastated the forest cover; but if the preexisting biotas were already in a state of dynamic change in response to varying climatic conditions, they would prove much more resilient to the disturbances that accompanied the development of Maya agriculture. And, by extension, the same argument can be applied to any assessment—conspicuously absent in the book as a whole—of the ecological impact of such nonagricultural food-getting activities as hunting, gathering, and fishing prior to or during the florescence of Maya civilization.

As paleoenvironmental evidence gradually accumulates, the possibility that the lowlands have experienced a greater degree of natural ecological change than is commonly supposed gains ground. The traditional view that the humid tropical forests of low latitudes largely escaped the major environmental changes that affected higher latitudes during the Pleistocene and early Holocene periods has recently come under attack. Research on the faunas and floras of the South American and African rain forests suggests that major changes in the distribution and biotic composition of the forests took place during the Pleistocene (Haffer 1969; Vuilleumier 1971; Meggers, Ayensu, and Duckworth 1973). It would be surprising if comparable changes had not occurred in the Maya lowlands, and indeed Covich cites recent paleolimnological work that provides evidence for changes in terrestrial and aquatic ecosystems in response to fluctuations in sea level, groundwater flow, and rainfall.

Changes in the seasonal incidence of rainfall probably exercised a crucial influence over the composition and distribution of plant and animal communities in the area, just as they do today. It is regrettable that in a book that so effectively explores the theme of past and present environmental diversity in the Maya lowlands, no comprehensive analysis is offered of present patterns of rainfall variability. Admittedly long-period climatic records for the area are sparse, but a spatial analysis of variations in average length of the dry season—as defined, for example, by Troll and Paffen (1963)—would have added an essential element to the overall picture of environmental diversity and would in particular have provided a framework for the debate about the role of long- and short-term fallow systems of cultivation in the Maya economy. Culbert, Magers, and Spencer (chap. 8) make a preliminary gesture in this direction with their table of average monthly precipitation at thirteen stations in the lowlands, but they neither define the dry (or wet) season(s) nor map spatial variations in its (their) occurrence. I can but agree with their self-stricture (p. 160, above) that "we consider the general neglect of regional weather data to be another symptom of the failure to come to grips with regional variation in subsistence potential."

SYSTEMS OF FOOD PROCUREMENT

As was implied at the start of this chapter, the theme that most conspicuously unites contributors to this book is rejection of the view that Maya agriculture was based solely on swidden cultivation. The myth of the milpa, as Hammond calls it (chap. 3), could only survive as long as the parallel assumption on which it rested, that of environmental uniformity in the Maya lowlands, persisted. The preceding discussion has demonstrated the death of that illusion; it is to be hoped that the book as a whole will effectively bury the swidden hypothesis too.

It is now possible to argue a priori for diversity in Maya subsistence from the ecological diversity of their lowland habitat. We should expect to encounter evidence for a multiplicity of food-getting activities across the spectrum from gathering, hunting, and fishing to forms of long-fallow, short-fallow, and continuous or "permanent" cultivation. It is gratifying but not surprising that this book contains an abundance of such evidence, but it is also clear that we are still far from understanding the geographical distribution, interrelationships, and relative importance of the various methods of food procurement that sustained Maya civilization. In fact, as this book demonstrates, there is still uncertainty over the recognition of the categories or systems of agricultural and nonagricultural food procurement that are appropriate to the analysis of Maya subsistence. At the risk of adding to terminological confusion and of eliciting the disapproval of the editors (who have sensibly tried to impose some semantic uniformity on their contributors) I shall examine the possible diversity of Maya subsistence in terms of a general (but not comprehensive) classification of food-procurement systems (table 15.1).

Although it may be thought beyond the brief of this book to consider nonagricultural sources of food available to the ancient Maya, it is unrealistic to focus attention exclusively on systems of cultivation. Even in modern agricultural economies the procurement of wild foods persists as a supplementary and sometimes prestigious activity that affords welcome occupational and nutritional variety in the domestic routine. Wild, especially aquatic, foods probably played a significant role in the Maya economy. Several contributors allude to the possible importance of fish in the diet of the Classic Maya. The assessment of this possibility is hampered by lack of direct evidence in the form of fish remains, but Puleston's experimental reconstruction of a raised field on the Hondo River appears to confirm the potential of the raised-field canals for providing fish, as suggested previously by Thompson (1974); and Harrison's argument (1977) that the *bajos* were shallow lakes may imply a degree of dependence on fish and other aquatic foods, whether or not the *bajos* were, as he suggests, intensively cultivated by a raised-field chinampa system of agriculture. The possible dietary contribution of aquatic food deserves keener investigation than it has so far received, particularly because fish represent an accessible and renewable source of protein in an environment not notably rich in terrestrial game and in a society lacking domesticated ungulates.

Hunting, too, probably made a regular if minor contribution to Classic Maya food supplies. As Wiseman points out, the lowlands support a fairly diverse mesofauna that present-day farmers still hunt. Whether extensions of swidden cultivation in the past actually increased populations of edge-loving fauna, as Wiseman

Table 15.1. Systems of Food Procurement

	Classic Maya Systems (known or postulated)	*Associated Features of the Cultural Landscape*
WILD-FOOD PROCUREMENT SYSTEMS		
Gathering of wild plants	Gathering, including fuel	———
Hunting of wild animals	Hunting, especially deer	Swiddens, seasonally burned savannas
Fishing	Fishing	Raised-field canals? *Bajo* lakes?
Manipulation of naturally occurring plant and animal populations.	Tending of preferred trees, shrubs, and vines	
	Management of deer and/or peccaries, etc.	Seasonally burned savannas?
CULTIVATION SYSTEMS		
Fallow systems		
Long-term swidden cultivation	Pioneering swidden	———
	Marginal-land swidden	———
Short-term sectorial cultivation	Flatland dry-field cultivation.	Stone-walled fields?
	Hillside dry-field cultivation	Linear hillside terraces
Continuous edaphic systems		
Enclosed-field cultivation	Hillside dry-field cultivation	Linear hillside terraces Stone-walled fields?
Horticulture	House-garden inter-cropping	———
Arboriculture	Ramon-tree cropping	Chambered chultunes? Stone-walled fields?
	Artificial rainforest	———
Continuous hydraulic systems		
Wetland cultivation	Raised fields: river (levee) type	Mounds, canals, causeways
	Raised fields: *bajo* (chinampa) type	Canals? Causeways? Mounds?
Dryland irrigation	Manual irrigation	Wells, chultunes, *aguadas*
	Flow irrigation	Check-dam and weir terraces, reservoirs and canals

suggests, is uncertain because the relative proportions of cleared and forested land at any one time are unknown; but, by attracting herbivores to the crops and weeds of the milpas it would have brought hunter and hunted into a closer and more spatially predictable relationship. Evidently this was not a first step that was to lead to ungulate domestication, as I have suggested it may have been in the ancient Near East (Harris 1977a:220–32), but it may have led to increased exploitation of deer, peccaries, and other game. The possibility of the semidomestication or free-range management of deer should also be considered. Perhaps the savannas, which Turner regards as relatively negative areas for agricultural purposes, were used in this way in addition to their presumed role as preferred hunting grounds. Critical examination of animal bones recovered from Maya sites might throw some light on the possibility that deer populations were brought into a state of semidomestication by selective manipulation (table 15.1).

There is scant evidence of the importance of wild plant foods among the ancient Maya, but observation of present-day Maya and other tropical Amerindian agriculturalists suggests that gathering plays a minor but significant part in the domestic economy. Wild plants, often harvested casually, yield edible, medicinal, and other products for household use, as no doubt they did in the Classic period. Wiseman rightly emphasizes the importance of fuel procurement and suggests that a wood-producing allotment system may have been developed by the prehistoric Maya on forest, swidden, or other agricultural land.

It is difficult to draw a sharp distinction between the gathering of wild plant foods, especially tree fruits, and the tending and actual planting of the most desired species, such as ramon, cacao, avocado, papaya, sapodilla, sapote, and the various species of *Annona.* When and to what extent the gathering of such useful plants gave way in the Maya lowlands to their deliberate cultivation is unknown and difficult to demonstrate archaeologically or paleoecologically. Wiseman makes a persuasive ecological case for the intensive production of tree, vine, root, and herbaceous crops in stands of artificial rain forest developed by selective clearance. Analogues of this postulated system of food production occur widely in the tropics, often in the form of house or dooryard gardens (Smith and Cameron 1977:99–100), and it is quite possible that the Classic Maya incorporated such a system of inter-cropping into their agricultural economy. If so, it can be envisaged as developing over a long time span from wild-plant gathering through the selective manipulation or tending of preferred forest trees, shrubs, and vines to the integration of crops of varied life forms and ecological requirements into this essentially arboricultural mode of production (table 15.1).

Closely comparable to Wiseman's artificial rain forest is Puleston's postulated system of kitchen-garden arboriculture, which is envisaged as focusing upon production of the highly nutritious and storable ramon seed. Puleston demonstrates convincingly that intensive ramon-tree cropping would have been extraordinarily productive in terms of yield measured against the time invested in collecting and transporting the ripe seeds. If his interpretation of the chambered chultunes as structures for storing ramon seeds is correct, the case is strong for ramon as a staple food in the diet of the Classic Maya of northeastern Peten. But, in view of the multiplicity of food-procurement systems that could have functioned in the area, including raised-field cultivation in Harrison's hypothetical *bajo* lakes (about which Puleston remains highly skeptical), it is difficult to accept the proposition that ramon-tree cropping was the dominant system of food procurement, "as important as maize has been in modern times." If direct paleoecological evidence of ramon could be recovered to set against the indirect archaeological evidence of the chultunes, the question of the relative importance of ramon-tree cropping in Classic Maya agriculture might be clarified.

Both artificial rain forest and ramon-tree cropping can be classified as edaphic or soil-dependent systems of cultivation in which fertility is maintained by the addition of organic matter so that continuous year-round cultivation is possible (table 15.1). Hydraulic systems—for which the defining criterion that makes continuous cultivation possible is control of surface- and soil-water conditions through wetland drainage or dryland irrigation—were also available to, and evidently practiced by, the Classic Maya (table 15.1). Siemens and Puleston's initial report (1972) of raised fields beside the Candelaria River has been followed by reports of similar raised field and canallike features in the Hondo and New river valleys of northern Belize (Hammond 1974b; Olson 1975; Puleston 1977; Siemens 1977), in the *bajos* of southern Quintana Roo (Harrison 1977), and possibly in *bajos* near Tikal (Dahlin

1976b). These relict landscape features vary in pattern and scale but occur in two distinct situations: on levees and other river margins, as along the Candelaria, Hondo, and New rivers, where they were presumably watered by seasonal floods and/or from diversion canals, and in the *bajos,* where seasonal or permanent lakes allowed a chinampa style of cultivation to be established. Until more field, and especially excavation, data are available, the extent, functions, and age of raised-field systems will remain controversial, as the conflicting interpretations of them in this book demonstrate. The evidence so far suggests that raised-field cultivation dates back (on the Hondo River) at least to 1400 B.C. (calibrated) and that maize and cotton were among the crops grown (Puleston 1977). Presumably this was a labor-intensive system of cultivation which made possible year-round cultivation by creating organic-rich planting surfaces and by regulating soil-moisture conditions. Like wet-paddy pond-field cultivation in south and east Asia, it no doubt had the ecological capacity to respond to increased demand with sustained increases in production. Thus relatively small areas of raised-field cultivation could have made a major contribution to the Classic Maya economy, and it is quite possible, as Hammond argues, that the raised fields were favored locales for the specialized production of cacao.

Whereas wetland cultivation by means of raised fields was associated with the southern lowlands, evidence for dryland irrigation comes, as is to be expected, from the more arid northern third of the Yucatan Peninsula. In this region remains of extensive reservoir and canal systems for water storage and distribution have been found (Matheny 1976). They are well developed at such civic-ceremonial centers as Uxmal, where there is evidence of six reservoirs and many feeder canals, and Edzna, where Matheny has traced 12 main canals that form a radial pattern focusing on the center of the settlement. The canals were evidently designed to collect and store rainwater and those north of the center fan out over an area of relatively good soil and are associated with over 200 house mounds. This strongly suggests that irrigation agriculture was practiced and it is possible that fertility was maintained by the addition to the fields of organic-rich sediments periodically cleaned out of the canals. In addition, garden plots were probably hand watered from *aguadas,* wells, and water-storing chultunes; but because of the karstic drainage of the northern peninsula it is unlikely that floodwater farming, which depends on seasonal surface flow, was practiced.

Among the more problematic features of the ancient Maya agricultural landscape are the extensive hillside terraces reported by Turner and others, principally near Becan in southern Campeche and Quintana Roo and in the Maya Mountains of southern Belize (Turner 1974a). Most of the Maya terraces are of the linear, sloping, dry-field type and were probably built to check erosional loss of topsoil and to create flatter planting surfaces with deeper soil than the natural hillsides afforded. Check-dam terraces in hillside gullies, and weir terraces built across channel bottoms to capture silt-laden runoff, are also reported from the Maya lowlands.

It is difficult to associate terraces as such with distinctive systems of cultivation, as too little is known of their agronomic functions. The check-dam and weir terraces may be regarded as small-scale hydraulic systems because their prime purpose is to modify natural water flow and because fertility is periodically renewed by the addition of water-borne silt. The more extensive linear dry-field terraces can, however, be classified either as continuous edaphic or as fallow systems according to whether fertility is maintained primarily by adding organic matter to the soil or by resting the soil from cultivation. Whether the Maya dry-field terraces were cultivated continuously or fallowed is unknown. Turner argues for "annual or near annual" cultivation on the grounds that "the time, expense, manpower, and organization necessary to construct and maintain the large-scale terrace systems were too great to have been wasted on a system of cultivation that merely approximated or slightly improved the swidden cycle." He also suggests that fertility was probably maintained by tillage and the addition of mulches, manures, and ash to the soil. That terrace construction and maintenance is necessarily more labor-demanding than the cultivation of flatlands of equivalent size cannot be assumed, as Bronson points out in chapter 14, and the organizational effort involved is clearly dependent on the time period over which any given set of terraces was constructed. If sets of terraces are developed by piecemeal addition over many centuries they do not require large-scale coordinated effort to build or to maintain and they are as likely to be cultivated under short-fallow cycles as to be continuously cropped. Until more evidence is available for the crops and cultivation techniques employed on the ancient Maya terraces it seems better to allow that they may either have been cropped annually or cultivated in short-fallow routines (table 15.1). Very possibly the Classic Maya cultivated hillside terraces by both methods.

Another relict feature of the Maya agricultural landscape, comparable to the hillside terraces, is the remnants of stone walls that occur extensively on the flatter lands of southern Campeche and Quintana Roo. Turner has mapped them in the Rio Bec region, where they are associated with relatively well-drained level surfaces but also extend onto terraced hillsides. The walls appear to demarcate fields or other land units, and Turner speculates that they may have served to deter predators and also as anti-hurricane windbreaks and walkways to facilitate movement in the wet season. He argues that the walls imply intensive agricultural land use and that they suggest "some type of individual or group ownership or control of the land, a tenure situation not prevalent among extensive, swidden farmers." It is true that permanent field boundaries tend not to be associated with swidden cultivation, except in areas where exclusion of domestic or feral livestock from cultivated plots is an integral part of the agricultural system, as it is for example with respect to pigs in the highlands of Papua New Guinea. If deer and/or peccaries, wild or semidomesticated, were sufficiently abundant to be a serious predatory nuisance to Classic Maya farmers, it is conceivable that the cut limestone walls were built to exclude them, but if so it is likely that the protected fields were cultivated by a more intensive routine than long-term fallow. Turner states that the well-drained flatlands with their calcareous loams, on which most of the stone walls are found, constitute the best agricultural zone because they are fertile and do not suffer significantly from erosion or flooding. It does seem improbable that such land, elaborately enclosed by stone-walled fields, was cultivated by swidden techniques. It is more likely that fields were cultivated continuously, with fertility maintained by inputs of organic matter, and/or short-term fallowing (table 15.1).

A range of relatively intensive techniques may have been applied to the enclosed fields, including the "intensive milpa" system mentioned by Wiseman and incorporated by Sanders (1973) into his model of lowland Maya agriculture. Intensive milpa implies a short-fallow cycle in which the land is cultivated either for longer than, or for as long as, it is fallowed (the latter routine can be equated with Sanders's "grass fallow" category, adopted from Boserup [1965], with a cultivation:fallow ratio of 1:1). Cultivation by short-fallow and more continuous edaphic methods can also be intensified—and probably was among the Classic Maya—by both multi- and inter-cropping. The feasibility of multi-cropping in the southern lowlands, where the dry season is shorter than farther north in the peninsula, is emphasized by Culbert, Magers, and Spencer; and both Sanders (1973) and Wiseman point to the increased productivity afforded by inter-cropping. For example, the incorporation of a drought-resistant root crop such as manioc into a milpa system focusing on maize, beans, and other annual seed crops allows production to be extended well into or through the dry season. As a leafy perennial, manioc also gives some protection to the soil, while the species diversity of inter-cropped milpas in general reduces the risk of plant disease and pest infestation.

It is possible that some of the enclosed fields were devoted to tree crops, either in mixed plantings analogous to Wiseman's artificial rain forest or in more monocultural plantations of such preferred species as ramon and cacao. Tree crops, with their deeper root systems and slower rates of maturation, allow more sustained agricultural exploitation of tropical soils than herbaceous annuals such as maize and beans. When annual seed crops are harvested most of the nutrients stored in the plant are removed from the field, whereas tree crops recycle nutrients more effectively. The stone walls may have demarcated areas devoted to long-term arboriculture, as well as to inter- and multi-cropped milpas, especially if cacao or ramon was raised intensively. Perhaps it is not beyond the bounds of possibility that the pattern of permanent enclosure served more than strictly agronomic functions. It is conceivable that it had a cadastral purpose associated with the levying of tax or tribute by the elites at civic-ceremonial centers. This possibility might gain some credence if a spatial and temporal correlation between field demarcation and civic-ceremonial centers could be demonstrated.

Finally we come to the system of cultivation that was for so long believed to be the sole or principal support of Classic Maya civilization: swidden or long-fallow, defined as a routine in which agricultural plots are cultivated for shorter periods than they are fallowed. Because swidden clearance and cropping is essentially ephemeral and not normally associated with permanent field boundaries or other lasting imprints on the landscape, it is notoriously difficult to demonstrate archaeologically. As several contributors point out, the assumption that the Maya economy was based on swidden owed its origin and persistence to the observed dominance of "shifting cultivation" in present-day Maya agriculture. The incompatibility of this assumption with the demonstrably higher population densities and more nucleated settlement patterns of the Classic period was a major factor in the rejection of the swidden hypothesis, but the question of the former importance of swidden relative to other systems of cultivation remains unresolved.

Paleoecological research offers the best hope of investigating this question. Wiseman attempts to do so using palynological and macrofossil data from the sedimentary record of Lakes Petenxil and Eckixil and concludes that on balance the evidence points there to short-fallow or more intensive systems of cultivation rather than to swidden. Certainly the limited paleoecological data available at present appear not to support the view that swidden cultivation was the mainstay of Classic Maya civilization. However, this is not to say that swidden did not contribute to the agricultural economy. Probably it functioned as a supplementary system of cultivation that provided the best means of exploiting the drier, steeper, and—initially—the more heavily forested areas. Such a marginal and pioneering function for swidden in a complex of Classic Maya cultivation systems is compatible both with the exiguous paleoecological evidence and with the role of swidden in many ethnographically known tropical societies that practice both intensive and extensive agriculture. It is the interpretation favored here, but it leaves aside the more difficult question of the position of swidden cultivation in the evolution of Maya agriculture, a controversial topic that is discussed briefly in the next section.

INTENSIVE AGRICULTURE AND MAYA CIVILIZATION

The obverse of the now discarded swidden hypothesis is that the florescence of Classic Maya civilization was based upon the development of intensive systems of cultivation. The varied evidence for such systems has been reviewed in the preceding section, but we have as yet little understanding of their relative age and importance in the Maya economy. It is tempting to speculate on this theme, but in so doing it is easy to fall into the trap of circular argument: Maya civilization depended on intensive agriculture; there is field evidence of intensive agriculture; the field evidence demonstrates that the Classic Maya population was large and its society complex, i.e., civilized. There are of course familiar nonagricultural criteria for recognizing Classic Maya society as civilized—for example, the existence of civic-ceremonial centers, monumental stone architecture, and a complex iconography including a calendric system—but we should hesitate before building agricultural criteria into any definition of Maya civilization.

The point that requires emphasis is that the presumed indicators of intensive cultivation now being recognized, such as raised fields, terraces, cut-stone field boundaries, canals, reservoirs, and chultunes, do not necessarily signal the existence of a dense population and a complex society. It is possible to cite examples of all of these features built and maintained by relatively small and simply organized tribal societies. Recent work in the Torres Strait Islands and western Papua demonstrates this for raised fields (Harris 1977b), as do comparative studies of raised fields in the Old World tropics by Denevan and Turner (1974) and of terraces by Wright (1962) and J. E. Spencer and Hale (1961). In his contribution to this volume Bronson argues—correctly in my view—that building raised fields and terraces is not necessarily more labor-demanding than cultivating areas of level, well-drained land of equivalent size. Nor does the existence of flights of terraces or spreads of raised fields necessarily imply direction of labor by a supratribal authority. The same can be—and often has been—said with reference to the construction and maintenance of irrigation canals and reservoirs, for example by Leach (1959) in an early critique of Wittfogel's concept of hydraulic civilization. Matheny relates this concept to the northern lowland Maya in his contribution and concludes that much of the evidence is for small-scale hydraulic works, as at Santa Rosa Xtampak, although "a central authority on the city level" is envisaged as responsible for the much larger and more complex hydraulic system at Edzna. This distinction implies that it is the scale and complexity of agricultural systems rather than just the existence of presumed intensive techniques of cultivation that determines whether a supratribal level of social organization should be inferred from the field evidence. And it is precisely in trying to assess the scale, relative importance, and interrelationships of Classic Maya cultivation systems that we encounter a paralyzing lack of information.

Several contributors make valiant attempts to tackle this problem. Harrison argues for the great extent and agricultural importance of raised fields in the *bajos* of southern Quintana Roo and possibly in *bajos* elsewhere in the lowlands. Turner supports Harrison's argument, makes the case for the large-scale development of hillside terraces and flatland field enclosures, and plausibly projects their geographical distribution in the Classic period. Puleston debates the interrelationships of terracing, raised-field cultivation, and ramon-tree cropping, and concludes that they were essentially mutually exclusive methods of agricultural intensification developed in different environmental situations and geographical areas. He further hypothesizes that the more labor-intensive systems of raised-field and terrace cultivation were best developed in peripheral areas where proportionately less effort was put into the construction of major architectural monuments, while in the Peten core area dependence on the less labor-intensive system of ramon-tree cropping allowed a greater investment of energy in monumental construction. This ingenious argument for an inverse relationship between labor-intensive cultivation and architectural achievement deserves to be tested as fresh evidence becomes available. However, a priori reasoning from environmental diversity and a knowledge of the characteristic complexity of traditional agricultural economies in the tropics suggests that heavy dependence on one system of cultivation—however energetically efficient it may be—is unlikely. It seems more probable that the Classic Maya depended throughout the lowlands on a blend of food-procurement systems that balanced minimization of risk through the maintenance of ecological diversity against maximization of output through economic specialization on such agronomically, nutritionally, and socially rewarding crops as maize, beans, ramon, and cacao.

A research direction that offers some prospect of advance in our understanding of the interrelationships of identifiable food-procurement systems is represented by Rice's analysis (chap. 4) of settlement and subsistence in the lake basins of Yaxha and Sacnab in Peten. He demonstrates the advantages of focusing on a specific region for which there is relatively adequate environmental and archaeological data, even though his delimitation by Thiessen polygon of the "immediate resource area" of the population is based on uncertain assumptions about the extent of the "sustaining or residential area aligned with the civic center of Yaxha." Given his starting assumptions, he produces persuasive reconstructions of changing population levels and subsistence activities from Middle Preclassic to Late Classic times and makes a convincing case for a "site-regional level of analysis."

One of the assumptions that is integral to Rice's analysis of agricultural change through time raises the last topic to be discussed here: that of the evolutionary relationship of extensive and intensive systems of cultivation in the Maya lowlands. Rice makes the orthodox assumption that extensive swidden preceded intensive systems of cultivation. He postulates that maize swidden remained the main agricultural strategy into the Late Preclassic period in the Yaxha-Sacnab region, but that population growth, increased demand for agricultural surpluses, and limited land resources forced shifts toward more intensive and/or productive systems of cultivation by the Early Classic period. Although direct evidence is lacking, he envisages a shift in staple crops from maize to ramon and possibly root crops in house-garden and short-fallow contexts, as well as the development of raised-field and terrace cultivation. Rice explicitly adopts Boserup's (1965) population-density-dependent model of agricultural intensification, as, with some qualification, does Turner, whereas Wiseman concludes that the pollen and macrofossil evidence from Lakes Petenxil and Eckixil allows but does not unequivocally support an evolution from early extensive to later intensive cultivation. Wiseman's own interpretation, based on a comparison of this evidence with the results he derives from simulation, envisages a Preclassic mosaic of scrub vegetation and maize fields (not necessarily all cultivated under long-fallow routines) giving way in the Classic period to dependence on "a suite of agricultural techniques, each fitting into its own environmental niche" rather than to sole dependence on short-fallow cultivation. His "maximum habitat model" parallels my own conception of the Classic Maya as dependent on a blend of ecologically diverse and economically specialized food-procurement systems. But it leaves open the question of how exclusively the agricultural economy of the Preclassic Maya depended on swidden cultivation.

As Hammond points out in his contribution, intensive methods of cultivation, such as the use of raised fields, terraces, and multi-cropping, are usually regarded as "innovations to supplement an existing swidden system by utilizing hitherto marginal terrain or increasing the efficiency of the swidden cycle itself." In contrast to this view, he suggests that small, highly productive agricultural plots such as raised or terraced fields may have been created, under no compulsion of population pressure, close to settlements. The time and effort involved in their construction and maintenance would not necessarily have exceeded that expended on travel to and from, and clearance and cultivation of, more distant swiddens. The implication is clear that local, intensive agriculture of this type could well have preceded the general adoption of swidden, which may itself have been a response to increasing demand generated by population growth and/or by the development of a tribute system emanating from civic-ceremonial centers.

This line of argument accords closely with a hypothesis I have previously advanced for the precedence in the tropics of "fixed-plot horticulture" of house-garden type over swidden cultivation (Harris 1973:399–402); and it reinforces the point made in the preceding section that swidden probably functioned in the Maya agricultural economy mainly as a marginal and pioneering technique of cultivation. As such it is likely to have been more important in the early Preclassic phase of agricultural evolution, when population densities were still relatively low and much land remained uncultivated, than during the florescence of Classic Maya civilization; but it is unlikely to have been either the only or the earliest system of cultivation practiced in the Preclassic Maya lowlands. House gardens and perhaps orchards or managed forest, as well as small raised fields on levees and swamp margins, probably played a more significant role than swidden in the evolution of Preclassic Maya subsistence, particularly if, as Puleston and Hammond believe, the initial pattern of penetration of the southern lowlands was riverine, with later adaptation to the forested interior away from the rivers. Hammond's (1977; Hammond et al. 1976) recent dating of the early Maya site of Cuello in northern Belize to 2600 B.C. (calibrated) suggests a much greater time depth for this process of penetration and adaptation than had previously been allowed, and Puleston's (1977) demonstration that raised-field canals were being dug there by 1400 B.C. (calibrated) gives some support to the postulate that such techniques of intensive cultivation already existed on a small scale early in Preclassic times.

The inferential case for the early development of small-scale intensive systems of cultivation implies a different and more complex evolutionary trajectory for pre-Hispanic Maya agriculture than is commonly assumed. In place of a simple progression from extensive to intensive cultivation, from swidden to short-term fallow to "permanent" agriculture, I envisage shifting emphases through time on a cluster of coexisting systems of food procurement. The earliest phases in the development of an agricultural economy probably saw the initiation on a small scale of house-garden, arboricultural, and raised-field cultivation close to settlements. At this stage the domestic economy may well have focused on the aquatic and riparian resources of rivers, lakes, and swamps, with swidden cultivation playing a significant but minor role as the usual means whereby forested land was brought under cultivation when demand for food and other crops increased.

With the growth in the number and size of settlements, especially civic-ceremonial centers, that occurred in Classic times, accelerating demand emanating from the centers and also generated by the overall increase in population led to greatly increased agricultural production. This increase was achieved partly through extension of the cultivated area and partly by intensifying production on already cultivated land. Forested hillsides were extensively swiddened and *bajo* floors may have been brought under chinampa-style raised-field cultivation; hillside terraces and enclosed fields on level land were evidently cultivated by short-fallow or continuous cropping routines; and plantations of ramon and other food-yielding trees were probably extended. Production may also have been raised by changes in crop complexes and rotations, especially through the elaboration of systems of multi- and inter-cropping.

Agricultural intensification in the Classic period is thus envisaged less as a process by which new and more productive and labor-intensive systems of "permanent" cultivation progressively replaced older and less productive fallow systems than as one which shifted the productive emphasis to those sytems, such as raised-field and ramon cultivation, that had the greatest inherent capacity to respond to increased demand with sustained increases in yield. As the agricultural economy developed in parallel with the social and institutional elaboration of Classic Maya civilization, so the integration of its component systems improved. Increased flow of information and goods between central and peripheral settlements stimulated refinements in spatial and temporal organization in farming areas as well as regional trade links. Puleston discusses the possibility that maize and other staple foods were traded over considerable distances, contrary to the views of Maya exchange expressed by Rathje (1971) and Tourtellot and Sabloff (1972), and he specifically suggests that maize production may have been intensified on raised fields and hillside terraces partly to supply the core (ramon-producing) area of northeastern Peten.

The lack of domesticated draft animals and wheeled vehicles must have limited the capacity of the Maya to trade bulk goods over long distances, and, as Bronson points out, unless the *bajos* were shallow lakes and water-borne transport was more highly developed than is commonly supposed, the Classic Maya centers "operated under a severe and unusual disadvantage" by comparison with early Asian cities. Dependence on human porters may well have limited the capacity of Maya centers to grow in size and in economic and political authority, and it is tempting to speculate that the difficulty of maintaining control over their hinterlands without more efficient means of transport may have been a significant factor in the eventual Maya collapse.

If much of the agricultural intensification that occurred during the Classic Period was achieved through improved integration and changes in the relative importance of preexisting systems of cultivation under the stimulus of increased subsistence, tribute, and trade demands, than the maintenance of high levels of production depended in large measure upon the stability of the social system and the continuity of information flows between settlements. If a center failed for whatever reason to maintain its authority, sacred or secular, over its hinterland, disintegration of the regional agricultural economy would be likely to follow. Examples abound of the "disintensification" of traditional agricultural systems under the impact of modern cash economies (see, for example, Brookfield 1927:39–41). Frequently this process takes the form of a shift from continuous, fixed-field cultivation to a fallowing system; for example in the Asian tropics the shift has often been from wet-paddy to swidden. The transition from Classic to Postclassic times in the Maya lowlands probably witnessed such shifts as regionally integrated economies became disarticulated with the demise of their civic-ceremonial centers. And it is easy to envisage this process, paralleled by a decline in population, leading in due course to the "disintensified" swidden-based economy of modern times, with its elusive traces of raised fields and other long since abandoned systems of cultivation.

Despite the new evidence and interpretations of Maya agriculture offered in this book, such traces of past human effort imprinted on the landscape still await full explanation. The field evidence and ethnoecological inferences on which the new interpretations are based are sufficiently well founded to overthrow the long established swidden hypothesis. But attempts to refine and to choose between other competing hypotheses are frustrated by lack of factual data on the distribution and function of settlements and on past environmental changes, as well as on the systems of cultivation themselves. An insufficiently detailed absolute chronology also hampers progress along the road toward a fuller understanding of pre-Hispanic Maya agriculture. This books takes us a long way down that road and tempts us again into the field, the laboratory, and the library in our efforts to understand the still enigmatic civilization of the lowland Maya.

16

GORDON R. WILLEY
Department of Anthropology, Harvard University

Pre-Hispanic Maya Agriculture: A Contemporary Summation

In this attempt to summarize the papers of the present volume the word *contemporary,* in the above title, is most appropriate. Knowledge and ideas about ancient Maya agriculture have changed rapidly and drastically in the last few years, and continue to change, so that any review must be dated as a kind of progress report. In addition to the rather surprising new data that have come in from field archaeology, geographers, geologists, palynologists, and botanists are helping the archaeologist revise his thinking about the ways in which the Maya managed their agricultural subsistence in the tropical forest lowlands.

As of this writing, however, and based upon a reading of the assembled papers, it is fair to say that three general conclusions, or at least working premises, have emerged. The first of these is simply that the old idea that the Lowland Maya lived by a swidden (slash-and-burn, milpa) system of maize cultivation alone is fallacious. Peter D. Harrison and B. L. Turner make this point very explicit, and all of the other authors allude to it in one way or another. Other farming techniques of greater productive potential must have been used by the Maya instead of, or in addition to, the swidden method; and, indeed, there is direct archaeological evidence that this was so.

A second conclusion relates to the first; in fact, in point of investigative procedure, it might be said to precede it. This is that Lowland Maya populations were much larger than was heretofore believed and, even more important, that they lived in larger and denser concentrations than long-fallow swidden cultivation would have been able to support. In other words, the settlement information that has come in over the past dozen years is inconsistent with the swidden hypothesis.

A third conclusion, or working premise, is that there was considerable and significant variability in agricultural practices as these were followed throughout the Maya lowlands. No single model can pertain to the entire area throughout its agricultural history. Differences in agriculture, obviously, were related to differences in environmental regions and niches, but it also seems probable that they were influenced by cultural choices.

The possible means of agricultural intensification—that is, the increase of agricultural production—were, it appears, numerous and varied. Frederick Wiseman (chap. 5) and Turner (chap. 9) list and discuss these. They include: short-fallow milpas or swidden, made possible by various techniques of crop rotation, companion planting or inter-cropping, hand weeding, mulching, and fertilizers; multiple annual cropping (as referred to by Culbert, Magers, and Spencer); "infield" or kitchen-garden farming; the production of diverse crops, including root crops and tree crops (especially the ramon nut); terracing; and raised-field farming, either along active streams or near still water. Of these, only terracing and raised fields leave appreciable direct archaeological traces; the others must be inferred from various lines of archaeological, palynological, or ethnohistoric-ethnographic evidences.

Although not addressing himself to terracing alone in his present papers, Turner (1974a, 1978) has done the most work on the subject. Currently, terraces are known from the ridge lands of the Rio Bec country in southern Campeche and from somewhat similar terrain in western Belize. They usually involve a degree of stone construction and appear to have been built both as silt traps and to protect slopes from erosion. In the Rio Bec region, where they have been well-studied, it is obvious that they represent a considerable expenditure of effort. They are to be distinguished from low stone walls which divide the nearby Rio Bec flat country into what look like demarcated field plots. The presence of these latter, though, suggests crowding and careful apportionment of agricultural lands, lending credence to the idea that the nearby hillslopes were exploited for terrace farming as a result of community needs. In view of this, and in the light of known heavy Late Classic settlement of the Rio Bec region, it seems probable that agricultural terracing here was largely a Late Classic phenomenon; however, it should be cautioned that this is still speculative. Elsewhere in the Maya lowlands agricultural terraces have been reported from Belize, where they are still said to be extensive on many of the hillslopes; however, these have not been plotted or described in any great detail.

Of all of the techniques of intensification, those involving raised fields and related forms of water control have recently attracted the most attention. Alfred Siemens and Dennis Puleston (1972) first called attention to such fields along the banks of the sluggish Rio Candelaria, on the western edge of the Maya lowlands. Since then these artificially raised garden areas—similar in principle to the Central Mexican lake chinampas—have been reported from along the Rio Hondo in northern Belize. On a more extensive scale claims have been made for their presence in old swamp or *bajo* areas in various places in the Maya Lowlands. Peter Harrison (chap. 13) estimates that a total of 2,460 square kilometers of such fields can be seen from the air in southern Quintana Roo, in the vicinity of the major site of Tzibanche. The evidence in question is seen as series of rectangular grid lines on the air photographs, such lines being assumed to be the separating canals between such raised cultivation plots. Similar phenomena have been reported elsewhere, including the vicinity of the great site of Mirador in the northern Peten and, perhaps, even more significantly in the Bajo de Santa Fe on the edge of Tikal. Are these *bajo* grid lines the remnants of raised-field-cultivation rectangles? Puleston is highly dubious and thinks it more likely that they are gilgai, natural formations caused by the deep cracking of mud flats. Clearly, on-the-ground exploration is indicated, for if raised-field agriculture was as extensive as the preliminary air photo reports suggest, Maya lowland subsistence must be reviewed in a whole new way. Even in the tropical forests, with problems of insect pests, the food production yield from the chinampa-like plots would have been enormously high. Is Tikal's great size to be attributed to such a subsistence resource?

The matter of the raised fields along some Maya lowland rivers and their putative presence in the *bajos* relates to what Siemens has had to say here about the karstic landscape which underlies most of this country. He observes that in this landscape there are two kinds of rivers: those that show little fluctuation in water level and those that have an appreciable rise and fall. It is the first type, with its "reservoir effects," that produces conditions favorable for raised fields, as in the instances of the Candelaria and Hondo rivers. Siemens also has something to say about riverine-*bajo* relationships. He points out that the destruction of the *bajos,* or their evolution from lakes to swamps, may not have been the result of silting, as in the original hypothesis, but the result of the downcutting of streams into the karstic beds and the draining, through this stream action, of the Peten lake waters into the Caribbean. This discussion takes us back to a reconsideration of the Cooke-Ricketson hypothesis about *bajo*-lake relationships, which was advanced forty years ago (Ricketson and Ricketson 1937). In a paper published elsewhere, Peter Harrison (1977) has resurrected this hypothesis, in spite of the Cowgill-Hutchinson (1963b) strictures against it—strictures with which Puleston (chap. 12) is still in agreement. In Harrison's paper, which has the catchy title, "The Rise of the *Bajos* and the Fall of the Maya," Tikal, and many other sites, are seen as dependent upon raised-field cultivation in what were then shallow lakes filled with raised fields or chinampas. With the silting of these *bajos,* as hypothesized by Cooke and Ricketson, such agriculture became less and less profitable, eventually bringing about the crisis that led to the great collapse in the ninth century. This leads me to a question: If the Siemens explanation of the "fall" of the *bajos,* that is, their drainage by the downcutting of streams, in turn related to the karstic uplift, is the correct explanation, would this reconcile the Cowgill-Hutchinson findings with the idea that the *bajos* had once been lakes? Or, to ask the question in another way, is it the presumed silting of the lakes that Cowgill and Hutchinson object to, or is it the presumption that they had been lakes at all?

I should like to make a partial digression at this point to say that there are things in the lowland Maya archaeological past that seem very consonant with a former lacustrine or still-water aquatic environment. These are seen in the imagery and symbolism of much of Maya Classic art. Hammond refers to some of this in his present paper, and both Harrison (1977) and Puleston (1977) develop this theme at some length. Puleston cites the water-lily motif, among many others, and especially the association of the water lily with the maize plant, and of both with the deity

Itzamna, whom he is inclined to interpret as a crocodile, the supreme animal of a tropical forest environment. These themes in Maya art do suggest an ambience of shallow lakes, swamps, and, perhaps, canals and lagoons that were made for raised-field agriculture.

Such Maya lowland water management or hydraulic engineering could also have served other purposes. Some years ago J. E. S. Thompson (1974) made the suggestion that the canals of the raised-field systems of the Rio Candelaria would have made ideal breeding and live-storage places for fish. This would have been an important subsistence supplement, as several of the writers in the present volume have commented. *Aguadas* and reservoirs near major lowland sites were obviously used for potable water storage. At Edzna, in Campeche, Ray Matheny has mapped and explored reservoirs, canals, and moats that served such purposes and also those of transportation and defense; according to Matheny, similar "waterworks" are known from Uxmal. Matheny points out that the "water complex" at Edzna, which had all of these functions and, perhaps, those of plant cultivation as well, was built into the original city planning and may have had ritual and aesthetic significances as well as these more practical ones. These findings and observations, while taking us away from our central theme of agriculture, do indicate, nevertheless, a depth of tradition on the part of the Maya in the manipulation of subsurface and surface water in which raised field farming would not have been a surprising part.

Another form of agricultural intensification that is referred to in several of the accompanying articles is that of "kitchen-garden" supplementation. Root crops were undoubtedly important in this regard, as Bennet Bronson (1966) indicated a decade ago. Orchard produce must also have been a part of this "infield" farming. It has also been argued by Dennis Puleston (1973) that orchards were considerably more than a mere supplement to maize cultivation; Puleston, again, makes this case very forcefully in the present volume (chap. 12). Maize cultivation, he states, was never important in the old "core area" of the Northeast Peten. Here, instead, the ramon nut was the principal crop from the beginning. Puleston feels that of all the farming techniques available to the Maya—including not only raised fields, terracing, and other intensification measures, but the swidden systems as well—harvesting from the ramon or breadnut tree was the most productive per man- or woman-hour of work, and he cites modern experiments to back his theory up. In this sense ramon-nut harvesting would have been the "line of the least resistance" for the Northeast Peten environmental niche—easier than simple swidden farming and infinitely more productive. Puleston points to the absence of terracing anywhere in the Northeast Peten or Tikal vicinity, a situation making the ramon-nut dependence of the large population concentrations here still more likely. One possible joker in the equation is the recently discovered possibility that the Bajo de Santa Fe, near Tikal, may have been filled with raised fields; as already noted, however, Puleston thinks that this possibility is very slight. Using the presence of chultunes as the archaeological clue to ramon-nut harvesting and storage, Puleston believes ramon-nut dependence was the principal economic mode in the Tikal region as early as the Late Preclassic and, perhaps, even before. The role of the ramon nut as the major staple for the Northeast Peten has been questioned by W. T. Sanders (1973:341), who, while conceding its value as a supplement, is hesitant to see it as the primary crop. He notes that nut-bearing trees are "notoriously variable in their yields from year to year" and that dependence upon them would therefore be risky. He also observes that the ramon nut, today, is considered rather a second-class food and a poor substitute for maize, and he thinks it likely that such attitudes prevailed in the past. The question remains open, especially in view of the possibility of raised field or chinampa cultivation in the nearby *bajos.* At this point another question occurs to me: If the lowland Maya of the Northeast Peten had such a reliable and easily obtainable food resource as Puleston believes the ramon nut to have been, why did they "collapse"? If Puleston is correct, this "collapse" must have had little or nothing to do with subsistence problems.

The second general conclusion or working premise, that lowland Maya population concentrations were too great for the carrying capacity of swidden maize farming alone, is touched upon by several of the contributors. Don Rice's house-mound counting in the Yaxha-Sacnab is a systematic example (chap. 4). He comes up with population estimates that climb from Middle Preclassic beginnings of 25 persons per square kilometer to 210 persons per square kilometer for the Late Classic (A.D. 600–800) climax. These Classic-period estimates, which are conservatively drawn, are well in excess of the carrying capacity of a one-to-four-year swidden fallow system. In Rice's opinion, agricultural intensification measures were taken to sustain this population growth. Another case would be that described by D. T. Vlcek and his coauthors (chap. 11). This concerns the Northern Lowland site of Chunchucmil. At the end of the Late Classic the large architectural center of Chunchucmil covered a square kilometer. Surrounding this were another 6 square kilometers of closely packed structures, with individual small mound groupings separated by boundary walls. Farther out is another 13 square kilometers of less densely packed small structures. An estimate of at least 12,000 persons is given for the inner zone of 6 square kilometers, a population far too large for the surrounding terrain to have supported by swidden farming. In the Chunchucmil example intensive cultivation in the immediate environs seems to be precluded by the nature of the setting and soils, and it is the archaeologists' opinion that foodstuffs must have been imported from elsewhere to sustain the population.

These two examples lead us into a consideration of the third conclusion or working premise, that of variability or variation in agricultural techniques, in time, in space, and by cultural choice. Wiseman has stated (p. 113) that "no single agricultural technique, either actual or hypothetical, will satisfy the requirements of the demographic, ecological, and palynological data." Viewing the Maya lowlands as a whole throughout its agricultural history it is difficult to dispute this statement. But beyond this point there is considerable difference of opinion as to the course of this variability, especially in the chronological dimension. What might be called the conventional view of Maya lowland agricultural development is that expounded by Sanders (1973) and generally accepted in the papers from the Santa Fe symposium on *The Classic Maya Collapse* (Culbert 1973). It is again set out in the second Santa Fe symposium on *The Origins of Maya Civilization* (Adams 1977; see especially the article by Sanders). According to this view, agricultural production steadily increased from Preclassic through Classic times, stimulated by population increases. Whether we follow a Boserup (1965) model or merely hold that there was an interlocking relationship, as yet not fully understood, between population growth and food supply, the assumption is that long-fallow swidden, with maize as the principal crop, was the initial agricultural system in the Maya lowlands. Then, as population grew, it became necessary to augment food production, and the intensification techniques came into existence, being variously and regionally deployed according to environmental conditions. In the Yaxha-Sacnab region Rice's settlement studies do seem to support this kind of a sequence. In the Middle Preclassic what he designates as the "tall upland vegetation zone" probably would have supported all of the regional population. This is an environmental zone well-suited to maize swidden cultivation, and the interpretation is further supported by the fact that most of the settlement of the period is confined to this zone. Settlement was dispersed through the zone, although even at this early time there are indications of an organizational center. Afterward, toward the end of the Late Preclassic period, with an increase in population, the first subsistence stress is suggested by the first occupation of the "moist slope" environmental zone. While there are no definite evidences of intensification techniques, either through terracing or clues to crop diversification, Rice speculates that maize was probably now supplemented with root crops and that an attempt may have been made to reduce the maize fallow cycle. By Classic times increased populations (as indicated by increased settlement) probably demanded ramon-nut harvesting in addition to the former crops. In Rice's opinion, the situation by this time allowed the population few options. They were exploiting all the agricultural possibilities of their environment, and that environment, in its upland and slope zones, was suffering from erosion as the result of agricultural activities. It is pertinent to note that in this instance there are no indications of raised fields having been constructed in the swampy areas of the lake shores. Whether or not this was a cultural choice or one in some way dictated by particular soil or drainage conditions is uncertain. As I say, Rice's work seems to support the conventional developmental picture although the data for intensification are somewhat equivocal, and the techniques or means used did not include either terracing or raised fields.

In the Rio Bec region, as already noted, Turner is of the opinion, although he advances it cautiously, that the very definite agricultural terracing found there is probably Late Classic. This implies that earlier farming methods were probably of the swidden type, and this is supportive of the conventional sequence. By and large, though, as of the present writing, the early-swidden-to-later-intensification methods sequence is largely a "logical" reconstruction based on the belief that in a tropical forest environment swidden farming is the simplest and easiest. That is, until population pressure begins to mount, food requirements are best satisfied, with the least expenditure of labor, by annual cutting and burning of the vegetation, planting, and harvesting, followed by a fallow cycle. We have seen that Puleston has challenged this belief with his ramon-nut theory, at least with reference to Tikal and the Northeast Peten. The conventional developmental model has also been challenged elsewhere and for other reasons.

Norman Hammond poses such a challenge in his paper (chap. 3) by suggesting that a raised field or chinampa technology was brought to the Maya lowlands by the first agricultural settlers, in Middle Preclassic or even Early Preclassic times. Presumably, such immigrants would have moved into the region from lower Central and South America. By farming this way, little Preclassic communities would have been able to maintain a relatively restricted area of residence and to expend less time and energy going to and from distant fields than would have been demanded under a swidden system. Eventually, with population buildup, more extensive farming would have been necessary. Some of this could have been carried out by enlarging raised fields and increasing their number, but when the population moved into terrain unsuited for this technology, swidden cultivation would have been practiced. Thus the conventional developmental sequence is turned around in this hypothesis. Hammond, as well as Puleston, cites early radiocarbon dates for raised fields in northern Belize, dates that carry the technique back to the second millennium B.C., so that there is at least some—although not very much—chronological evidence to the effect that raised-field intensive farming has a great antiquity in the Maya lowlands.

Other kinds of variability have been discussed in several of the papers. Culbert and his colleagues, using modern ethnographic data, refer to the possibility that multiple-cropping, or the growing of two or even three harvests per year, may have been practiced in the past, as it is today, in the Poptun region. Were certain regions of favorable soils and rainfall more advantageous than others? Does this apply to the Northeastern Peten, the region that appears to have been the original "core" of the development of Classic Maya civilization? Or were the advantages here to be found in the availability of the ramon tree, following Puleston's suggestion?

Most interesting in regard to this matter of variability is the factor of cultural choice. It is, of course, difficult to explain. Vlcek, Garza, and Kurjack cannot explain the location of the organizational center of Chunchucmil on the basis of agricultural potential of the immediately surrounding land. Given the settlement evidences there, food to support the resident population must have been brought in from elsewhere, although probably not from a very great distance. In the Chunchucmil case it is a possibility that salt resources and the exploitation of and trade in this commodity were responsible for the city's location. And yet there are no easy answers. In the concluding section of his impressive paper (chap. 14) in which he compares Tikal, Angkor, Prambanan, and Anuradhapura, sites of tropical lowland settings in various parts of the world, Bennet Bronson states that neither favorable agricultural soils, nonagricultural resources, nor sitings for trade-route advantages will explain the location of such cities. He also makes the point that in comparing the Maya and southeast Asian civilizations he feels that the greatest weakness of the former, in the sense of developmental potential, was a logistic one, the ability to move goods, especially bulk goods like foodstuffs, over long distances. Such a weakness or limitation might give more force to the argument that urban development for the Maya would have been more closely tied to, even if not completely confined by, food resource regions. But, as we have seen, there do seem to be exceptions.

Let me close with some personal conclusions. These are over and above the three general conclusions with which I began this summary and with which, I think, most of us are probably in agreement. In addition, it would now be my first speculation that all of the cultivation techniques which have been reviewed here were probably known from the time of the earliest farming settlements in the Maya lowlands. The one possible exception would be terracing, but even of this I am not sure, for silt-trapping, on a small scale, is probably a very old technique. Second, as to the sequence of techniques, I am not sure, nor do I think that anyone else can be at our present state of knowledge. Working the sequence out by securing the right kinds of evidence is going to be very difficult and something that will be with us for a long time. It would be my guess that this developmental sequence will vary from place to place. What is clear is that population size, although perhaps fluctuating downward temporarily during the Protoclassic and, again, at the time of the Classic Hiatus, moved generally upward until the Terminal Late Classic, accompanied by a deployment of agricultural techniques to take advantage of as many possibilities as could be discerned in the light of existing technology. Third, I am in agreement with those who have emphasized the importance of cultural choice or decision making. It is a factor to be reckoned with along with the natural environmental and technological ones. Ideas are a part of any ecological equation dealing with humans. Fourth and finally, let me say that after reading all of these assembled papers I am still convinced—whatever the farming technologies employed by the Lowland Maya—that certain kinds of urban development, indeed those aspects most closely associated in our minds with the formal definition of the word *urban,* the close-spaced residential districts of Teotihuacan or Tenochtitlan, or the ancient Middle East, were not feasible in this tropical forest environment on a preindustrial level. Perhaps this is overstated, and I might be willing to modify it to say certain *degrees* (rather than *kinds*) of urban development, or to change "on a preindustrial level" to "without more effective logistical support"; but I think my meaning is essentially clear. This is not to deny a number of important urban or civilized functions to Tikal; but its 50,000 persons dispersed over 165 square kilometers (Haviland 1969, 1970) makes for not only a quantitatively but a qualitatively different entity than does Teotihuacan's 100,000 to 200,000 residents packed within a zone of 21 square kilometers (Millon 1973). The lowland Maya "ceremonial center," or "vacant city," concept has undoubtedly been overpolarized and overdone, for there can be no denying the many urban qualities of such great centers as Tikal; we are dealing, however, with a continuum in sizes, population densities, and functions. This continuum is, I think, to be viewed in the course of lowland Maya developmental prehistory, and it also has value for comparative projections of the Maya vis-à-vis other Mesoamerican developments. In my opinion, the Classic Maya failure of the ninth century A.D. might be described as a failure to proceed far enough on the ceremonial-center-to-true-city continuum. This is a digression from the strict theme of Lowland Maya agriculture, but the connections and implications are there for any Mesoamericanist to see.

17

B. L. TURNER II
Department of Geography, University of Oklahoma

PETER D. HARRISON
Middle American Research Institute

Implications from Agriculture for Maya Prehistory

Views concerning the nature of pre-Hispanic Maya agriculture and subsistence as outlined in this volume have undergone considerable modification during the past decade as the amount of evidence specific to the subject has increased. The blossoming of new and reevaluated data pertinent to ancient lowland subsistence has been the result of expanded research interests in the Maya and their habitats by specialists from various disciplines. As we have seen, the general consensus of most specialists actively engaged in field research is a rejection of the traditional swidden or milpa thesis and the adoption of a more variable subsistence model that includes numerous modes of food production and trade. As the evidence against the swidden thesis increases it is becoming apparent that the lowland Maya were not an exceptional instance among early civilizations, but that they shared most, if not all, of the agricultural attributes that comparable cultures maintained.

MODES OF MAYA FOOD PRODUCTION

Agriculture was the principal food source of the lowland Maya civilization. Systems of agriculture varied through time and space in the lowlands, ranging from simplistic, extensive systems of cultivation to elaborate, intensive ones. This theme is highlighted by Wiseman (chap. 5), among others; his pollen work has led him to reject the concept of monocultural systems of agriculture, such as a total reliance on swidden or intensive monocropping of maize. Numerous suggestions have been made as to the types of agriculture utilized by the Maya, including swidden, kitchen gardens, orchard gardens, artificial rain forests, raised fields, and terraces. The presence of ancient terraces and raised fields in the lowlands confirm that these two forms of cultivation were used by the Maya. The other systems of agriculture are inferred, although it seems reasonable to assume that most of them were utilized during pre-Hispanic times, especially swidden (see Barrera, Gómez-Pompa, and Vásquez-Yanes 1977).

A critical point of disagreement concerns the significance of any one type of agriculture in time and space. We believe that those methods required to sustain crop production were pursued whenever and wherever the need arose, and for the most part lowland agriculture was not impeded by so-called marginal environments or by limited Maya agricultural expertise. The evidence to date simply does not support a restricted view of lowland cultivation.

The specific types of cultivation employed by the Maya depended largely on the quality and amount of land available, the crops utilized, and other factors. In the northeastern segment of the central lowlands, for example, the Maya pursued large-scale raised-field agriculture. The fact that much of this area contained seasonally inundated land and that it required considerable manipulation to cultivate apparently did not hinder Maya cultivators.

The importance of raised-field cultivation in the lowlands is attested by the number of fields that have been observed at varying locations, including northern Belize and adjacent sectors of Peten, southern Quintana Roo, the Candelaria region of Campeche, sectors of Tabasco (Arturo Gómez-Pompa, personal communication), and Tres Bocas, Veracruz (Peter Schmidt, personal communication). Most of the ancient raised fields have been observed only from the air, with ground identification of the fields in the Candelaria River Basin and in northern Belize.

Puleston suggests that many, if not most, of the reported raised fields observed from the air may be gilgai and that the distribution of the agricultural features should be assumed to correspond only with those fields that have been verified on the ground. This warning is well taken, especially when the features that are observed aerially differ in appearance from comparable verified fields. Too much should not be abstracted from limited data. We believe, however, that the gilgai argument is incorrect, and that those features that conform to certain patterns and sizes and that are located in appropriate habitats will eventually be confirmed as artificially constructed fields and/or systems of water control.

To our knowledge the gilgai that have been observed in the lowlands are small—about a square meter. No gilgai have been reported in the Maya region that approach the size of the larger raised fields, which commonly exceed 200 square meters. Furthermore, while gilgai in other regions of the world (generally colder or more arid environs than the lowlands) are often regular and rectangular in design, they rarely maintain the precision of angularity and pattern reported for Maya raised fields (see chap. 13). Several Maya raised-field locations are also crossed by large canals, such as the elbow-jointed canal near Nicolás Bravo, Quintana Roo, attesting the manipulated character of the *bajo* zones in which the relic fields are reported (figs. 17.1, 17.2).

The various ground verifications of artificial features in the lowlands are perhaps the most telling evidence against the gilgai argument. To our knowledge, every rectangular or linear feature in the Maya region that has been reported as a suspected raised field or canal has proved on ground examination to be an artificial construction. To date, adequate ground examination is lacking for the sighted features in the Bajo de Santa Fe near Tikal, and therefore those features must remain controversial. Among examples that have been verified are the canals at Edzna that from the air look more like gilgai than do the raised-field systems in the Maya region.

Despite the success of aerial observation in identifying ancient systems of land manipulation in the Maya region, many more reported features need to be examined. Perhaps most critical is the examination of the extensive raised-field systems reported for southern Quintana Roo, the largest network of reported fields in Mesoamerica. If proven to be relics, they will have significant repercussions for interpretations of lowland Maya agriculture, population, and trade. These features occur in *bajos,* although an

Figure 17.1 Reported large canals near Nicolás Bravo, Quintana Roo, Mexico. The light-colored vegetation is situated on raised surfaces, and the dark vegetation is in depressions. All vegetation is a 4-to-5-meter-high scrub forest. The canals are approximately 25 meters wide.

Figure 17.2 Reported raised fields near Nicolás Bravo, Quintana Roo, Mexico. The light-colored and higher vegetation of rectangular pattern is probably situated on relics of raised platforms of dirt. This pattern is strikingly similar to the known raised fields in the Maya area. The length of the longer patterns approaches 50 meters.

ancient river system may have existed, and their study should provide critical information necessary to evaluate Siemens's discussion of the distinctions between Peten and more northern *bajos.*

The presence of relic terraces and field demarcation (stone walls) in the Maya lowlands is well noted and their significance accepted, but several important questions need clarification. Why, for instance, do reports of these features, so prevalent in the Rio Bec Zone (field demarcation extends across most of the Yucatan Peninsula), grow less common to the south in Peten? The Peten Maya knew how to terrace and certainly had a need for this practice where sloping terrain was cultivated intensively. Despite the suggested need, reports of relic terraces in the Peten away from the foothills of the Maya Mountains are limited to a brief note by Turner (1974a:124) on a ravine about ten kilometers southwest

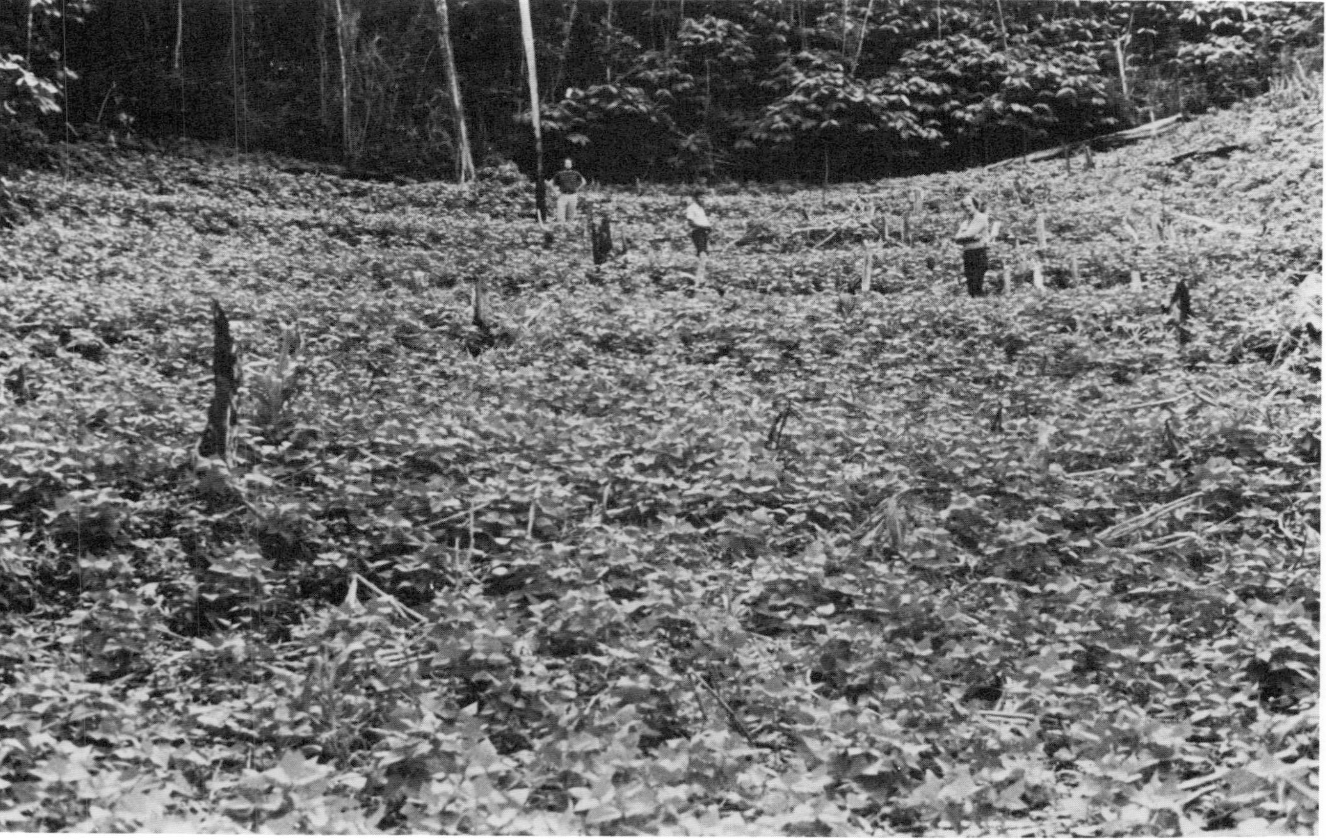

Figure 17.3. Remnants of ancient terraces near Lake Yaxha, Peten, Guatemala. The men are standing on three of the six visible terraces (flat surfaces), which have been constructed across a steep ravine.

of Yaxha (fig. 17.3). Also of note is a reference by Blom (1946:5) to terraces "in Belize and in the Peten." Perhaps the paucity of reports of terracing and field demarcation reflects the effort extended to search for these features or denotes an ancient agricultural emphasis on orchard gardens (Puleston), artificial rain forests (Wiseman), or, more likely, *bajo* manipulation (Harrison).

Puleston has raised questions about the dating of terraces in the Maya region, apparently inferring that they may be of Postclassic origin. Dating terraces is a difficult procedure because of the poor preservation of cultural remains within the structure and the absence of plaster to designate levels of construction. House sites, a logical association with terraces, can be dated more accurately than the stone walls. The configuration of a field system with a house site at the summit of a hill, surrounded by terraces crossing the slopes (fig. 17.4) is a strong indication that the site and the walls were probably contemporaneous, although some researchers remain skeptical.

Fortunately, the Maya often constructed platforms of stone that are structurally part of the terrace systems (Turner 1974b:310–11). These platforms tend to be over a meter high and filled with sufficient rubble to contain datable cultural remains. Ceramic materials from two such platforms on two different terrace systems in the Rio Bec region suggests that the features were constructed after A.D. 600 and A.D. 830, respectively (Turner 1974b:321–22). These dates correspond with the Late and Terminal Classic periods of heavy population concentrations in the Rio Bec Zone as determined by house site and structure studies. Since the Rio Bec region was sparsely occupied after A.D. 1050 (the end of the Terminal Classic period for the region), it is extremely doubtful that the Postclassic inhabitants had the work force or the need to construct the terrace systems. The most logical conclusion is that the elaborate network of walls and related features was built during the later stages of Classic Maya occupation, although initial terrace constructions may have begun earlier.

Field demarcation apart from terraces raises serious interpretative problems. Do the demarcated plots that are so prevalent across the Yucatan Peninsula represent ancient fields of intensive cultivation? If so, what type of agriculture was pursued within them? The sizes of the plots, usually less than one hectare, and the house sites that are generally contained within them suggest an intensive

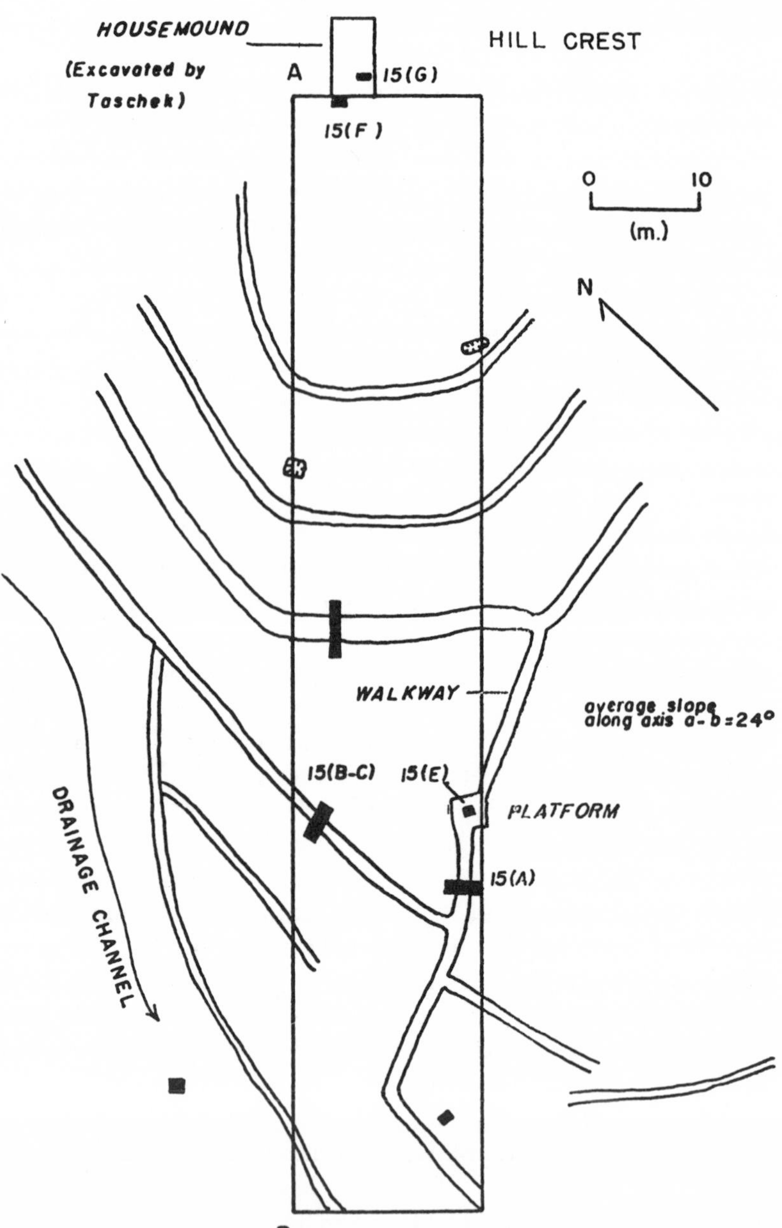

Figure 17.4. Sketch of a segment of a terraced hillside near Xpujil, Campeche, Mexico. Note the large walls running upslope and the characteristic house mound on the hilltop. The large rectangle represents the area cleared of bush. The dark squares and rectangles represent locations of excavations. The house site was excavated by Jennifer Tascheck Ball.

gardening system, as noted by Harris (chap. 15), in which case swidden or other types of staple cultivation probably took place at a distance from the house sites and plots. In numerous instances, however, the demarcated plots extend over such large areas, as reported by Vlcek and his colleagues, that it is difficult to imagine the Maya farmer walking to the proposed distant outfields. Rather, importation of food is suggested. Much more work is needed on this topic.

INTENSITY OF LOWLAND AGRICULTURE

The level of agricultural intensification that the lowland Maya were capable of sustaining requires significant reexamination in light of the recent evidence. Without doubt the lowlanders were not limited to extensive, swidden levels of intensity. The large-scale stoneworks and earthworks attest levels of intensification much higher than those generally associated with swidden. The controversy now centers on the levels of intensification with which the ancient agricultural features were associated.

Agricultural form or type must not be confused with intensity in examining this problem. *Type* refers to the technical aspects of the system of cultivation, such as slash-and-burn, field raising, or terracing. *Intensity* refers to inputs or outputs of the agricultural system, although it is recognized that certain types of agriculture are commonly related to certain intensities of cultivation. *Input measures* refer to labor or capital intensification. *Output measures* refer to the amount of production from a *constant source of land over a specified period of time.* The output measure, which has been adopted as the reference of agricultural intensity in this text, is strongly associated with the frequency of and the skills employed in cultivation, but also is infiuenced by the types of cultivars, environment, and other variables. Given the current status of the data pertaining to pre-Hispanic Maya agriculture, the frequency of cultivation or the crop-fallow ratio are adequate measures of agricultural intensity. As the quality of the data improves, however, more elaborate measures that better reflect agricultural output should be adopted (see Turner and Doolittle 1978).

The distinction between agricultural form and intensity requires explicit recognition because of recent developments regarding interpretations of Maya cultivation in which the two terms are utilized either in a confusing manner or as synonyms. Drawing from West African parallels, Netting (1977) has proposed that the Maya may have employed an agricultural system based on kitchen gardening within or near settlements and other types of cultivation at more distant locations. Apparently, several students of the Maya implicitly and erroneously have interpreted Netting's use of the term *kitchen garden* to infer some sort of extensive agriculture or, at least, a form of agriculture that cannot compare favorably in terms of intensity with other forms of agriculture. Netting (personal communication) neither suggests nor implies this interpretation, but uses the term in reference to intensive—high input and output—cultivation. Other interpretations of Netting's terminology are not warranted.

It is important to recognize that agricultural intensification varied spatially and temporally throughout the lowlands and that various levels of intensity may have been in use at any one place and time. The major concern, however, is the proper interpretation of the maximum intensity that the Maya were able to sustain. Sanders (1973:362) has proposed that the lowland Maya probably did not exceed a crop-fallow ratio of 1:1 (one year of cultivation to one year of fallow). He views this intensity level as a liberal assessment, since grass invasion of the cultivated land would have presented enormous labor problems.

We take issue with Sanders's assessment. Studies of vegetation succession in the Maya lowlands do not support the grass-invasion hypothesis. Cultivated land in the Rio Bec region, for example, is invaded by several weeds, but within a few months of fallow various ferns and composites are the dominant species. Most of the grasslands in the Maya region are probably edaphic and not the result of past cultivation. We agree with Sanders that intensive cultivation would often have required large amounts of labor, but we think that in numerous cases the Maya exceeded a 1:1 crop-fallow ratio.

The presence of relics of stone terraces and raised fields are evidence of intensive cultivation, although the precise levels of intensity are difficult to determine. This assessment must not be confused with arguments concerning societal organization associated with agricultural types or intensification. While Harris is correct in noting that both raised fields and stone terraces (as well as irrigation networks) are often constructed by "simply organized tribal societies," the level of societal complexity apparently does not affect the intensity of cultivation. Denevan and Turner's (1974) study of raised fields in the Old World tropics indicates that this cropping technique is generally associated with intensive cultivation, regardless of the people involved. Terraces and raised-field works may be constructed slowly over lengthy periods of time by simply organized peoples, but this cannot be interpreted as necessarily affecting labor inputs per field or the frequency of cultivation per field. The natives of Frederick-Hendrick Island, for example, have constructed small-scale raised-field complexes over periods of years, but these fields are intensively cultivated (Serpenti 1965).

Mesoamerican peoples were astute farmers, and the Maya were no exception. We suggest that the pre-Hispanic lowlanders had the ability to cultivate the same parcel of land for lengthy periods of time with only short periods of fallow. The ancient terraces and raised fields do not indicate that intensive cultivation was limited to these features. Indeed, numerous level but well-drained areas that received adequate precipitation probably were the prime agricultural lands for the Maya and may have been the most intensively cultivated with the excepiton of raised fields. Unfortunately, these flatlands could be cropped regularly without leaving obvious evidence to indicate some of the techniques utilized for cultivation. As a result, attention is focused on lands with terraces and raised fields, since for these features comparisons can be made with contemporary systems in similar environmental circumstances.

FOOD SOURCES

Cultivation and Collection

The significance of particular cultivars and other sources of food utilized by the pre-Hispanic Maya deserves more detailed consideration than has been given in this volume. Problems of pollen preservation in the lowlands will continue to hinder research efforts in this direction. Perhaps opal phytolith analysis will prove a boon to recovering plant remains, although much further work is required to demonstrate the utility of this technique for the identification of tropical flora. Regardless of the research problems, it is becoming clear that the lowland Maya utilized a large variety of culitvated and collected foods and that the importance of any single cultivar or wild food will be difficult to prove.

That maize (*Zea mays*) was an important food for the lowland Maya is indisputable. Its dominance in terms of percentage of lowland diet has been questioned on several occasions, however, such as Bronson's (1966) diligent root-crop argument. Puleston (1974b) has gone as far as to suggest that maize was eaten primarily by the elite classes in the central Peten and that the mainstay of the lower classes was ramon (*Brosimum alicastrum*). According to Puleston's argument, the significance of ramon in the diet of the central lowlanders should have increased as populations reached their Late Classic peaks. This trend probably should be discernible as an increase in ramon pollen during the period in question; as more food was required the lowlanders would preserve more ramon trees and the relative amount of ramon pollen would increase. Palynological studies by Wiseman, however, demonstrate no significant change through time in *Brosimum-Cecropia* pollen, suggesting that the presence of ramon in the Central Maya Zone did not increase during the Late Classic period. Wiseman (personal communication) has further confirmed the statistical significance of an increase in maize pollen for the same period, suggesting that the cultivation of maize in relation to the collection of ramon was increasing in importance in the Central Zone during the Late Classic period. This result is precisely the opposite of that predicted by the ramon thesis.

Wiseman's results are open to numerous interpretations, some of which he will present elsewhere in the near future. Regarding the maize-ramon discussion, however, it should be noted that this new evidence seriously challenges the ramon thesis. This thesis is based on two tenuous assumptions, namely the present distribution of the ramon as an indicator of the significance of this tree more than 1,000 years ago, and the function of the double-chambered chultunes that occur in the central Maya region.

None of the suggested functions of the double-chambered chultun have gained wide acceptance, despite Puleston's (1971) assertions that they were utilized as storage pits for ramon nuts. While ramon-nut storage may have been the chultun's basic function in the central Peten, it is difficult to explain why damp, subterranean storage facilities would have been favored over elevated, breeze-blown containers. By far the most questionable aspect of the ramon thesis, however, is the assumption that the present distribution of the ramon reflects past distribution. The clustering of ramon within sites may represent an affinity of this species for disturbed conditions. Until botanical studies solve this question, the ramon thesis remains speculative. These problems, the new data offered by Wiseman and others, and the arguments concerning the variability of the nut's productivity (Sanders 1973) lead us tentatively to reduce the significance of ramon in the normal diet of the pre-Hispanic Maya, although we do not question its use as a dietary supplement or as a famine food.

Intensive examination of *bajos* and "rural" terrain in the central lowlands of Peten, the region to which the ramon thesis applies, may help resolve the issue. If relics of agricultural features are found in relation to either terrain type, then we should look to domesticated plants as the key element in the diet of past inhabitants. To date, thorough ground surveys in the central zone away from major civic-temple centers have been limited and generally have not included areas lying much more than ten kilometers from the heart of the centers. Based on the network of ancient agricultural features that extends outward from Becan, it should not be surprising to find such features at considerable distances from a center the size of Tikal. Although undated, terraces that appear to be ancient have been found about thirty-five kilometers southeast of Tikal and more detailed ground examination should uncover other such evidence (fig. 17.3).

An extremely large number of cultivated and wild plants was available to the lowland Maya for food, fiber, dye, and other uses. Lundell (1939) has compiled a lengthy list of these plants, of which several of the more important are noted here. Beans (*Phaseolus vulgaris*) and squashes (*Cucurbita moschata* and *C. pepo*) were undoubtedly cultivated separately and intercropped with maize. Also cultivated were a variety of roots and tubers, the importance of which may have rivaled that of maize: sweet potato (*Ipomoeo batatas*), manioc (*Manihot esculenta* and *M. dulcis*), malanga (*Xanthosoma violaceum*), and jicama (*Pachyrhizus erosus*). Other important crops were the tomato (*Lycopersicum esculentum*), chayote (*Sechium edule*), and chaya (*Jatropha aconitifolia*). Domesticated and semidomesticated plants included, among others, the ramon, mamey apple (*Calocarpum mammosum*), avocado (*Persea americana*), zapote (*Achras zapote*), and papaya (*Carica papaya*). Several other important plants included cacao (*Theobroma cacao*), chiles (*Capsicum annum, C. frutesceus,* and *C. baccatun*), cotton (*Gossypium*), and henequen (*Agave sisalana*).

Further consideration must be given to the respective roles of luxury and utilitarian crops as influences on pre-Hispanic Maya agriculture. Much of the Maya realm is prime land for the cultivation of tropical fruits, cacao, cotton, and henequen. The possible significance of cacao has been raised in this volume by Hammond, but other crops may have provided important inter- and intraregional trade goods, especially cotton and henequen. Future work should examine the possibility of ecologically favorable zones for specialty crops in the lowlands and the significance of these zones to regional agriculture and trade.

Fishing, Hunting, and Animal Husbandry

Bronson's queries concerning the protein sources available to the Maya are critical to all examinations of lowland agriculture and subsistence. Considerations of protein sources are particularly important in light of the data indicating that the lowlands often contained substantial populations. Aquatic resources as a major source of protein, especially fish, among the pre-Hispanic Maya have drawn considerable speculation of late (Lange 1971; D. E. Puleston and O. S. Puleston 1971). J. E. S. Thompson (1974) has postulated that fish were a sufficiently important protein source for the lowlanders that they were obtained from specially constructed fish traps or ponds. That the Maya practiced a sophisticated form of fish collection is a reasonable assumption, and that they may have practiced pisciculture is an intriguing idea that deserves exploration. At this moment, however, the evidence for either practice on an elaborate scale is extremely speculative, and theoretical arguments in their support must be cautious of several pitfalls.

Thompson's fish trap argument is directed only to the long, linear canals found by Siemens and Puleston (1972) in the Candelaria River Basin (also see Matheny, chap. 10). Thompson does not include the rectangular raised fields that also occur in the Candelaria Basin in his thesis. The latter features were undoubtedly constructed for purposes of cultivation, although auxiliary gathering of aquatic resources may have taken place. The size of the raised-field surfaces in relation to the surrounding ditches is too large to explain the features simply as spoil banks from the ditches, despite the notions of Thomas Schorr (cited in Thompson 1974: 301). This conclusion is based on the comparative evidence of the size and form of contemporary raised fields (Denevan and Turner 1974) and of prehistoric fish ponds (e.g., Kikuchi 1976). The pre-Hispanic Maya were excellent engineers and it is doubtful that their efforts to construct canals, traps, or ponds would have resulted in the large raised surfaces that have been found in the lowlands. Furthermore, early Spanish accounts alluded to and documented the cultivation of raised surfaces similar to those in the Maya region in Venezuela (Castellanos 1955:539; Gumilla 1945:430–31).

Other than canals not associated with raised fields, the most likely areas for Maya fish traps or ponds are the shallow lakes and *bajos* that occur throughout the lowlands. To date, however, evidence of lake ponds or diking in lakes is lacking. The extension of pisciculture to *bajos* would require considerable hydraulic manipulation. Nevertheless, researchers should keep a sharp watch for possible evidence of ancient fish farms or traps in *bajos* and other hydromorphic zones in the lowlands.

The pre-Hispanic Maya were actively engaged in hunting with the use of the bow and arrow, atlatl, snare, deadfall trap, spiked pit, and net trap (C. Thomas 1882:97; Franco 1969). The large number of game hunted by the Maya have been discussed by Gann (1918:24), Roys (1931:347), and Lange (1971), and need not be reiterated here. Absent in the discussions of Maya hunting and collecting are considerations of habitat modifications wrought by the Maya and the effect of these modifications on wild animal populations in the lowlands. Future examinations must account for this factor in determining the significance of hunting to the pre-Hispanic Maya.

Animal husbandry among the Maya is an often ignored topic that deserves careful examination, as noted by Harris (chap. 15). The lowlanders had the domesticated dog (*Canis familiares* or *C. caibaeus*), which they probably fattened and ate, as was the practice in other parts of Mesoamerica. A reevaluation of the literature indicates that the Maya may have tamed, semidomesticated, and possibly domesticated several other animals.

Bishop Landa (Tozzer 1941:201) reported that the postconquest Maya raised a large number of fowl, including parrots, turkeys, and others:

> They have domesticated [tame?] fowls, which they raise in great quantities in their houses like hens and cocks, though they are troublesome to raise. . . . Some people raise doves [*Columbigallina rufipennis* Bonaparte] as tame as ours and they multiply rapidly. They raise a certain kind of large white mallard [Muscovy] duck [*Cairina Moschata*]. . . .

The bishop (Tozzer 1941:127) also reported that Maya women let

> deer suck their breast, by which means they raise them and make them so tame that they never will go into the woods, although they take them and carry them through the woods and raise them there.

The possibility that deer (*Odocoileus toltecus*) were at least semidomesticated by the Maya is very real (see Harris, chap. 15). Several early Spanish accounts of exploration in the Maya region report the docility of deer to the intruders (Means 1917:30), suggesting previous adaptation toward humans.

Landa also raises the issue of the semidomestication or taming of the coatimundi (*Nasua narica yucatanica*) by the Maya. He notes (Tozzer 1941:204–5) that:

> The Indian women raised them and they leave nothing which they do not root over and turn upside-down and it is an incredible thing how wonderfully fond they are of playing with the Indian women and how they clean them of lice and they always go to them and will have nothing to do with a man in their lives. There are many of them and they always go in herds in a row, one after the other, with their snouts thrust in each others' tails. . . .

The impact of these various animals on Maya subsistence deserves further consideration, although the possiblity exists that some, such as the Muscovy duck, were post-Hispanic introductions into the Maya region.

Agricultural Trade

Most studies of Maya trade have centered on the exchange of elite goods and postulated trade networks, particularly in Postclassic times (Chapman 1957; J. E. S. Thompson 1964; Sabloff and Rathje 1975). Major trade in agricultural goods and the effects that such trade might have had on patterns of Maya cultivation previous to the Postclassic period have been largely ignored. This situation is the result of the long-prevalent view that the "ecological uniformity" of the lowlands impeded the development of trade (L. A. Parsons and Price 1971; Tourtellot and Sabloff 1972), and of the paucity of evidence indicating major trading by the Classic Maya for items other than elite goods (Sabloff 1974). The arguments favoring major trade activity prior to the Postclassic have failed to consider agricultural trade for various reasons, the most apparent being the ecological homogeneity thesis (Rathje 1972). We believe that the evidence in this volume (Vleck, Garza, and Kurjack, chap. 11), coupled with that which is already in the literature (see Dillon 1975), raises legitimate questions concerning the role of pre-Hispanic Maya trade in foodstuffs, and that future agricultural considerations of the ancient lowlands must begin to consider trade.

Evidence that the Maya may have engaged in major trade for agricultural goods is largely inferential, and acceptance of long-distance trading in staple items is probably contingent on proof that inland trade was water borne. Siemens has postulated a trade-route network for the Tikal region, and Matheny provides interesting evidence that canal routes may have been utilized by the Maya in the Tabascan area and along the Campeche Coast. The data are insufficient, however, to allow judgments on the presence or absence of relic inland water routes or to establish the chronologies of the canals.

The size of some Maya sites suggests that pre-Hispanic populations were sufficiently large to have warranted food production from areas lying considerable distances from the site. It is not unreasonable to assume that Tikal may have been too large to have fed itself and had to rely on the importation of food items from nearby areas. The extensive zone of terraces in western Belize raises questions of food trade to sites such as Tikal. If the immediate terrace zone were not densely occupied—and the data appear to substantiate this assumption—then the terraces may be interpreted as an agricultural extension of the densely settled Peten lowlands. Food could have been transported along the Macal-Chiquibul-Mopan-Belize river system and via the Holmul River to the interior.

The presence of large coastal sites reported by Vleck and his colleagues offers another intriguing bit of evidence in support of major trade in agricultural goods by the lowland Maya. We find it extremely doubtful that the populace of Chunchucmil could have sustained itself on the one-quarter-hectare plots that surround the house sites of the center. We further concur with the authors that the paucity of soil in the immediate vicinity of the site suggests that large-scale cultivation would have required considerable land manipulation, for which no evidence is presented, or that some food must have been brought to the site from other locales.

Chunchucmil may well have owed its existence to salt trade or to some other specialized function, such as henequen production. Despite arguments to the contrary, salt probably was a major long-distance-trade item for the lowland Maya (Blom 1932:535–36; J. E. S. Thompson 1964:16, Dillon 1975:98–104). Sodium is an essential element for the human body, although the necessary quantity is not clear (Kaunitz 1956; Block 1963). While sodium can be obtained from various sources—which means that salt itself may be a luxury item, as noted by Puleston (chap. 12)—two lines of evidence suggest that salt was a principal source of sodium for the pre-Hispanic Maya. As Block (1963:89) notes, most vegetarian-based diets require an additional two to five grams of mineral salts per person per day. The sheer size of the ancient lowland populace would have necessitated considerable maintenance of appropriate vegetable materials, such as palm leaves, in order to have obtained sufficient quantities of sodium from this source. We feel that the amount of land devoted to agriculture and other land uses would have made such maintenance difficult and that salt trade would probably have been a more efficient means of providing sodium to the diet of the lowlanders. Furthermore, once introduced to mineral salt, the human body may have a tendency to become "addicted" to it, craving much larger dosages of the mineral than it needs (Kaunitz 1956:1141; Block 1963:89). The Maya did utilize mineral salt and probably developed a "salt habit," as do most human populations. These two arguments, and the fact that salt was probably the major meat and fish preservative available to the Maya, add considerable weight to the view that salt was an important item to the pre-Hispanic lowlanders and that long-distance trading for this item took place. Indeed, the survival of the northern Yucatecan Maya into Postclassic times may have some connection with coastal salt production.

AGRICULTURAL GROWTH IN THE MAYA LOWLANDS

Direct evidence of the developmental sequence of Maya agriculture is sparse, despite the recent evidence from Belize (Puleston 1977; Hammond 1977). This problem has stimulated the use of agricultural growth models to project the sequence of development in the lowlands. Environmental theses have been influential in the past, stressing the limiting nature of the "marginal" or "hostile" lowland forest to agricultural growth among the Classic Maya. Recently, Boserup's (1965) thesis that environmental barriers to agricultural growth are limited, and that this growth corresponds largely to population pressures, has been most influential. The details of this thesis have been evaluated elsewhere and need not be reiterated here (Spooner 1972; Turner, Hanham, and Portararo 1977). It is sufficient to note that the environmental theses, as stated, are probably incorrect, and that Boserup's thesis has been useful in reconstructing the *broader* patterns of pre-Hispanic agricultural growth in the lowlands. Both theoretical arguments and data concerning the cultivation of the Maya have reached a level of sophistication that demands more complex considerations than the views that have been advanced.

Recent studies by Brown and Podelefsky (1976) and Turner and his colleagues (1977) have demonstrated a strong statistical relationship between population density (a crude measure of population pressure) and agricultural intensities among subsistence-type cultivators in the tropics. These works add strength to Boserup's and Brookfield's (1962) basic observations and indicate that variations in population density through time and space in the Maya lowlands were probably associated with various levels of agricultural intensity, assuming that most Maya populations were primarily subsistence oriented. If Maya farmers attempted to maximize agricultural efficiency (derive the most output per unit of input), a general tendency toward extensive, long-fallow systems and intensive, short- to no-fallow systems should have existed where population densities were low and high, respectively. Perhaps as many as 60 percent of the intensities of agricultural systems among the Maya may have been attributable to population factors (Turner, Hanham, and Portararo 1977).

Additional variables may also help explain patterns of pre-Hispanic Maya cultivation. Turner and his colleagues, following Brookfield's (1972) lead, have demonstrated that environmental factors are the second most important influence on agricultural intensity after population density. Unlike some of their predecessors, they do not see this influence as limiting or restraining to agricultural growth. All land may be viewed as part of a continuum of agricultural feasibility, ranging from marginal land that requires considerable manipulation to culitvate to optimal land that requires minimal preparations to cultivate. As population pressures mount in marginal agricultural zones, agricultural intensities rise quickly because the time and labor expended to make the land usable are not economically justifiable unless intensive cultivation ensues. Cultivation intensifies rapidly on optimal land also because the environmental quality is such that a high agricultural efficiency can be maintained without rotating or fallowing fields. In short, agricultural intensities tend to be greater per level of population density where environmental extremes in terms of agricultural feasibility are encountered.

This argument suggests that Maya sites or zones that had similar population densities may not have had similar intensities of cultivation. Those sites situated in more marginal or in optimal zones were probably associated with greater intensities of cultivation than similar-sized sites located in more intermediate habitats for agriculture. If this is true, then more work is required to determine the environmental extremes for agriculture in the lowlands. At this point several zones that appear to have been more marginal for agriculture are those that had sparse or infertile soils and long dry seasons, such as parts of northern and western Yucatan, or that had problems of inundation, such as Quintana Roo or northern Belize. Zones of well-watered alluvial soils such as the Copan Valley, or well-drained colluvial soils (Rendolls) with adequate rainfall may be examples of optimal agricultural lands.

Other factors that may also have influenced agricultural growth in the Maya lowlands include crop types; emphasis on hunting, collecting, fishing-pisciculture, and animal husbandry; the amount of land devoted to forest or forest products; trade or commercial agriculture; and taxation. If the Maya did participate in large-scale trading of food staples, then the subsistence-based models of agriculture must be modified to incorporate aspects of market-type models. At this juncture we feel that most Maya populations produced most of their own foods, although instance of substantial reliance on short- or medium-range food trade, as may have existed at Tikal and Chunchucmil, may have been more common than has been previously thought.

Given the foregoing discussion and Boserup's concept of agricultural efficiency, several sketches of the growth of agriculture through time and space in the Maya lowlands may be developed. These sketches assume that when provided a choice, subsistence farmers tend to select that mode and level of agriculture that provides the most return per unit of effort. Furthermore, these sketches are simplistic and do not account for what may appear to be economically irrational decisions. Ritual and other special factors that influenced Maya farmers or elite decision-makers and in turn affected agriculture in pre-Hispanic times are not known and are not considered here.

Scenario A. The most common sketch, that supported by Sanders (1973) and Turner (1974b), views the Maya as having entered the lowlands as incipient farmers and slowly spreading across the lowlands in search of better farmland, such as the well-drained Rendolls of the interior ridge lands or the better-drained sectors of certain river valleys. Initial cultivation would have been some sort of swidden with relatively long fallow periods because land was still plentiful. As population pressure began to build among variously located groups, several events probably took place. Some of the populace moved to settle more distant land (hierarchical diffusion), helping alleviate some of the pressure. Cultivation nearer the population buildups was intensified, and more land at the peripheries of the settled zones was utilized (contagious diffusion). As more and more land was incorporated into the systems of each settled area, travel time to the outer fields became a sufficient economic stimulus to warrant the establishment of other farmsteads and, eventually, population clusters. Through the processes of hierarchical and contagious diffusion, agriculture spread across the better agricultural lands in the Maya realm.

Faced with further population growth and, perhaps, increasing food consumption per population, the Maya began to cultivate more marginal land near centers of population. The time and effort devoted to this task intensified agriculture. Finally, during the later stages of the Classic period, pressures on agriculture reached such proportions that numerous regions of the lowlands were cultivated intensively with a variety of techniques. Intensity levels reached stages where land was often demarcated into small plots and terraces were even utilized on shallow slopes. Certain areas may have found it profitable to concentrate on certain crops and to trade for other crops with neighboring zones, but this idea is highly speculative (see also Harrison 1977).

After the Classic Maya collapse in the central lowlands, the pressure for food production decreased drastically and in numerous regions almost ceased to exist as populations diminished. In turn, agriculture disintensified, reverting to long-fallow swidden throughout the central lowlands. Marginal agricultural land was abandoned, raised fields eroded, and terraces decayed. Intensive cultivation during Postclassic times persisted only in the northern lowlands and in certain small regions of population clusters, such as Tayasal, in the central and southern lowlands.

Scenario A is supported by at least three pieces of evidence. The earliest recorded Maya site at Cuello, Belize, seems to have been supported in part, if not principally, by swidden cultivation on better-drained land (Hammond, 1977), fitting the expected pattern. Also, the farmstead and settlement patterns in most of the central and southern lowlands appear to be associated with optimal zones for cultivation (Voorhies 1972; Green 1973; Eaton 1975). Finally, agricultural growth in the Rio Bec Zone of the central Maya lowlands apparently fits this developmental sequence. Recent discoveries in northern Belize, however, suggest that this sketch is not applicable to the entire lowlands and that alternative sketches need examination.

Scenario B. The second sketch results from the very early dates of 1400 B.C. (calibrated ^{14}C) for intensive raised-field cultivation in the Rio Hondo Valley by Siemens and Puleston. It has been posited that this evidence indicates that the Maya populated and cultivated the lowlands first through riverine terrain, practicing localized intensive cultivation, and that only after the river systems of the eastern and western peripheries of the central lowlands were filled did they spread inland, adopting swidden cultivation, and, eventually, ramon collection (D. E. Puleston and O. S. Puleston 1971).

The riverine scenario deserves careful consideration because of the early dates assigned to the Rio Hondo fields and because of the apparent propensity of the pre-Hispanic Maya for raised-field cultivation. The riverine thesis has several problems. It does not account for agricultural development in the northern lowlands, where rivers do not exist, unless it is assumed that agriculture in the northern zone considerably postdates cultivation in the central lowlands. Sketch B also envisions the Maya as entering the lowlands as well-developed, sophisticated agriculturalists, prompting questions as to the origins of the people. Finally, it contradicts the concept of agricultural efficiency by suggesting that the early Maya (colonists?) deliberately chose to pursue a more strenuous and less efficient form of agriculture in the floodplains than was probably necessary.

Most of the floodplains on the eastern peripheries of the Maya lowlands have limited well-drained land and suffer from serious problems of inundation. The inundated sections of the floodplains are not prime agricultural lands unless significantly modified. The well-drained ridge or uplands adjacent to the floodplains offer better cropping conditions for incipient cultivators, especially if initial population levels were low. How do we justify the colonists' choice of agriculturally inefficient floodplain cultivation over the efficient upland cultivation? A hostile or constricting element (perhaps an indigenous pre-Maya people) may have prevented expansion away from the floodplain, forcing the early agriculturalists to cluster for defense and to manipulate the inundated zone. Another alternative is that the floodplain farmers may have been agricultural specialists in search of suitable environs for cultivation of particular crops, perhaps cacao as suggested by Hammond. The most likely reasons for the incipient riverine pattern are accessibility to water or a much earlier growth in agriculture and population in the uplands than has been previously considered. If none of the above (and no other similar factor) are related to the early intensified agriculture in the riverine areas, then the Maya were operating on an economic rationale that appears nonoperative among subsistence farmers or among other frontier situations (Margolis 1977).

Scenario C. The Cuello site (Hammond 1977) offers alternative evidence to sketch B, indicating that upland swidden cultivation predates Hondo floodplain agriculture and that early raised-field cultivation in the lowlands need not necessarily be explained by an intrusive colonization force or unusual economic decision making. An assemblage of the latest evidence leads us to scenario C.

Incipient cultivators in the lowlands probably spread across the upland zones employing various long-fallow swidden systems of agriculture, but also relying heavily on home gardens (Harris 1973:339–402), collecting, hunting, and fishing. As population pressures mounted in the upland zones, these early Maya shifted their subsistence base more toward agriculture in order to support the growing populace (see Cohen 1977). This shift toward the dominance of agriculture took place at dates much earlier than previously suspected, about 2500 B.C. if not before (Hammond 1977:127). Also at very early dates, certain populations began to concentrate for socioeconomic reasons that are not clear. By the first millennium B.C., some local populations were sufficiently large to promote the development of intensive cultivation in the Hondo River Valley (Puleston 1977). At first the Hondo represented a marginal agricultural environment because of inundation problems, but once local land shortages developed and the effort was extended to manipulate the problem, the floodplain was converted to a prime agricultural environment. The establishment of raised-field cultivation in the Hondo Valley represented such an economic investment that intensive cultivation of the adjacent uplands was diminished.

It is interesting to speculate as to why the Hondo Valley developed so rapidly. Its position as a trade route on the eastern peripheries of the lowlands offers an explanation. If trade was a factor, however, we would expect other river valleys on the eastern and, perhaps, the western peripheries to have a similar early development. This proposition is not substantiated by the evidence at this time, but it is a problem worth pursuing, especially in the valleys that extend into the central lowlands.

Despite the early intensive cultivation of certain areas, the average agricultural development in the lowlands probably followed the pattern suggested in sketch A, a move from extensive to intensive agriculture from the Formative through the Terminal

Classic periods, although the levels of intensity increased and decreased at various times in various zones. By the later stages of the Classic period, large sectors of the lowlands were under intensive cultivation while other areas, such as the pine ridges of Belize and Peten, were sparsely utilized for agriculture.

AGRICULTURE, STATES, AND URBANISM

The numerous associations that have been made between state or urban development and agriculture are well known and need not be reiterated. Several of these relationships deserve special consideration, however, because they have been used as arguments explaining the "uniqueness" of the Maya civilization and because the data presented in the text have direct bearing on them. These arguments include stress theses of state growth and environmental theses of urban development.

The hydraulic thesis as developed by Steward (1949) and Wittfogel (1957) was one of the first stress arguments to see the Maya as a unique instance of state formation, because evidence that the pre-Hispanic lowlanders practiced large-scale irrigation was not available (and remains unavailable) and because their location in a seasonally wet, tropical forest was interpreted to mean that hydraulic works were not needed, or were prohibited by the environment.

The lowland Maya inhabited a realm in which—with the exception of the northwestern coast of Yucatan—insufficient precipitation was not a critical agricultural factor, barring occasional droughts or attempts to cultivate the less watered regions in the dry season. Nevertheless, many of the areas occupied by the Maya required the use of numerous cultivation techniques. Irrigation probably was not one of the more important of these measures, although Matheny's work may require a reevaluation of this assessment.

Drainage of excessive water appears to have been a more critical hydraulic technique for agriculture than irrigation, especially in the central and southern Maya lowlands. The initial hydraulic thesis, however, did not consider field raising or drainage, nor have later evaluations of the thesis (Mitchell 1973). We concur with Puleston and Harris that these techniques are instances of hydraulic agriculture, but this conclusion neither counters the basic weakness of the hydraulic thesis nor adequately explains the different levels of state development attributed to the civilizations of the highlands and lowlands of Mesoamerica.

The data presented in this text and elsewhere have demonstrated that the Maya excelled as cultivators as much as any pre-Hispanic New World people. Their agricultural efforts supported large populations throughout various and numerous sections of the lowlands. It should be recognized that the number of reported ancient terraces, demarcated fields, irrigation networks, and raised fields in the Maya lowlands, taken as a whole, surpasses similar reports for any highland area prior to the Postclassic period.

This comparison is not intended to demean the significance of the great highland centers, but is offered in response to arguments that emphasize an agricultural distinction between the highlands and the lowlands of Mesoamerica in terms of the sophistication or the magnitude of agrotechnologies. The cropping systems emphasized in both broad environmental zones differed technologically only in respect to environmental circumstances and it is doubtful that they differed considerably in labor or organizational requirements. In short, it may be difficult to demonstrate that major differences in agrotechnologies existed between the highlands and lowlands, although discrepancies in state growth probably occurred.

Carneiro's (1970) provocative circumscription thesis is an attempt to fit state growth among all early civilizations, including the Classic Maya, into a general explanatory framework. This thesis emphasizes warfare, resulting from competition for land and resources, as a necessary condition for state growth. Competition is envisioned as resulting from stress by circumscribed agricultural land, resources, or population. Our comments concern the thesis only as it applies to *stress* and the Mesoamerican controversy. We leave discussions of warfare and its role in state development to others.

The circumscription argument was formulated during the period in which the swidden thesis of pre-Hispanic Maya agriculture was dominant. Since swidden cultivation implied small populations and low stress, Carneiro (1970:375) explained state growth among the Maya in terms of social circumscription. He argued that given the large amount of land per capita necessary for swidden cultivation, even a low population density could have produce a certain amount of goods or resources. For early developing civilizations this production pressure (stress) was primarily ment as a possible factor in the state development of the Classic Maya, the data in this text suggest that an alternative view of how stress may have affected state development in the highlands and lowlands of Mesoamerican is necessary.

Stress may be viewed as the pressure placed on any locale to produce a certain amount of goods or resources. For early developing civilizations this production pressure (stress) was primarily associated with subsistence agriculture, although as states evolved emphasis shifted to market agriculture. Initially population density, interacting with the physical environment, was the key factor creating stress, but as higher levels of state organization developed, such factors as taxation, market production, coercion, and increased per-capita resource consumption also combined with population density to influence production pressure (for a similar discussion of stress creating a shift from hunting and collecting to agriculture, see Cohen 1977). To simplify discussion, however, we shall assume that levels of stress can be largely attributed to the density of population and the quality of the physical habitat.

The concept of the agricultural feasibility continuum (Turner, Hanham, and Portararo 1977:392) can illuminate the stress argument for cultivators. Habitats that are marginal for agriculture require considerable manipulation to cultivate, so incipient agriculture in these environs requires large amounts of labor and skills. In this circumstance, even low levels of population density will stimulate high levels of stress and, presumably, high levels of sociopolitical organization to counter the stress. Moderate habitats for cultivation, given the same low levels of population density, will incur lower levels of stress and less sociopolitical organization because the cropping conditions are superior to marginal habitats. In the moderate habitats, less labor and fewer skills are required to produce the resources necessary to sustain the populace than in the marginal environs. The same level of population density in optimal agricultural habitats creates even less stress than in either of the other two environs because conditions for cultivation are outstanding, requiring minimal labor and skills and minimal sociopolitical organization. In this scheme, increasingly larger densities of population are needed to create equivalent stress as habitats range in agricultural feasibility from marginal to optimal conditions. This argument only accounts for variations in levels of stress among early societies and makes no attempt to justify Carneiro's position that warfare and state growth result from the stress.

Many of the highland valleys in Mesoamerica, such as the Teotihuacan Valley, are composed largely of marginal agricultural habitats, that is, they are situated at some distance from water sources, in places where mesophytic cropping conditions are limited (see Sanders and Price 1968:93–98). As population growth occurred, people gravitated to the optimal and moderate agricultural habitats, the better-watered and -drained lands along lake shores, rivers, and springs, creating high densities of population. The result was high levels of stress, and concomitant agricultural intensification with the use of irrigation (Sanders 1977), despite the quality of the land. The alternative was to spread into the adjacent poorly watered or inundated lands, where cropping conditions were more marginal. Ultimately the growth of population was such that agriculture was expanded into the marginal lands, but only under high levels of stress.

In contrast to the highlands, the Maya lowlands offered considerably more moderate and, perhaps, optimal agricultural conditions. As populations grew, the Maya could readily expand over large areas of moderate and, often, optimal habitats, alleviating the buildup of unusually high levels of stress in the optimal environs for cultivation. It is presumed that this alternative was generally accepted because it was economically more efficient than creating high levels of stress in certain zones. The number of moderate agricultural habitats, such as the sufficiently watered ridge lands, did not always prevent high levels of stress from occurring. In some instances, densities of population increased such that even the moderate and optimal habitats were carefully managed with high labor input and elaborate systems of cultivation, and marginal habitats, such as inundated zones, were utilized similarly. The Maya lowlands as a whole, however, offered superior agricultural conditions—that is, the lowlands were less agriculturally circumscribed—and would have required considerably larger average population densities to have created a degree of stress equivalent to that which developed in certain highland valleys.

If this assessment of the stress argument is correct, then we should expect to find that the highland valleys, in which high levels of population density occurred, had superior levels of sociopolitical organization to those found in the lowlands. Furthermore, we should expect to find discrepancies in the sociopolitical organization between different agricultural habitats in the Maya lowlands that had equivalent densities of population. To our knowledge this situation has not been demonstrated, but then it has not been examined either.

It is becoming difficult to demonstrate that major differences existed among Mesoamerican civilizations in scales of agriculture or in agrotechnologies prior to the Postclassic period (see Bronson, chap. 14, and Harris, chap. 15). Furthermore, the evidence increasingly suggests that both the highlands and the lowlands often contained specific areas of densely settled populations, although the overall density of certain regions in the highlands probably exceeded the average density of the lowlands at any particular time. Despite the similarities in the development of agricultural skills and population, discrepancies apparently existed in state development, the Classic Maya being generally credited with lesser status in sociopolitical organization than Teotihuacan. The Maya agricultural data suggest that the hydraulic thesis or its expansion to include the entire spectrum of agrotechnology does not adequately explain these differences. Certain aspects of the circumscription thesis may be able to explain the discrepancies insofar as the development of stress is concerned, but its validity in terms of the data and its suppositions concerning the role of warfare are suspect. Furthermore, all arguments utilizing stress, agricultural scale, or agricultural technology as explanatory mechanisms of state growth must account for discrepancies found among other societies, both prehistoric and contemporary.

Karl Butzer (1976) contends that a direct association between the scale of agrotechnology and state development in early Egypt did not exist. He argues that irrigation agriculture was carried out on a local level long after a state hierarchy of power developed. Several groups from highland New Guinea offer support to Butzer's argument that intensive agriculture need not be directed by complex bureaucratic institutions. These groups practice highly intensive raised-field agriculture with only a rudimentary level of state development (see Brookfield and Brown 1963; Rappaport 1967; E. Waddell 1972). These data and interpretations raise serious questions for all stress theories of state development and are difficult to refute. We may find in the future that our agricultural continuum argument holds only for the development of agriculture and not for state growth, *or* that agricultural development is a necessary but not a sufficient condition for state development.

Arguments addressing the issue of urban growth in the highlands and lowlands of Mesoamerica often suffer from similar problems ascribed to various theses of state growth. The problem is complicated by differences in interpretations of urbanism and by disagreements over the proper classification of Maya population centers. Haviland (1969, 1970) and Kurjack (1974) have argued that Tikal and Dzibilchaltun, respectively, had sufficient population, nucleation, and social organization to be considered urban. Sanders (1973:345–59) forcefully disputes these assessments, noting that the distribution of house sites and, hence, population densities of the highland and lowland centers differed greatly. Teotihuacan maintained a densely nucleated pattern of settlement while lowland sites displayed a much more loosely structured and scattered settlement pattern.

If urbanization is defined as the tendency toward nucleation of settlement, in combination with population growth and societal specialization, then the process or urbanization can be viewed as a secondary result of the factors that lead to state formation. Urbanization is viewed here as a secondary process because it depends on the development of sociopolitical organization. That is, the interaction of population growth and environmental circumstances may stimulate sociopolitical organization that, in turn, may stimulate settlement nucleation and specialization. The interplay of these factors can be illustrated diagrammatically (fig. 17.5). This scheme is obviously oversimplified and does not account for exotic influences that may alter subsistence stress, sociopolitical growth, or the level of urbanization. Nevertheless we find the stress thesis compelling and visualize two broad patterns developing among early Mesoamerican cultures (fig. 17.6). While *A* and *B*

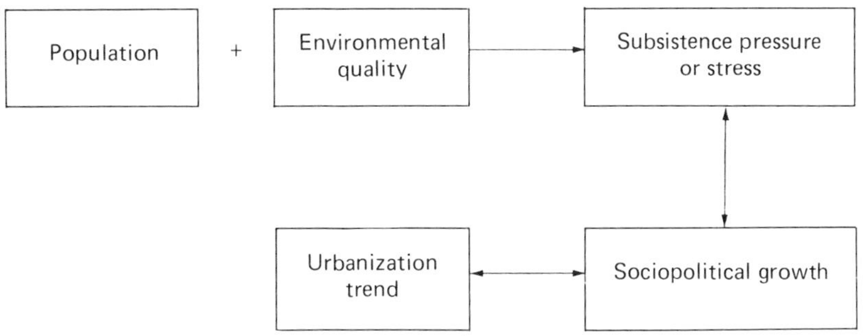

Figure 17.5. Diagrammatic relationship of some factors affecting sociopolitical growth and urbanization.

Figure 17.6. Patterns of cultural development indicating alternative responses to internal stress.

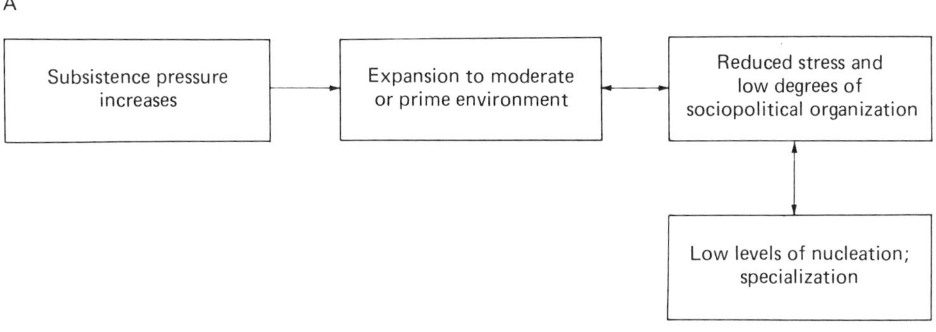

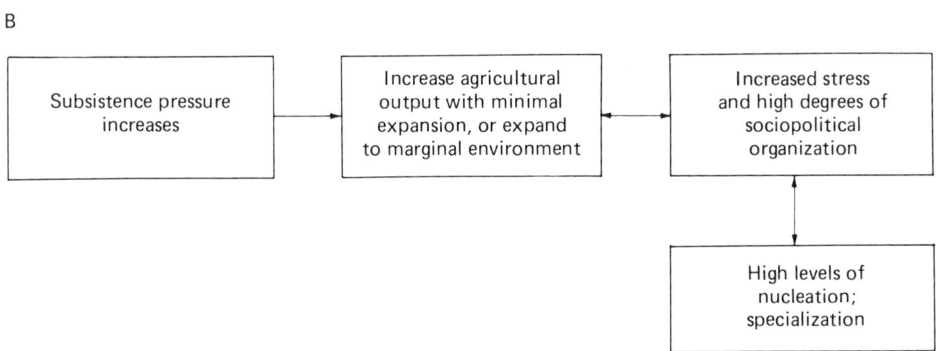

(fig. 17.5) represent the two basic processes that may have developed in Mesoamerica, continual increases in subsistence pressure may ultimately have forced a group following the *A* pattern to move to pattern *B* once expansion into moderate and prime environments was no longer possible.

We view most highland Mesoamerican groups as having entered pattern *B* much earlier than the lowland groups. The lowland Maya as a whole probably entered pattern *B* during the Late Classic, but never reached similar developmental levels of urbanization in most areas because of the collapse. Northern Maya groups attained higher levels of urbanization than the central and southern Maya groups because of greater stress, given their population levels and quality of lands for cultivation. A paradoxical issue that detracts from this argument and necessitates further consideration is the apparent abundance of relics of Maya agricultural activity in certain central lowland zones that suggest rather high levels of stress. These relics occur without evidence of a high level of concomitant development of settlement nucleation.

AGRICULTURE AND CLASSIC COLLAPSE

The possibility that Maya agriculture may have played a causative role in the collapse of the lowland Classic civilization is an old theme, extending at least back to O. F. Cook (1921). The arguments are that the lowland environment was too fragile to support long-term, intensive cultivation of any kind or that the Maya did not possess the skills and techniques to cultivate the forest zone properly. The evidence suggests that such arguments are suspect.

Innumerable relics indicate the manner in which the lowland Maya faced the problems of soil erosion, inundation, and moisture control. We think it a fair assumption that a people who took on such agricultural-engineering feats as terracing, irrigation, field raising, and drainage also possessed the capabilities to replenish soil fertility through mulching, manuring, burning, or other similar procedures. We contend that no substantial reasons exist to suggest that insufficient agricultural know-how was a cardinal collapse factor.

We have evidence of large-scale intensive agriculture in the pre-Hispanic lowlands. Such agriculture probably existed from Preclassic times to the collapse in the central and southern lowlands, and into historic times in the northern lowlands. Inferences that large-scale environmental catastrophes resulted from this cultivation are extremely speculative and based on scanty data. The evidence of soil erosion at Tikal is a case in point. The temporal sequence of this erosion has not been established, and it is not known whether the erosion was connected with the occupation of the site or with its immediate abandonment. More crucial, it is not known whether the erosion was connected with cultivation per se or with the intensity of land use for housing and construction. Indeed, it is doubtful that the type of agriculture that would have been practiced in interior Tikal would have precipitated erosional problems; the kitchen garden/orchard garden pattern that is ascribed by some to the site is usually a stable system of cultivation in terms of soil erosion.

Sanders's (1973:362–65) discussion of the role of agriculture in the collapse deserves consideration. He argues that the Maya intensified agriculture to the grass-fallow stage, but only at great expense because of the difficulty in maintaining soil fertility and combating grass invasion. The result of the grass-fallow routine was a reduction in cultivable land and food production such that the core area had to import food from the peripheries. When the foodstuffs from the peripheries were cut off, the core region could not sustain its population and the collapse ensued.

This argument is a bit confusing because the concepts of *grassland conversion* and *grass succession* are apparently mixed. The former concept applies to the alteration of a habitat from forest (or some other biotic condition) to grassland; the latter concept refers to a temporary successional sequence of vegetation as it reverts from a cultivated to a more natural biotic stage, presumably climax conditions. The evidence from the lowlands does not support either case; Sanders's conclusion (1973:362) that "there is no question that grass invasion occurs [in the Maya lowlands]" is not justified at this time.

Regardless of our position concerning the precise role of grass succession or conversion, Sanders is correct in noting that intensification of agriculture in several lowland habitats was undertaken only with considerable effort and expense, as it is everywhere except under certain optimal agricultural conditions. The Classic

Maya probably had the capability, however, to sustain intensive agriculture for lengthy periods of time without serious deterioration of the physical habitat for cultivation. Despite this assessment, Sanders's suggestion that the core region became dependent on imported foodstuffs from the peripheries has merit. This importation probably was not the consequence of the technical inability of the core region to feed itself, but rather was the result of a populace that devoted a large measure of its energies to other affairs and that found it convenient or economical to rely on imports for a portion of its subsistence. This reliance may have been such by the Classic period that once it was cut off or lost, the core region could not shift its economy quickly enough to support the population, so that collapse ensued.

The problem with this interpretation, as with most collapse arguments that involve agriculture, is that it does not account for the almost total abandonment of certain zones in the central core region, nor does it explain the collapse and abandonment of sections of the periphery. Nevertheless, we feel that the concept has some merit and that more attention should be given to the problem, especially in regard to the dichotomy between the cultural collapse itself and the ultimate abandonment of various lowland regions.

Other problems confronting a purely agricultural interpretation of the collapse involve spatial chronology. Copan is apparently one of the first large centers to collapse, although it is situated in some of the best agricultural land in the Maya region. Agriculturally it is difficult to explain why Copan should collapse before numerous Peten and northern Yucatecan sites.

Harrison's (1977) *bajo* argument does not account for the fall of Copan, but it does offer a testable case for the northward movement of the collapse from the central Peten into Quintana Roo. His thesis (chap. 13) assumes that *bajos* were once shallow-watered, marshy basins and that the central zone centers were dependent on their manipulation for agriculture, water, and trade. Initially Harrison suggested that mismanagement of agriculture or other land usages near the *bajos* created siltation problems that altered the hydrology of the depressions. This alteration played havoc with the crucial food-water resource role of the *bajos* and thus led to the collapse of numerous centers.

This argument suggests neither that a limiting environment

forced a collapse nor that the Maya were technologically incapable of coping with the tropical forest. Rather, Harrison has assumed that the Maya simply may not have recognized the siltation problem until it was too late. Although this interpretation may be correct, others may be more viable in light of the evidence. Perhaps a more plausible explanation of the hypothetical siltation is that sociopolitical disruptions led to agricultural mismanagement that caused siltation. Environmental or climatic factors could have changed the nature of the *bajos* (if they changed). A crucial research step at this juncture is to examine archaeologically and ecologically a lowland *bajo* zone that contains relics of Maya manipulation.

FUTURE STUDIES

Interest in problems of Maya subsistence has focused primarily on agriculture to the disregard of other procurement systems. Historically this situation developed out of the minimal research on problems of Maya subsistence and the dominance of the swidden thesis. Recently the focus on agriculture has been sustained by numerous attacks on the swidden thesis, which required research directed to the collection of evidence of pre-Hispanic agriculture other than swidden, not to supplementary food items that the Maya utilized. Other factors have also contributed to the emphasis on agriculture. The sparseness of vegetable and animal remains that is often encountered in the humid lowlands has inhibited data collection pertaining to hunting, collecting, fishing, and animal husbandry. Repeated examinations of middens at Becan and its hinterlands by the 1973 Rio Bec Ecological Project (directed by R. E. W. Adams), for example, resulted in no significant recovery of macrofossils, bones, or other such remains of food materials. Excavations in other sectors of the lowlands (e.g., the Tikal project) have been more successful, but in general preservation problems have hindered research in this direction. Finally, agricultural studies have been emphasized recently because contemporary investigations indicate that cultivated food plants maintain a much stronger association with population densities among cultivators than do other types of food (Turner, Hanham, and Portararo 1977). This result suggests that, given limited research funding, the broader reconstruction of the subsistence systems of the pre-Hispanic Maya may be best facilitated by focusing on agriculture.

Regardless of the recent emphasis on pre-Hispanic Maya agriculture, our knowledge of the topic is superficial, and much further research is required. While numerous problems are unsolved, the critical thrusts of research efforts should be directed to establishing the nature of pre-Hispanic habitats and habitat utilization, especially for agriculture, and the environmental ramifications of past agriculture. Each of these study areas will required multidisciplinary research efforts similar to those described by Karl Butzer (1975).

Several ecological questions must be addressed immediately. The simplicity with which the lowland habitats have been treated by some scholars and the willingness of others to apply ecological data as if all lowland habitats were uniform are alarming. The xerophytic, highly karsted plains of northern Yucatan are difficult to equate with the mesophytic, faulted foothills of central Belize. Similarly, the poorly drained *bajo*-depressions (poljes) throughout the lowlands offer striking physical contrasts to the adjacent well-drained slope lands. To treat the macro and micro areal variability of lowland habitats too simplistically is to err.

The temporal variability in lowland habitats is another crucial problem to be confronted. The paleoecological record for the Maya area is not clear, but it seems to indicate that no major climatic changes took place in the lowlands during Maya occupation. Subtle climatic changes or other environmental changes may have occurred, but proper interpretations of the evidence to this effect are difficult to evaluate. The ramifications of small changes in precipitation characteristics, drainage patterns, or other environmental variables for agriculture in various lowland habitats are not thoroughly understood, and further work is needed before prognoses of environmental deterioration in the lowlands can be properly evaluated. Also, recognition that the pre-Hispanic Maya had the capabilities to manipulate their habitats on a large-scale basis will require reinterpretation of many of the paleoecological data in regard to past ecological conditions in the lowlands.

A second research thrust should be the continuation of searches for evidence of pre-Hispanic land usages, especially usages for food procurement. This research requires continued ground and aerial surveys for vestiges of agricultural and settlement patterns and of transportation routes, such as canals. Perhaps the most critical land-use issue at this time concerns the degree of manipulation of *bajos* during pre-Hispanic times and the extent to which the Maya may have utilized irrigation techniques. In conjunction with these research efforts, superior data on the productivity of various modes of cultivation that the Maya pursued are needed. Information of this type is, of course, speculative in that documentation of the precise cropping procedures and techniques utilized by the Maya in various habitats is not available. Nevertheless, experimental cultivation with a variety of techniques and procedures in various lowland habits will provide essential information. To date, experimental cultivation with intensive systems utilized by the pre-Hispanic Maya has been limited to several raised fields in Belize (Puleston 1977) and Tabasco (Gómez-Pompa and Venegas 1976).

A third research emphasis is a synthesis of the preceding two, involving the ecological ramifications of various agricultural and related activities throughout the lowlands. Specifically, data are needed on the short- and long-range effects of various types of cultivation on lowland soils, vegetation, and climates. This information will provide spinoffs, such as the effects of changes in vegetation on faunal populations and distributions and, ultimately, on ancient hunting. In brief, we need evidence with which to evaluate the possibilities and probabilities that the pre-Hispanic Maya degraded their environs beyond their abilities to utilize them to support their large populations.

These research thrusts are but a few that are needed to assess pre-Hispanic Maya agriculture. The works presented in this volume have demonstrated that numerous other topics relevant to lowland subsistence problems require investigation. These topics include, among others, the significance to agriculture of alternative food-procurement systems, regional specialization in crops, inter and intraregional trade, commercial cultivation, and "urban"-rural relations.

References

ADAM, D. P.

1974 "Palynological Applications of Principal Component and Cluster Analyses," *United States Geological Survey Journal of Research* 2:727–42.

ADAM, D. P., AND P. J. MEHRINGER, JR.

1975 "Modern Pollen Surface Samples—An Analysis of Subsamples," *United States Geological Survey Journal of Research* 3:733–36.

ADAMS, RICHARD E. W. (ED.)

1977 *The Origins of Maya Civilization* (Albuquerque: University of New Mexico Press, School of American Research Advanced Seminar Series).

"AGRICOLA"

1965 *Handbook for the Ceylon Farmer* (Colombo: Studio Times).

ALLCHIN, F. R.

1969 "Early Cultivated Plants in India and Pakistan," in *The Domestication and Exploitation of Plants and Animals,* ed. P. J. Ucko and G. W. Dimbleby (London: Duckworth & Co.).

ALLEE, N. C.

1962 "Measurement of Environmental Factors in Tropical Rainforest of Panama," *Ecology* 7:273–302.

ALLEE, N. C., A. E. EMERSON, O. PARK, AND K. P. SCHMIDT

1949 *Principles of Animal Ecology* (Philadelphia: W. B. Saunders Co.).

ALTSCHULER, MILTON

1958 "On the Environmental Limitations of Mayan Cultural Development," *Southwestern Journal of Anthropology* 14:189–96.

ANDERSON, EDGAR

1952 *Plants, Man, and Life* (Berkeley and Los Angeles: University of California Press).

ANDREWS, E. WYLLYS, IV

1965 "Archaeology and Prehistory in the Northern Lowlands: An Introduction," in *Handbook of Middle American Indians,* vol. 2, *Archaeology of Southern Mesoamerica, Part 1,* ed. G. R. Willey (Austin: University of Texas Press).

1969 "The Archaeological Use and Distribution of Mollusca in the Maya Lowlands," in *Middle American Research Institute Publication 34* (New Orleans: Tulane University).

ANDREWS, GEORGE F.

1975 *Maya Cities: Placemaking and Urbanization* (Norman: University of Oklahoma Press).

ARMILLAS, PEDRO

1971 "Gardens on Swamps," *Science* 174:653–61.

BALL, JOSEPH W.

1973 "Ceramic Sequence at Becan, Campeche, Mexico" (Ph.D. diss., University of Wisconsin–Madison).

1974 "A Regional Ceramic Sequence for the Rio Bec Area," in *Preliminary Reports on Archaeology Investigation in the Rio Bec Area, Campeche, Mexico,* Middle American Research Institute Publication 31 (New Orleans: Tulane University).

BALL, JOSEPH W., AND E. WYLLYS ANDREWS V

1975 "The Polychrome Pottery of Dzibilchaltun, Mexico: Typology and Archaeological Context," in *Middle American Research Institute Publication 31* (New Orleans: Tulane University).

BANCROFT, HUBERT H.

1883 *The Native Races of the Pacific States of Western America,* vol. 2 (San Francisco: A. C. Bancroft and Co.).

BARRERA, A., A. GÓMEZ-POMPA, AND C. VÁZQUEZ-YANES

1977 "El manejo de las selvas por las Mayas sus implicaciones silvícolas y agrícolas," *Biotica* 2:47–61.

BARTLETT, ALEXANDRA S., AND ELSO S. BARGHOORN

1973 "Phytogeographic History of the Isthmus of Panama During the Past 12,000 Years," in *Vegetational History in Northern Latin America,* ed. A. Graham (New York: Elsevier Publishing Co.)

BARTLETT, HARLEY HARRIS

1936 *A Method of Procedure for Field Work in Tropical American Phytogeography based upon a Botanical Reconnaissance in parts of British Honduras and the Peten forest of Guatemala. Botany of the Area, Miscellaneous Paper No. 1,* Carnegie Institution of Washington Publication no. 481 (Washington, D.C.).

1962 "Possible Separate Origins and Evolution of the Ladang and Sawah Types of Tropical Agriculture," in *Proceedings of the Ninth Pacific Science Congress, 1957,* vol. 4 (Bangkok: Department of Science).

BEMMELEN, R. W. VAN

1956 "The Influence of Geologic Events on Human History," *Verhandelingen van het Koninklijk Geologisch-Mijnboukundig Genootschap* 16:19–36.

BILLINGS, W. D.

1970 *Plants, Man and the Ecosystem,* 2d ed. (Belmont, Calif.: Wadsworth Publishing Co.).

BLANTON, RICHARD E.

1976 "Anthropological Studies of Cities," in *Annual Review of Anthropology 5* (Palo Alto: Annual Reviews).

BLOCK, M. R.

1963 "The Social Influences of Salt," *Scientific American* 209:88–98.

BLOM, FRANS

1932 "Commerce, Trade, and Monetary Units of the Maya," in *Middle American Research Institute Publication 5* (New Orleans: Tulane University).

1946 "Apuntes sobre los ingenieros Mayas," *Irrigación en México* 27:5–16.

BLUST, R.

1976 "Austronesian Culture History: Some Linguistic Inferences and Their Relations to the Archaeological Record," paper presented at the Annual Meeting of the Association for Asian Studies, Toronto.

BOECHARI

1973 "Some Considerations on the Problem of the Shift of Mataram's Center from Central to East Java in the Tenth Century A.D.," paper presented at Colloquy on Early South East Asian History, University of London.

BOSERUP, ESTER

1965 *The Conditions of Agricultural Growth: The Economics of Agrarian Change Under Population Pressure* (Chicago: Aldine Publishing Co.).

BOTKIN, DANIEL B., AND MATTHEW J. SOBEL

1975 "The Complexity of Ecosystem Stability," in *Ecosystem Analysis and Prediction,* ed. S. A. Levin (Philadelphia: Society for Industrial and Applied Mathematics).

BRADBURY, JOHN P.

1971 "Paleolimnology of Lake Texcoco, Mexico: Evidence from Diatoms," *Limnology and Oceanography* 16:180–200.

BRADBURY, JOHN P., AND DENNIS E. PULESTON

1974 "A Palynological Investigation of Maya Agriculture," paper presented at the Seventy-third Annual Meeting of the American Anthropological Association, Mexico City.

BRAINERD, GEORGE W.

1954 *The Maya Civilization* (Los Angeles: Southwest Museum).

1956 "Changing Living Patterns of the Yucatan Maya," *American Antiquity* 22:162–64.

1958 *The Archaeological Ceramics of Yucatan,* University of California Anthropological Records, no. 19 (Berkeley and Los Angeles).

BRASSEUR DE BOURBOURG, CHARLES ETIENNE

1865 *Rapport sur les ruines de Mayapan et d'Uxmal au Yucatan (Mexique), adressé à Son Excellence M. Le Ministre de L'Instruction Publique* (Paris: Imp. Imperial).

BROHIER, R. L.

1934 *Ancient Irrigation Works in Ceylon,* part 2 (Colombo: Government Press).

BRONSON, BENNET

1966 "Roots and the Subsistence of the Ancient Maya," *Southwestern Journal of Anthropology* 22:251–79.

1972 "Farm Labor and the Evolution of Food Production," in *Population Growth: Anthropological Implications,* ed. B. Spooner (Cambridge, Mass.: M.I.T. Press).

1975 "The Earliest Farming: Demography as Cause and Consequence," in *Population, Ecology, and Social Evolution,* ed. S. Polgar (The Hague: Mouton).

BROOKFIELD, HAROLD C.

1962 "Local Study and Comparative Method: An Example from Central New Guinea," *Annals of the Association of American Geographers* 52:242–54.

1972 "Intensification and Disintensification in Pacific Agriculture: A Theoretical Approach," *Pacific Viewpoint* 13:30–48.

BROOKFIELD, HAROLD C., AND PAULA BROWN

1963 *Struggle for Land, Agriculture and Group Territories Among the Chimbu of the New Guinea Highlands* (London: Oxford University Press).

BROOKS, H. K., J. COOLEY, E. S. DEEVEY, H. VAUGHAN, AND H. YEZDANI

1973 "Lakes Yaxha and Sacnab, Twin Basins in the Central Maya Area of Guatemala," paper presented at the Ninth Congress of the International Union for the Study of the Quaternary, Christchurch, New Zealand.

BROWN, M. C., AND S. C. FORD

1973 "Caves and Groundwater Patterns in a Tropical Karst Environment, Jamaica, West Indies," *American Journal of Science* 273:622–33.

BROWN, PAULA, AND AARON PODOLEFSKY

1976 "Population Density, Agricultural Intensity, Land Tenure, and Group Size in the New Guinea Highlands," *Ethnology* 15:211–38.

BUDOWSKI, G.

1970 "The Distinction Between Old Secondary and Climax Species in Tropical Central American Lowland Forests," *Tropical Ecology* 11:44–48.

BULLARD, WILLIAM R.

1960 "Maya Settlement Pattern in Northeastern Peten, Guatemala," *American Antiquity* 25:355–72.

1964 "Settlement Pattern and Social Structure in the Southern Maya Lowlands During the Classic Period," *Actas y memorias del XXXV Congreso Internacional de Americanistas,* vol. 1 (Mexico City), pp. 279–87.

1970 "Topoxte, a Postclassic Maya Site in Peten, Guatemala," in *Monographs and Papers in Maya Archaeology,* ed. W. R. Bullard, Papers of the Peabody Museum of Archaeology and Ethnology, vol. 61 (Cambridge, Mass.: Harvard University).

BULMER, S.

1975 "Settlement and Economy in Prehistoric Papua, New Guinea," *Journal de la Société des Oceanistes* 46:7–75.

BURKILL, I. H.

1951 "The Rise and Decline of the Greater Yam in the Service of Man," *Advancement of Science* 7:443–48.

1966 *A Dictionary of the Economic Products of the Malay Peninsula* (Kuala Lumpur: Ministry of Agriculture and Cooperatives).

BUTZER, KARL W.

1975 "The Ecological Approach to Archaeology: Are We Really Trying?" *American Antiquity* 40:106–7.

1976 *Early Hydraulic Civilization in Egypt: A Study in Cultural Ecology* (Chicago: University of Chicago Press).

CAIN, S. A., AND G. M. CASTRO

1959 *Manual of Vegetation Analysis* (New York: Harper & Row).

CARNEIRO, ROBERT L.

1967 "On the Relationship Between Size of Population and Complexity of Social Organization," *Southwestern Journal of Anthropology* 23:234–43.

1970 "A Theory of the Origin of the State," *Science* 169:733–38.

CARR, R. F., AND J. E. HAZARD

1961 Map of the Ruins of Tikal, El Peten, Guatemala, in *Tikal Report,* no. 11 (Philadelphia: University of Pennsylvania, Univeristy Museum).

CARTER, WILLIAM E.

1969 *New Lands and Old Traditions: Kekchi Cultivators in the Guatemalan Lowlands,* Latin American Monograph no. 6 (Gainesville: University of Florida Press).

CASTELLANOS, JUAN DE

1955 *Eligías de varones ilustres de Indias,* vol. 1 (Bogotá: Editorial ABC).

CHANG, J-H.

1968 "The Agricultural Potential of the Humid Tropics," *Geographical Review* 58:333–61.

CHANG, K. C.

1958 "Study of Neolithic Social Groupings: Examples from the New World," *American Anthopologist* 60:298–334.

CHAPMAN, ANNE M.

1957 "Port of Trade Enclaves in Aztec and Maya Civilizations," in *Trade and Market in the Early Empires,* ed. K. Polanyi, C. Arensberg, and H. Pearson (Glencoe: Free Press).

CHEVEY, P., AND F. LE POULAIN

1940 "La pêche dans les eaux douces cambodgiennes," *Bulletin Economique de l'Indochine* (42d yr.):39–83, 260–331.

CHISHOLM, MICHAEL
1968 *Rural Settlement and Land Use* (London: Hutchinson Publishing Group).

CHOW, VEN TE (ED.)
1964 *Handbook of Applied Hydrology* (New York: McGraw-Hill).

CLAESSEN, H. J. M.
1973 "Despotism and Irrigation," *Bijdragen* 129:70–85.

CLARK, C., AND M. HASWELL
1970 *The Economics of Subsistence* (London: Macmillan & Co.).

COE, MICHAEL D.
1961 "Social Typology and the Tropical Forest Civilizations," *Comparative Studies in Society and History* 4:65–85.
1966 *The Maya* (New York: Frederick A. Praeger).

COE, MICHAEL D., AND KENT V. FLANNERY
1967 "Early Cultures and Human Ecology in South Coastal Guatemala," in *Smithsonian Contributions in Anthropology,* vol. 3 (Washington, D.C.).

COE, WILLIAM R.
1957 "Environmental Limitations on Maya Culture: A Reexamination," *American Anthropologist* 59:328–35.
1965 "Tikal: Ten Years of Study of a Mayan Ruin in the Lowlands of Guatemala," *Expedition* 8:5–56.

COGGINS, CLEMENCY C.
1975 "Paintings and Drawing Styles at Tikal" (Ph.D. diss., Harvard University).

COHEN, MARK N.
1977 *The Food Crisis in Prehistory* (New Haven: Yale University Press).

COMITÉ COORDINADOR DE HIDROLOGÍA Y METEOROLOGÍA
1968 *Datos meteorológicos mensuales* (Guatemala City: Ministerio de Comunicaciones y Obras Públicas).

CONDOMINAS, , G.
1957 *Nous avons mangé la forêt* (Paris: Mercure de France).

CONKLIN, H. C.
1957 *Hanunóo Agriculture,* F.A.O. Forestry Development Paper no. 12 (Rome: Food and Agriculture Organization).

COOK, ORATOR F.
1921 "Milpa Agriculture: A Primitive Tropical System," in *Annual Report of the Smithsonian Institution, 1919* (Washington, D.C.).

COOK, SHERBURNE F.
1972 *Prehistoric Demography,* McCaleb Module in Anthropology, Addison Wesley Modular Publications (Reading, Mass.).

CORTESÃO, A. (ED. AND TRANS.)
1944 *The Suma Oriental of Tomé Pires* (London: Cambridge University Press for the Hakluyt Society).

COURSEY, D. G.
1967 *Yams* (London: Longmans, Green).
1972 "The Civilizations of the Yam," *Archaeology and Physical Anthropology in Oceania* 7:215–33.

COVICH ALAN P.
1976 "Recent Changes in Molluscan Species Diversity of a Large Tropical Lake (Lago de Peten, Guatemala)," *Limnology and Oceanography* 21:51–59.

COVICH, ALAN P., AND MINZE STUIVER
1974 "Changes in Oxygen 18 as a Measure of Long-Term Fluctuations in Tropical Lake Levels and Molluscan Populations," *Limnology and Oceanography* 19:682–91.

COWGILL, URSULA M.
1961 "Soil Fertility and the Ancient Maya," *Transactions of the Connecticut Academy of Arts and Sciences* 42:1–56.
1962 "An Agricultural Study of the Southern Maya Lowlands," *American Anthropologist* 64:273–86.
1971 "Some Comments on Manihot Subsistence and the Ancient Maya," *Southwestern Journal of Anthropology* 27:51–63.

COWGILL, URSULA M., AND G. EVELYN HUTCHINSON
1963a "Ecological and Geochemical Archaeology in the Southern Maya Lowlands," *Southwestern Journal of Anthropology* 19:267–86.
1963b "El Bajo de Santa Fe," *Transactions of the American Philosophical Society* 53 (part 7):1–51.
1966 "The Chemical History of Laguna de Petenxil," *Memoirs of the Connecticut Academy of Arts and Sciences* 17:121–26.

CULBERT, T. PATRICK
1973 *The Classic Maya Collapse* (ed.) (Albuquerque: University of New Mexico Press, School of American Research Advanced Seminar Series).
1974 *The Lost Civilization: The Story of the Classic Maya* (New York: Harper & Row).

CULBERT, T. PATRICK, MARA L. SPENCER, AND PAMELA C. MAGERS
1976 "Slash-and-burn Agriculture in the Maya Lowlands," paper presented at the Forty-second International Congress of Americanists, Paris.

DAHLIN, BRUCE
1974 "Settlement Patterns in Northern Belize," paper presented at the Seventy-third Annual Meeting of the American Anthropological Association, Mexico City.
1976a "Cropping Cash in the Maya Protoclassic," paper presented at the Second Cambridge Symposium on Recent Research in Mesoamerican Archaeology, Cambridge.
1976b "Preliminary Investigations of Agronomic Potentials in Bajos Adjacent to Tikal, Peten, Guatemala," paper presented at the Forty-second International Congress of Americanists, Paris.

DAMES, M. L. (TRANS. AND ED.)
1921 *The Book of Duarte Barbosa* (London: Hakluyt Society).

DAMPIER, CAPT. WILLIAM
1906 *Dampier's Voyages,* 2 vols., ed. John Masefield (London: Ballentyne Press).

DAUBENMIRE, R. F.
1959 "Canopy Coverage Method of Vegetation Analysis," *Northwest Science* 33:43–64.
1968 *Plant Communities: A Textbook of Plant Synecology* (New York: Harper & Row).
1972 "Ecology of *Hyparrhenia Rufa* (Nees) in Derived Savanna in Northwestern Costa Rica," *Journal of Applied Ecology* 9:11–23.

DAVIS, MARGARET B.
1969 "Palynology and Environmental History During the Quaternary Period," *American Scientist* 57:317–32.
1973 "Redeposition of Pollen Grains in Lake Sediment," *Limnology and Oceanography* 18:44–52.

DAVIS, MARGARET B., L. B. BRUBAKER, AND T. WEBB III

1973 "Calibration of Absolute Pollen Influx," in *Quaternary Plant Ecology,* ed. H. J. B. Birks and R. G. West (London: Blackwell Scientific Publications).

DAVIS, RONALD B.

1974 "Stratigraphic Effects of Tubificids in Profundal Lake Sediments," *Limnology and Oceanography* 19:466–88.

DEBLOOIS, EVAN I.

1970 "Archaeological Researches in Northern Campeche, Mexico" (Dept. of Sociology and Anthropology, Weber State College, Ogden, Utah).

DEEVEY, EDWARD S.

1973 Proposal for renewal of research support, NSF Grant GB32150.

1976 "Holocene Forests and Maya Disturbance near Lake Quexil, Peten, Guatemala," paper presented at the Second International Symposium on Paleolimnology, Mikolaiki, Poland.

in press "Holocene Forests and Maya Disturbance near Lake Quexil, Peten, Guatemala," *Polish Archives of Hydrobiology*

DEEVEY, E. S., H. VAUGHN, AND G. B. DEEVEY

1977 "Lakes Yaxha and Sacnab, Peten, Guatemala: Planktonic Fossils and Sediment Focusing," in *Interactions Between Sediments and Fresh Water,* ed. H. L. Golterman (The Hague: W. Junk).

DENEVAN, W. M.

1970 "Aboriginal Drained-Field Cultivation in the Americas," *Science* 169:647–54.

DENEVAN, W. M., AND B. L. TURNER II

1974 "Forms, Functions, and Associations of Raised Fields in the Old World Tropics," *Journal of Tropical Geography* 39:24–33.

DERANIYAGALA, S.

1972 "The Citadel of Anuradhapura 1969: Excavations in the Gedige Area," *Ancient Ceylon* 2:48–169.

DILLON, BRIAN D.

1975 "Notes on Trade in Ancient Mesoamerica," in *Three Papers on Mesoamerican Archaeology,* Contributions of the University of California Archaeological Research Facility, no. 24 (Berkeley and Los Angeles).

DIREKTORAT LANDUSE

1969–70 *Peta Penggunaan Tanah: 1:50,000,* sheets 47/BX2, 48/BX1, 48/BW3 (Jakarta: Ministry of the Interior).

DIVISION D'AGRONOMIE

1972 *Monographie des cultures au Cambodge,* Institut Français de Pondichéry, Travaux de la Section Scientifique et Technique, vol. 4, fasc. 3 (Phnom Penh: Ministry of Agriculture).

DOEHRING, DONALD O., AND JOSEPH H. BUTLER

1974 "Hydrogeologic Constraints on Yucatan's Development" *Science* 186:591–95.

DOMROS, M.

1974 *The Agroclimate of Ceylon* (Wiesbaden: Franz Steiner).

DRUCKER, PHILLIP, AND ROBERT F. HEIZER

1960 "A Study of the Milpa System of La Venta Island and Its Archaeological Implications," *Southwestern Journal of Anthropology* 16:36–45.

DUDAL, R., AND F. R. MOORMAN

1964 "Major Soils of South-East Asia," *Journal of Tropical Geography* 18:54–80.

DUMOND, DONALD E.

1961 "Swidden Agriculture and the Rise of Maya Civilization," *Southwestern Journal of Anthropology* 17:301–16.

DUMONT, R.

1957 *Types of Rural Economy* (London: Methuen & Co.).

EATON, JACK D.

1972 "A Report on the Excavation of Chicanna, Campeche, Mexico," *Cerámica de Cultura Maya* 8:42–61.

1975 "Ancient Agricultural Farmsteads in the Rio Bec Region of Yucatan," in *Contribution of the University of California Archaeological Research Facility no. 27* (Berkeley and Los Angeles).

EDELMAN, C. H., AND R. BRINKMAN

1962 "Physiography of Gilgai Soils," *Soil Science* 94:366–70.

EMERSON, R. A., AND J. H. KEMPTON

1935 "Agronomic Investigations in Yucatan," *Carnegie Institution Yearbook* 34:138–42.

ERASMUS, CHARLES J.

1965 "Monument Building: Some Field Experiments," *Southwestern Journal of Anthropology* 21:277–301.

EVANS, JOHN G.

1972 *Land Snails in Archeology* (London: Seminar Press).

EWEL, J., AND R. MYERS

1974 "Preliminary Vegetation Studies at Yaxha, Guatemala" (ms., Department of Botany, University of Florida, Gainesville).

EYSVOOGEL, W. F.

1951 "The Relationship of Soil Characteristics to Irrigation Programs in Indonesia," in *Proceedings of the U.N. Scientific Conference on the Conservation and Utilization of Resources,* vol. 4 (United Nations).

FAEGRI, KNUT, AND JOHN S. IVERSEN

1964 *Textbook on Pollen Analysis* (New York: Hafner Press).

FARMER, B. H.

1957 *Pioneer Peasant Colonization in Ceylon* (London: Oxford University Press).

FISHER, C. A.

1964 *South East Asia: A Social, Economic, and Political Geography* (London: Methuen & Co.).

FLANNERY, KENT V.

1972 "The Cultural Evolution of Civilization," in *Annual Reviews of Ecology and Systematics 3* (Palo Alto: Annual Reviews).

1973 "The Origins of Agriculture," in *Annual Review of Anthropology 2* (Palo Alto: Annual Reviews).

1976 *The Early Mesoamerican Village* (New York: Academic Press).

FLEMING, STUART

1976 "Radiocarbon Dating," in *Dating in Archeology* (New York: St. Martin's Press).

FRANCO , JOSÉ L.

1969 "Snares and Traps in Codex Madrid," in *Notes on Middle American Anthropology and Ethnology,* vol. 5 (New York: AMS Press).

FREY, DAVID G.
1964 "Remains of Animals in Quaternary Lake and Bog Sediments and Their Interpretation," *Archiv fur Hydrobiologie, Ergebnisse der Limnologie* 2:1–114.

FRY, R. E.
1969 "Ceramics and Settlement in the Periphery of Tikal, Guatemala" (Ph.D. diss., University of Arizona).

GADE, DANIEL W., AND R. RIOS
1972 "Chaquitaella: The Native Footplough and Its Persistence in the Central Andean Agriculture," in *Tolls and Tillage,* vol. 2 (Copenhagen: National Museum of Denmark).

GALLENKAMP, CHARLES
1959 *Maya: The Riddle and Rediscovery of a Lost Civilization* (New York: David McKay Co.).

GANN, T. W. F.
1918 *The Maya Indians of Southern Yucatan and Northern British Honduras,* Bureau of American Ethnology Bulletin no. 64 (Washington, D.C.).
1925 *Mystery Cities* (London: Duckworth & Co.).
1926 *Ancient Cities and Modern Tribes: Exploration and Adventure in Maya Lands* (New York: Charles Scribner's Sons).

GANN, T. W. F., AND J. ERIC S. THOMPSON
1931 *The History of the Maya from the Earliest Time to the Present Day* (New York: Charles Scribner's Sons).

GARDNER, M. R., AND W. R. ASHBY
1970 "Connectance of Large Tynamical (Cybernetic) Systems: Critical Values of Stability," *Nature* 228:784.

GATES, WILLIAM
1937 *Yucatan Before and After the Conquest* (Baltimore: Maya Society).

GAUSSEN, H., P. LEGRIS, M. VIART, AND L. LABROE
1964 *Carte internationale du tapis vegetal, Ceylon* (Colombo: Ceylon Survey Department).
1965 *Notice de la feuille Ceylon,* Institut Français de Pondichéry, Travaux de la Section Scientifique et Technique, hors série no. 5.

GEERTZ, CLIFFORD
1959 "Form and Variation in Balinese Village Structure," *American Anthropologist* 61:991–1012.
1963 *Agricultural Involution* (Berkeley and Los Angeles: University of California Press).

GERSTENHAUER, A.
1960 "Der tropische Kegelkarst in Tabasco (Mexiko)," 3 Geomorph., Supp. 2, *Internationale Beiträge zur Karst-morphologie:* 22–48.
1966 "Beiträge zur Geomorphologie des mittleren u. nördlichen Chiapas (Mexiko) unter besonderen Berücksichtigung des Karstformenschatzes," in *Frankfurter Geographische Hefte,* no. 4 (Frankfurt: Kramer).

GOLLEY, F. B., J. T. McGINNIS, R. G. CLEMENTS, G. I. CHILD, AND M. J. DUEVER
1975 *Mineral Cycling in a Tropical Moist Forest Ecosystem* (Athens: University of Georgia Press).

GOLLEY, FRANK B., AND ERNESTO MEDINA
1975 "Ecological Research in the Tropics," in *Tropical Ecological Systems,* ed. F. B. Golley and E. Medina (New York: Springer-Verlag).

GOLOUBEW, V.
1941 "L'Hydraulique urbaine et agricole à l'époque des rois d'Angkor," *Bulletin Economique de l'Indochine* (44th yr):9–18.

GÓMEZ-POMPA, ARTURO, C. VÁZQUEZ-YANES, AND S. GUEVARA
1972 "The Tropical Rain Forest: A Nonrenewable Resource," *Science* 177:762–65.

GÓMEZ-POMPA, ARTURO, AND RAÚL VENEGAS
1976 "La Chinampa Tropical," *Informa, Comunicado Numero 5* (Xalapa: Instituto de Investigaciones sobre Recursos Bióticos).

GOODMAN, DANIEL
1975 "The Theory of Diversity-Stability Relationships in Ecology," *Quarterly Review of Biology* 50:237–66.

GOOR, M. L. VAN
1919 *Korte Gids voor de Tempelbouwvallen in de Prambanan-Vlakte,* Ourheidkundige Dienst in Nederlandsch-Indie (Weltevreden: Landsdrukkerij).

GOPALAN, C., B. V. RAMA SASTRA, AND S. C. BALASUBRAMANIAN
1971 *Nutritive Values of Indian Foods* (Hyderabad: National Institute of Nutrition).

GORDON, B. LEROY
1969 *Anthropogeography and Rainforest Ecology in Bocas del Toro Province, Panama,* Office of Naval Research Report, Contract 3656(03) NR 388 067 (Berkeley: Department of Geography, University of California).

GORMAN, C.
1974 "Modèles à priori et la Préhistoire de la Thailande," *Etudes Rurales* 53–56:41–71.

GORMAN, C., AND PISIT CHAROENWONGSA
1976 "Ban Chiang: A Mosaic of Impressions from the First Two Years," *Expedition* 18:14–26.

GOULDEN, CLYDE E.
1969 "Temporal Changes in Diversity," in *Diversity and Stability in Ecological Systems* (Upton: Brookhaven National Laboratory).

GOULDEN, CLYDE E., AND G. EVELYN HUTCHINSON
1966 "Plant Microfossils," *Memoirs of the Connecticut Academy of Arts and Sciences* 17:67–73.

GOUROU, P.
1940 *L'Utilisation du sol en Indochine Française* (Paris: Paul Hartmann, for the Centre d'Etudes de Politique Etrangère).
1955 *The Peasants of the Tonkin Delta* (New Haven: Human Relations Area Files Press).

GRAF, A. B.
1957 *Exotica: Pictorial Cyclopedia of Indoor Plants* (Rutherford, N. J.: Roehrs Co.).

GRAHAM, ALAN
1975 "Late Cenozoic Evolution of Tropical Lowland Vegetation in Veracruz, Mexico," *Evolution* 29:723–35.
1976 "Studies in Neopical Paleobotany, 2, The Miocene Communities of Veracruz, Mexico," *Annals of the Missouri Botanical Garden* 63:787–842.

GREEN, ERNESTENE L.
1973 "Locational Analysis of Prehistoric Maya Sites in Northern British Honduras," *American Antiquity* 38:279–93.

GREENLAND, D. J.
1975 "Bringing the Green Revolution to the Shifting Cultivator," *Science* 190:841–44.

GRONEMAN, J.

1893 *Tjandi Parambanan* (The Hague: Marinus Nijhoff).

GROSLIER, B. P.

1958 *Angkor et le Cambodge au XVIe siècle d'après les sources Portugaises et Espagnoles,* Annales du Musée Guimet, Bibliothèque d'Etudes, vol. 63.

GROSLIER, B. P., AND J. ARTHAUD

1968 *Angkor: Hommes et Pierres* (Paris: B. Arthaud).

GUMILLA, JOSÉ

1945 *El Orinoco ilustrado* (Madrid: Tipigrafía Clásica Española).

GUZMÁN, L. E.

1962 "Las Terrazas de los antiguos Mayos Montoñesos, Chiapas, Mexico," *Revista Interamericana de Ciencias Sociales* 1:398–406.

GYUK, IMRE, AND ROBERT HARRISON

1975 "Environmental Degradation and the Collapse of the Classic Maya," in *Man-Environment Interactions: Evaluations and Applcations, Part I, Unit I, Man-Environmental Themes* (Stroudsberg, Pa.: Dowden, Hutchinson, and Ross).

HAFFER, J.

1966 "Speciation in Amazonian Forest Birds," *Science* 165:131–37.

HALL, D. G. E.

1968 *A History of South-East Asia* (London: Macmillan & Co.).

HALL, E. R., AND K. R. KELSON

1959 *The Mammals of North America,* 2 vols. (New York: Ronald Press).

HALL, K. R.

1975 "Khmer Commercial Development and Foreign Contacts under Suryavarman I," *Journal of the Economic and Social History of The Orient* 18:318–36.

HALL, ROBERT L.

1976 "Ghosts, Water Barriers, Corn and Sacred Enclosures in the Eastern Woodlands," *American Antiquity* 41:360–64.

HALLSWORTH, E. G., GWEN K. ROBERTSON, AND F. R. GIBBONS

1955 "Studies in Pedogenesis in the New South Wales, VII: The 'Gilgai' Soils," *Journal of Soil Science* 6:1–31.

HAMMOND, NORMAN

1972 "Locational Models and the Site of Lubaantun: A Classic Maya Centre," in *Models in Archaeology,* ed. D. L. Clarke (London: Methuen & Co.).

1974a "The Distribution of Late Classic Maya Major Ceremonial Centres in the Central Area," in *Mesoamerican Archaeology: New Approaches,* ed. N. Hammond (Austin: University of Texas Press).

1974b "Preclassic to Postclassic in Northern Belize," *Antiquity* 48:177–89.

1975 *Lubaantun: A Classic Maya Realm,* Monographs of the Peabody Museum of Archaeology and Ethnology, no. 2 (Cambridge, Mass.: Harvard University).

1976a "Agricultural Intensification in the Maya Lowlands," paper presented at the Forty-second International Congress of Americanists, Paris.

1976b "The Early Preclassic in the Maya Lowlands," paper presented at the Forty-first Annual Meeting of the Society for American Archaeology, St. Louis.

1977 "The Earliest Maya," *Scientific American* 236:116–33.

HAMMOND, N., D. C. PRING, R. BERGER, V. R. SWITSUR, AND A. P. WARD

1976 "Radiocarbon Chronology for Early Maya Occupation at Cuello, Belize," *Nature* 260:579–81.

HANKS, L. M.
1972 *Rice and Man: Agricultural Ecology in Southeast Asia* (Chicago: Aldine-Atherton).

HARDOY, JORGE E.
1973 *Pre-Columbian Cities* (New York: Walker and Co.).

HARNER, MICHAEL L.
1970 "Population Pressure and the Social Evolution of Agriculturalists," *Southwestern Journal of Anthropology* 26:67–86.

HARRIS, DAVID R.
1969 "Agricultural Systems, Ecosystems, and the Origins of Agriculture," in *The Domestication and Exploitation of Plants and Animals,* ed. P. J. Ucko and G. W. Dimbleby (London: Duckworth & Co.).
1972 "Swidden Systems and Settlement," in *Man, Settlement, and Urbanism,* ed. Peter J. Ucko, Ruth Tringham, and G. W. Dimbleby (London: Duckworth & Co.).
1973 "The Prehistory of Tropical Agriculture: An Ethno-ecological Model," in *The Explanation of Culture Change: Models in Prehistory,* ed. A. C. Renfrew (London: Duckworth & Co.).
1977a "Alternative Pathways Toward Agriculture," in *The Earliest Agriculture,* ed. C. A. Reed (The Hague: Mouton).
1977b "Subsistence Strategies Across Torres Strait," in *Sunda and Sahul: Prehistoric Studies in Southeast Asia, Melanesia, and Australia,* ed. J. Allen, J. Golson, and R. Jones (London: Academic Press).

HARRISON, PETER D.
1974 "Archaeology in Southwestern Quintana Roo: Interim Report of the Uaymil Survey Project," paper presented at the Forty-first International Congress of Americanists, Mexico City.
1975 "Intensive Agriculture in Southern Quintana Roo, Mexico: Some New Lines of Evidence and Implications for Maya Prehistory," paper presented at the Fortieth Annual Meeting of the Society for American Archaeology, Dallas.
1977 "The Rise of the *Bajos* and the Fall of the Maya," in *Social Process in Maya Prehistory: Studies in Memory of Sir Eric Thompson,* ed. N. Hammond (London: Academic Press).

HAUCK, FORREST RICHARD
1973 "The Edzna Hydraulic Complex: Initial Investigation" (M.A. thesis, Brigham Young University).
1975 "Preconquest Maya Overland Routes on the Yucatan Peninsula and Their Economic Significance" (Ph.D. diss., University of Utah).

HAVILAND, WILLIAM A.
1963 "Excavation of Small Structures in the Northeast Quadrant of Tikal, Guatemala" (Ph.D. diss., University of Pennsylvania).
1965 Prehistoric Settlement at Tikal, Guatemala," *Expedition* 7:14–23.
1968 "Ancient Lowland Maya Social Organization," in *Middle American Research Institute Publication 26* (New Orleans: Tulane University).
1969 "A New Population Estimate for Tikal, Guatemala," *American Antiquity* 34:429–33.
1970 "Tikal, Guatemala, and Mesoamerican Urbanism," *World Archaeology* 2:186–97.
1972 "Family Size, Prehistoric Population Estimates, and the Ancient Maya," *American Antiquity* 37:135–39.

HELLMUTH, NICHOLAS M.
1971 "Some Notes on the Ytza, Quejache, Verapaz Chol, and Tonquegua Maya" (ms).
1972 "Excavations Begin at Maya Site in Guatemala," *Archaeology* 25:148–49.

HESTER, JOSEPH A.

1954 "Natural and Cultural Bases of Ancient Maya Subsistence Economy" (Ph.D. diss., University of California, Los Angeles).

HIGBEE, EDWARD

1948 "Agriculture in the Mayan Homeland," *Geographical Review* 38:457–64.

HIGHAM, C. H.

1973a "Economic Change in Prehistoric Thailand," paper presented at Colloquy on Early South-East Asia, University of London.

1973b "The Prehistory of the Southern Khorat Plateau," paper presented at Colloquy on Early South-East Asia, University of London.

HIRSHBERG, R. I., AND J. F. HIRSHBERG

1957 "Meggers' Law on Environmental Limitation on Culture," *American Anthropologist* 59:890–91.

HIRTH, F., AND W. W. ROCKHILL (TRANS. AND ED.)

1966 *Chau Ju-Kua: His Work on the Chinese and Arab Trade in the Twelfth and Thirteenth Centuries, Entitled 'Chu-Fan-Chi'* (New York: Paragon Reprints).

HO, P.-T.

1977 "The Indigenous Origins of Chinese Agriculture," in *The Earliest Agriculture,* ed. C. E. Reed (The Hague: Mouton).

HO, T. L.

1961 "Essais d'engrais dans les rizières du Cambodge," *Journal d'Agriculture et de Botanique Appliquée* 8:191–99.

HOCART, A. M. (ED)

1924 *Memoirs of the Archaeological Survey of Ceylon,* vol. 1 (Colombo).

HOGBIN, H. I.

1938 "Tillage and Collection: A New Guinea Economy," *Oceania* 9:127–51, 286–325.

HOPKINS, J. W.

1968 "Prehispanic Agricultural Terraces in Mexico" (M.A. thesis, University of Chicago).

HUNTINGTON, ELLSWORTH

1915 *Civilization and Climate* (New Haven: Yale University Press).

1917 "Maya Civilization and Climatic Change," in *Proceedings of the Nineteenth International Congress of Americanists* (Washington, D.C.).

JACOBS, JANE

1969 *The Economy of Cities* (New York: Random House).

JAIN, S. K., AND D. K. BANERJEE

1974 "Preliminary Observations on the Ethnobotany of the Genus Coix," *Economic Botany* 28:38–42.

JANZEN, DANIEL H.

1970 "The Unexploited Tropics," *Bulletin of the Ecological Society of America* 51:4–7.

1973 "Tropical Agroecosystems," *Science* 182:1212–19.

JENNINGS, JESSE N.

1971 *Karst* (Cambridge, Mass.: M.I.T. Press).

JONES, CHRISTOPHER

1977 "Inauguration Dates of Three Late Classic Rulers of Tikal, Guatemala," *American Antiquity* 42:28–60.

JOYCE, T. A.
1926 "Report on the Investigations at Lubaantun, British Honduras, in 1926," *Journal of the Royal Anthropological Institute of Great Britain and Ireland* 56:207–30.

JOYCE, T. A., J. C. CLARK, AND J. E. S. THOMPSON
1927 "Report on the British Museum Expedition to British Honduras, 1927" *Journal of the Royal Anthropological Institute of Great Britain and Ireland* 57:295–323.

KAUNITZ, H.
1956 "Causes and Consequences of Salt Consumption," *Nature* 175:1141–44.

KIKUCHI, WILLIAM K.
1976 "Prehistoric Hawaiian Fishponds," *Science* 193:295–99.

KIRKBY, A. V.
1973 *The Use of Land and Water Resources in the Past and Present Valley of Oaxaca,* Memoirs of the Museum of Anthropology, University of Michigan, no. 5 (Ann Arbor).

KNOX, R.
1966 *An Historical Relation of Ceylon* (1681; Dehiwala: Tisara Prakasayo).

KURJACK, EDWARD B.
1974 *Prehistoric Lowland Maya Community and Social Organization: A Case Study at Dzibilchaltun, Yucatan, Mexico,* Middle American Research Institute Publication 38 (New Orleans: Tulane University).

LA BARRE, WESTON
1970 "Old and New World Narcotics: A Statistical Question and an Ethnological Reply," *Economic Botany* 24:73–80.

LANGE, FREDERICK W.
1971 "Marine Resources: A Viable Subsistence Alternative for the Prehistoric Lowland Maya," *American Anthropologist* 73:619–39.

LEACH, EDMUND R.
1959 "Hydraulic Society in Ceylon," *Past and Present* 15:2–25.
1961 *Pul Elija: A Village in Ceylon* (Cambridge: Cambridge University Press).

LeGRAND, H. E.
1973 "Hydrological and Ecological Problems of Karst Regions," *Science* 179:859–64.

LEGRIS, P., AND F. BLASCO
1972 *Notice de la Carte Cambodge,* Institut Français de Pondichéry, Travaux de la Section Scientifique et Technique, hors série no. 11.

LEHMAN, J. T.
1975 "Reconstructing the Rate of Accumulation of Lake Sediment: The Effect of Sediment Focusing," *Quaternary Research* 5:541–50.

LEHMANN, H.
1954 "Der Tropische Kegalkarst des verschiedenen Klimazonen," *Erdkunde* 8:130–39.

LEHMANN, H., K. KRÖMMELBEIN, AND W. LÖTSCHERT
1956 "Karstmorphologische, geologische und botanische Studien in der Sierra de los Organos auf Cuba," *Erdkunde* 10:185–203.

LI, H.-L.
1970 "The Origin of Cultivated Plants in Southeast Asia," *Economic Botany* 24:3–23.

LIKENS, GENE E., AND MARGARET B. DAVIS
1975 "Post-glacial History of Mirror Lake and Its Watershed in New Hampshire, U.S.A.: An Initial Report," *Verhanlungen Internationale Vereinigung Fur Theoretische und Angewandte Limnologie* 19(4):982–93.

LINARES, O. F.
1976 " 'Garden Hunting' in the American Tropics," *Human Ecology* 4:331–50.

LINTON, RALPH
1940 "Crops, Soils, and Culture in America," in *The Maya and Their Neighbors,* ed. C. L. Hay et al. (New York: Appleton-Century).
1955 *The Tree of Culture* (New York: Alfred A. Knopf).

LLOYD, JOEL J., AND GABRIEL DENGO
1960 "Continued Drilling May Uncover Oil in Guatemala's Petén," *Oil & Gas Journal* 58:208–12.

LOGAN, MICHAEL H., AND WILLIAM T. SANDERS
1976 "The Model," in *The Valley of Mexico: Studies in Pre-Hispanic Ecology and Society,* ed. E. R. Wolf (Albuquerque: University of New Mexico Press, School of American Research Advanced Seminar Series).

LOTHROP, SAMUEL K.
1924 *Tulum: An Archaeological Study of the East Coast of Yucatan,* Carnegie Institution of Washington Publication no. 335 (Washington, D.C.).

LOWE-McCONNELL, R. H.
1975 Fish Communities in Tropical Freshwaters (London: Longman Group).

LUNDELL, CYRUS L.
1933a "The Agriculture of the Maya," *Southwest Review* 19:65–77.
1933b "Archaeological Discoveries in the Maya Area," *Proceedings of the American Philosophical Society* 72:147–79.
1934 "Preliminary Sketch of the Phytogeography of the Yucatan Peninsula," in *Contributions to American Archaeology,* no. 12, Carnegie Institution of Washington Publication no. 436 (Washington, D.C.).
1937 *The Vegetation of Peten,* Carnegie Institution of Washington Publication no. 478 (Washington, D.C.).
1938 "Plants Probably Utilized by the Old Empire Maya of Peten and Adjacent Lowlands," *Papers of the Michigan Academy of Science, Arts, and Letters* 24:37–56.
1940 "The 1936 Michigan-Carnegie Botanical Expedition to British Honduras," in *Botany of the Maya Area, Miscellaneous Paper no. 14,* Carnegie Institution of Washington Publication no. 522 (Washington, D.C.).
1961 "The Flora of Tikal," *Expedition* 3:39–43.

LUNET DE LAJONQUIERE, E.
1911 *Inventaire descriptif des monuments du Cambodge,* Publications de l'Ecole Française d'Extrême Orient (Paris: Imprimerie Nacionale).

McCOURT, D.
1955 "Infield and Outfield in Ireland," *Economic History Review* 7:369–76.

MacNEISH, R. S.
1964 "Ancient Mesoamerican Civilization," *Science* 143:531–37.

MALDONADO-KOERNELL, MANUEL
1964 "Geohistory and Paleogeography of Middle America," in *Handbook of Middle American Indians,* vol. 1, *Natural Environment and Early Cultures,* ed. Robert C. West (Austin: University of Texas Press).

MARCUS, JOYCE
1973 "Territorial Organization of the Lowland Classic Maya," *Science* 180:911–16.

MARGOLIS, MAXINE

1977 "Historical Perspectives on Frontier Agriculture as an Adaptive Strategy," *American Ethnologist* 4:42–64.

MATHENY, RAY T.

1976 "Maya Lowland Hydraulic Systems," *Science* 193:639–46.

MATHEWSON, KENT

1977 "Maya Urban Genesis Reconsidered: Trade and Intensive Agriculture as Primary Factors," *Journal of Historical Geography* 3:203–15.

MA TUAN-LIN

1883 *Ethnografie des peuples étrangères à la Chine,* trans. D'Hervey de St. Denys (Geneva).

MAY, ROBERT M.

1973 *Stability and Complexity in Model Ecosystems* (Princeton: Princeton University Press).

1976 "Patterns in Multi-Species," in *Theoretical Ecology, Principles and Applications* (Philadelphia: W. B. Saunders Co.).

MEANS, P. A.

1917 *History of the Spanish Conquest and the Itza,* Papers of the Peabody Museum of Archaeology and Ethnology, vol. 7 (Cambridge, Mass.: Harvard University).

MEGGERS, BETTY J.

1954 "Environmental Limitation on the Development of Culture," *American Anthropologist* 56:801–24.

MEGGERS, B. J., E. S. AYENSU, AND W. D. DUCKWORTH (EDS.)

1973 *Tropical Forest Ecosystems in Africa and South America: A Comparative Review* (Washington, D.C.: Smithsonian Institution Press).

MERCER, HENRY C.

1975 *The Hill-Caves of Yucatan* (1896; rpt., Norman: University of Oklahoma Press).

MILLON, RENÉ

1973 *Urbanization at Teotihuacan, Mexico,* vol. 1, *The Teotihuacan Map* (*Parts 1 and 2, Text and Maps*) (Austin: University of Texas Press).

MILLS, J. V. G. (TRANS. AND ED.)

1907 *Ying-Yai Sheng-Lan: The Overall Survey of the Ocean's Shores* (1443; London: Hakluyt Society).

MIOTKE, FRANZ-DIETER

1973 "Die Tieferlegung der Oberflächen zwischen Mogoten in Puerto Rico (Östlich Arecibo)," in *Neue Ergebrisse der Karstforschung in den Tropen und im Mittelincerraum,* ed. A. Semmel, Vorträge des Frankfurter Karstsymposiums (Wiesbaden: Franz Steiner Verlag).

MITCHELL, WILLIAM P.

1973 "The Hydraulic Hypothesis: A Reappraisal," *Current Anthropology* 14:532–34.

MOHR, E. J. C.

1945 "The Relation Between Soil and Population Density in the Netherlands Indies," in *Science and Scientists in the Netherlands Indies,* ed. P. Honig and F. Verdoorn (New York: Board for the Netherlands Indies, Surinam, and Curacao).

MORLEY, SYLVANUS G.

1938 *The Inscriptions of Petén* (Washington, D.C.: Carnegie Institution).

1946 *The Ancient Maya* (Stanford: Stanford university Press).

1956 *The Ancient Maya,* 2d ed., rev. by G. Brainerd (Stanford: Stanford University Press).

1958 *The Ancient Maya,* 3d ed., rev. by G. Brainerd (Stanford: Stanford University Press).

MOSIÑO ALEMÁN, PEDRO A., AND ENRIQUETA GARCÍA

1974 "The Climate of Mexico," in *World Survey of Climatology,* vol. 11, *Climates of North America,* ed. R. A. Bryson and F. K. Hare (New York: Elsevier Scientific Publishing Co.).

MUELLER-DOMBOIS, D., AND H. ELLENBERG

1974 *Aims and Methods of Vegetation Ecology* (New York: John Wiley & Sons).

MULLER, FLORENCIA

1960 *Atlas Arguelógico de la República Mexicana,* vol. 2, *Campeche* (Mexico City: Instituto Nacional de Antropología e Historia).

NAROLL, RAOUL

1962 "Floor Area and Settlement Pattern," *American Antiquity* 27:587–89.

NATIONAL ACADEMY OF SCIENCES

1975 *Underexploited Tropical Plants with Promising Economic Value* (Washington, D.C.).

NED. AARDRIJKSKUNDIG GENOOTSCHAP

1938 *Atlas van Tropisch Nederland* (Batavia: Topografischen Dienst in Nederlandsch-Indië).

NELSON, FRED W.

1973 *Archaeological Investigations at Dzibilnocac, Campeche, Mexico,* Papers of the New World Archaeological Foundation, no. 33 (Provo: Brigham Young University Press).

NETTING, ROBERT McC.

1968 *Hill Farmers of Nigeria: Cultural Ecology of the Kofyar of the Jos Plateau* (Seattle: University of Washington Press).

1974 "Agrarian Ecology," *Annual Review of Anthropology 3* (Palo Alto: Annual Reviews).

1977 "Maya Subsistence: Mythologies, Analogies, Possibilities," in *The Origins of Maya Civilization,* ed. R. E. W. Adams (Albuquerque: University of New Mexico Press, School of American Research Advanced Seminar Series).

NICHOLLS, L.

1921 "Malaria and the Lost Cities of Ceylon," *Indian Medical Gazette* 56:47–61.

NICHOLLS, C. W.

1959 "Irrigation," in *University of Ceylon History of Ceylon,* ed. N Attygalle (Colombo: Ceylon University Press).

NUTTONSON, M. Y.

1963 *The Physical Environment and Agriculture of Vietnam, Laos, and Cambodia* (Washington, D.C.: American Institute of Crop Ecology).

OCHSE, J. J., M. J. SOULE, JR., M. J. DIJKMAN, AND C. WEHLBURG

1961 *Tropical and Subtropical Agriculture,* vol. 1 (New York: Macmillan Co.).

OGDEN, J. G., III

1969 "Correlation of Contemporary and Late Pleistocene Pollen Records in the Reconstruction of Postglacial Environments in Northeastern North America," *Mitteilungen International Verein. Limnologie* 17:64–77.

OLSON, GERALD W.

1969 "Description and Data on Soils of Tikal, El Peten, Guatemala, Central America" (mimeo 69-2, Department of Agronomy, Cornell University).

1974 "Field Report on Soils Sampled Around San Antonio in Northern Belize (British Honduras)" (mimeo 74-23, Department of Agronomy, Cornell University).

1975 "Study of Soils in the Sustaining Area Around San Antonio in Northern Belize (British Honduras)" (mimeo 75-1, Department of Agronomy, Cornell University).

OLSON, GERALD W., AND DENNIS E. PULESTON

1972 "Soils and the Maya," *Americas* 24:33–39.

OLSON, G. W., A. H. SIEMENS, D. E. PULESTON, G. CAL, AND D. JENKINS

1975 "Ridged Fields in British Honduras," *Soil Survey Horizons* 16:9–12.

ORIANS, GORDON H.

1975 "Diversity, Stability, and Maturity in Natural Ecosystems," in *Unifying Concepts in Ecology,* ed. W. H. Van Dobben and R. H. Lowe-McConnell (The Hague: Junk).

OWER, LESLIE H.

1927 "Features of British Honduras," *Geographical Journal* 70:373–86.

1928 "The Geology of British Honduras," *Journal of Geology* 36:494–509.

1929 *The Geology of British Honduras* (Belize: Clarion).

PALERM, ANGEL, AND ERIC R. WOLF

1957 "Ecological Potential and Cultural Development in Mesoamerica," in *Studies in Human Ecology,* Anthropological Society of Washington and Pan American Union Social Science Monograph no. 3 (Washington, D.C.: Pan American Union).

PANABOKKE, C. R.

1967a *Ceylon General Soil Map* (Colombo: Survey Department of Ceylon).

1976b *Soils of Ceylon and Fertilizer Use* (Colombo: Ceylon Association for the Advancement of Science).

PARANAVITANA, S.

1936 *The Excavations in the Citadel of Anuradhapura,* Memoirs of the Archaeological Survey of Ceylon, vol. 3 (Colombo).

PARSONS, JAMES J.

1969 "Ridged Fields in the Rio Guayas Valley, Ecuador," *American Antiquity* 34:76–80.

PARSONS, JAMES J., AND W. D. DENEVAN

1967 "Pre-Columbian Ridged Fields," *Scientific American* 217:93–100.

PARSONS, LEE A., AND BARBARA J. PRICE

1971 "Meosamerican Trade and Its Role in the Emergence of Civilization," in *Observations on the Emergence of Civilization in Mesoamerica,* ed. R. F. Heizer and J. A. Graham, Contributions of the University of California Archaeological Research Facility, no. 11 (Berkeley and Los Angeles).

PATRICK, RUTH, AND CHARLES W. REIMER

1966 *The Diatoms of the United States,* vol. 1 (Philadelphia: Academy of Natural Sciences).

PEARSALL, DEBORAH M.

1977 "Phytolith Analysis of Archeological Soils: Evidence for Maize Cultivation in Formative Ecuador," *Science* 199:177–78.

PEARSE, A. S., EDWIN P. CREASER, AND F. G. HALL

1936 *The Cenotes of Yucatan* (Washington, D.C.: Carnegie Institution).

PELLIOT, P. (TRANS. AND ED.)

1951 *Mémoires sur les coûtumes du Cambodge de Tcheou Ta-Kouan,* a new version with commentary (Paris: Adrien-Maisonneuve)

PENDERGAST, DAVID M.

1968 "Four Maya Pottery Vessels from British Honduras," *American Antiquity* 33:379–82.

PICKERSGILL, B., AND C. B. HEISER

1977 "Origins and Distribution of Plants Domesticated in the New World Tropics," in *The Earliest Agriculture,* ed. C. E. Reed (The Hague: Mouton).

POHL, M.
1974 "The Contribution of Hunting to Present-Day Maya Nutrition," paper presented at the Seventy-third Annual Meeting of the American Anthropological Association, Mexico City.

POORE, M. E. D.
1962 "The Method of Successive Approximation in Descriptive Ecology," *Advances in Ecological Research* 1:35–68.

PRESCOTT, J. A.
1931 *The Soils of Australia in Relation to Vegetation and Climate,* Council of Scientific and Industrial Research in Australia, Bulletin 52 (Canberra).

PRICE, L. GREER
1974 "Ostracode Communities from Lake Chichancanab, Yucatan, Mexico" (M.A. thesis, Washington University, St. Louis).

PULESTON, DENNIS E.
1968a "*Brosimum alicastrum* as a Subsistence Alternative for the Classic Maya of the Central Southern Lowlands (M.A. thesis, University of Pennsylvania).
1968b "New Data from Tikal on Classic Maya Subsistence," paper presented at the Thirty-third Annual Meeting of the Society for American Archaeology, Santa Fe.
1969 "Settlement Patterns and Tree Crops," paper presented at the 136th Annual Meeting of the American Association for the Advancement of Science, Boston.
1971 "An Experimental Approach to the Function of Classic Maya Chultuns," *American Antiquity* 36:322–36.
1973 "Ancient Maya Settlement and Environment at Tikal, Guatemala: Implications for Subsistence Models" (Ph.D. diss., University of Pennsylvania).
1974a "Experimental Agriculture as a Method for Testing Models of Ancient Subsistence Systems," paper presented at the Seventy-third Annual Meeting of the American Anthropological Association, Mexico City.
1974b "Intersite Areas in the Vicinity of Tikal and Uaxactun," in *Mesoamerican Archaeology: New Approaches,* ed. N. Hammond (Austin: University of Texas Press).
1976 "Experimenting with the Ecology of a Complex Prehistoric Agricultural System," paper presented at the Forty-first Annual Meeting of the Society for American Archaeology, St. Louis.
1977 "The Art and Archaeology of Hydraulic Agriculture in the Maya Lowlands," in *Social Process in Maya Prehistory: Studies in Memory of Sir Eric Thompson,* ed. N. Hammond (London: Academic Press).

PULESTON, DENNIS E., AND DONALD W. CALLENDER, JR.
1967 "Defensive Earthworks at Tikal," *Expedition* 9:40–48.

PULESTON, DENNIS E., AND OLGA STAVRAKIS PULESTON
1971 "An Ecological Approach to the Origins of Maya Civilization," *Archaeology* 24:330–37.

PULESTON, DENNIS E., AND PETER O. PULESTON
in press "El ramón, como base de la dieta de los Maya Antiguos," *Antropología e Historia de Guatemala.*

PULESTON, OLGA STAVRAKIS, AND DENNIS E. PULESTON
1974 "A Processual Model for the Rise of Classic Maya Civilization in the Southern Lowlands," *Proceedings of the 40th International Congress of Americanists* 1:119–24.

RANDS, ROBERT L.

1973 "The Classic Maya Collapse: Usumacinta Zone and Northwestern Periphery," in *The Classic Maya Collapse,* ed. T. P. Culbert (Albuquerque: University of New Mexico Press, School of American Research Advanced Seminar Series).

RAPPAPORT, ROY A.

1967 *Pigs for the Ancestors: Ritual in the Ecology of a New Guinea People* (New Haven: Yale University Press).

RATHJE, WILLIAM L.

1971 "The Origin and Development of Lowland Classic Maya Civilization," *American Antiquity* 36:275–85.

1972 "Praise the Gods and Pass the Metates: A Hypothesis of the Development of Lowland Rainforest Civilizations in Middle America," in *Contemporary Archaeology,* ed. Mark P. Leone (Carbondale: Southern Illinois University Press).

1973 "Classic Maya Development and Denouement: A Research Design," in *The Classic Maya Collapse,* ed. T. P. Culbert (Albuquerque: University of New Mexico Press, School of American Research Advanced Seminar Series).

RAYNOR, G. S., E. C. OGDEN, AND J. V. HAYES

1972 "Dispersion and Deposition of Corn Pollen from Experimental Sources," *Agronomy Journal* 64:420–27.

REINA, RUBEN E.

1967 "Milpas and Milperos: Implications for Prehistoric Times," *American Anthropologist* 69:1–20.

RENVOIZE, B. S.

1972 "The Area of Origin of Manihot Esculenta as a Crop Plant," *Economic Botany* 26:352–60.

RICE, DON S.

1974 *The Archaeology of British Honduras: A Review and Synthesis,* Occasional Publications in Anthropology, Archaeology Series, no. 6, University of Northern Colorado, Museum of Anthropology (Greeley).

1976 "The Historical Ecology of Lakes Yaxha and Sacnab, El Peten, Guatemala" (Ph.D. diss., Pennsylvania State University).

1977a "A Comparison of Approaches for Investigating the Heterogeneity and Potential Productivity of the Lowland Maya Environment," paper presented at the Forty-second Annual Meeting of the Society for American Archaeology, New Orleans.

1977b "Middle Preclassic Maya Settlement in the Central Maya Lowlands," *Journal of Field Archaeology* (in press).

RICHARDS, P. W.

1952 *The Tropical Rain Forest* (Cambridge: Cambridge University Press).

RICKETSON, OLIVER G., AND EDITH B. RICKETSON

1937 *Uaxactún, Guatemala, Group E, 1926–1931,* Carnegie Institution of Washington Publication no. 477 (Washington, D.C.).

ROBLES RAMOS, R.

1958 "Geología y geohidrología," in *Las recursas naturales del Sureste y zu aprovechamiento,* vol. 2 (Mexico City: Instituto Mexicano Recursos Naturales Renovables).

ROYS, RALPH L.

1931 *The Ethnobotany of the Maya,* Middle American Research Institute Publication no. 2 (New Orleans: Tulane University).

1943 *The Indian Background of Colonial Yucatan,* Carnegie Institution of Washington Publication no. 548 (Washington, D.C.).
1957 *The Political Geography of the Yucatan Maya,* Carnegie Institution of Washington Publication no. 613 (Washington, D.C.).

RUPPERT, KARL, AND J. H. DENISON
1943 *Archaeological Reconnaissance in Campeche, Quintana Roo, and Peten,* Carnegie Institution of Washington Publication no. 543 (Washington, D.C.).

RUZ LHUILLIER, ALBERTO
1970 *The Civilization of the Maya* (Mexico City: Instituto Nacional de Antropología e Historia).

RZEDOWSKI, J., AND ROGERS McVAUGH
1966 "Vegetación de Nueva Galicia," *Contributions of the University of Michigan Herbarium* 9:1–123.

SABLOFF, JEREMY A.
1971 "The Collapse of the Classic Maya Civilization," in *The Patient Earth,* ed. J. Harte and R. H. Socolow (New York: Holt, Rinehart and Winston).
1974 "Old Myths, New Myths: The Role of Sea Traders in the Development of Ancient Maya Civilization," in *The Sea in the Pre-Columbian World,* ed. E. P. Benson (Washington, D.C.: Dumbarton Oaks Research Library).

SABLOFF, JEREMY A., AND WILLIAM L. RATHJE
1975 "The Rise of a Maya Merchant Class," *Scientific American* 233:72–82.

SABLOFF, JEREMY A., AND GORDON R. WILLEY
1967 "The Collapse of Maya Civilization in the Southern Lowlands: A Consideration of History and Process," *Southwestern Journal of Anthropology* 23:311–36.

SÁNCHEZ, P. A., AND S. W. BUOL
1975 "Soils of the Tropics and the World Food Crisis," *Science* 188:598–603.

SANDERS, WILLIAM T.
1962 "Cultural Ecology of the Maya Lowlands, Part 1," *Estudios de Cultural Maya* 2:79–121.
1963 "Cultural Ecology of the Maya Lowlands, Part 2," *Estudios de Cultura Maya* 3:203–41.
1972 "Population, Agricultural History, and Societal Evolution in Mesoamerica," in *Population Growth: Anthropological Implications,* ed. B. Spooner (Cambridge, Mass.: M.I.T. Press).
1973 "The Cultural Ecology of the Lowland Maya: A Reevaluation," in *The Classic Maya Collapse,* ed. T. P. Culbert (Albuquerque: University of New Mexico Press, School of American Research Advanced Seminar Series).
1977 "Environmental Heterogeneity and the Evolution of Lowland Maya Civilization," in *The Origins of Maya Civilization,* ed. R. E. W. Adams (Albuquerque: University of New Mexico Press, School of American Research Advanced Seminar Series).

SANDERS, WILLIAM T., AND BARBARA J. PRICE
1968 *Mesoamerica: The Evolution of a Civilization* (New York: Random House).

SARKAR, N. K.
1957 *The Demography of Ceylon* (Colombo: Ceylon Government Press).

SAUER, JONATHAN
1967 *Geographic Reconnaissance of Seashore Vegetation of the Mexican Gulf Coast,* Coastal Studies Series, no. 21 (Baton Rouge: Louisiana State University Press).

SAUL, FRANK P.

1972 *The Human Skeletal Material of Altar de Sacrificios: An Osteobiographic Analysis,* Papers of the Peabody Museum of Archaeology and Ethnology, vol. 63, no. 2 (Cambridge, Mass.: Harvard University).

SAXE, ARTHUR A., AND HENRY T. WRIGHT

1966 "Terracing in the Maya Mountains of British Honduras: A Test Excavation at Cubetas Viejas," paper presented at the Thirty-first Annual Meeting of the Society for American Archaeology, Reno.

SCHOLES, FRANCE V., AND RALPH L. ROYS

1968 *The Maya Chontal Indians of Acalan-Tixchel* (Norman: University of Oklahoma Press).

SCHUFELDT, P. W.

1950 "Reminiscences of a Chiclero," in *Morleyana* (Santa Fe: School of American Research and Museum of New Mexico).

SECRETARÍA DE RECURSOS HIDRAÚLICOS (MEX.), DIRRECÍON DE HIDROLOGÍA

1962 *Boletín Hidrológico,* no. 17.

SEMPLE, ELLEN C.

1911 *Influences of Geographic Environment* (New York: Holt and Co.).

SENEWIRATNE, S. T., AND R. R. APPADURAI

1966 *Field Crops of Ceylon* (Colombo: Lake House).

SERPENTI, L. M.

1965 *Cultivators of the Swamps: Social Structure and Horticulture in a New Guinea Society* (Assen: Royal Van Gorlum).

SHREVE, FORREST

1937 "Lowland Vegetation of Sinaloa," *Bulletin of the Torrey Botanical Club* 64:605–13.

SHREVE, FORREST, AND IRA L. WIGGINS

1964 *Vegetation and Flora of the Sonoran Desert,* 2 vols. (Stanford: Stanford University Press).

SIEMENS, ALFRED H.

1976 "Karstic Constraints on Prehispanic Land Use and Transportation in the Southern Maya Lowlands," paper presented at the Forty-second International Congress of Americanists, Paris.

1977 "Some Patterns Seen from the Air," *Journal of Belizean Affairs* 5:5–21.

SIEMENS, ALFRED H., AND DENNIS E. PULESTON

1972 "Ridged Fields and Associated Features in Southern Campeche: New Perspectives on the Lowland Maya," *American Antiquity* 37:228–39.

1977 "Raised Fields and Related Features in Northern Belize" (ms).

SIMMONS, CHARLES S., JOSÉ M. TARANO, AND JOSÉ H. PINTO Z.

1959 *Clasificación de reconocimiento de los suelos de la República de Guatemala* (Guatemala City: Ministerio de Agricultura, Instituto Agropecuario Nacional, Servicio Cooperativa Inter-Americana de Agricultura).

SMITH, C. EARLE, JR., AND MARGUERITA L. CAMERON

1977 "Ethnobotany in the Puuc, Yucatan," *Economic Botany* 31:93–110.

SOIL CONSERVATION SERVICE

1960 *Soil Classification: A Comprehensive System, 7th Approximation* (Washington, D.C.).

1970 *Soil Taxonomy of the National Cooperative Soil Survey* (Washington, D.C.).

SPENCER, J. E.
1963 "The Migration of Rice from Mainland Southeast Asia into Indonesia," in *Plants and the Migrations of Pacific Peoples: A Symposium,* ed. J. Barrau (Honolulu: University of Hawaii Press).
1964 "Agricultural Terracing in China," in *Symposium on Land Use and Mineral Deposits in Hong Kong, Southern China, and South-East Asia,* ed. S. G. Davis (Hong Kong: Hong Kong University Press).
1966 *Shifting Cultivation in Southeastern Asia,* University of California Publications in Geography, no. 19 (Berkeley and Los Angeles).

SPENCER, J. E., AND G. A. HALE
1961 "The Origin, Nature, and Distribution of Agricultural Terracing," *Pacific Viewpoint* 2:1–40.

SPIER, PETER, AND ALICE J. HALL
1975 "A Traveler's Tale of Ancient Tikal," *National Geographic* 148:799–811.

SPOONER, BRIAN (ED.)
1972 *Population Growth: Anthropological Implications* (Cambridge, Mass.: M.I.T. Press).

SQUIRE, E. G.
1858 *The States of Central America* (New York: Harper & Bros.).

STADELMAN, RAYMOND
1940 "Maize Cultivation in Northwestern Guatemala," *Carnegie Institution of Washington, Contributions to American Anthropology and History* 33:83–263.

STEENIS, C. G. G. J.
1965 "Concise Plant Geography of Java," in *Flora of Java,* ed. C. A. Backer and R. C. Bakhuizen van den Brink (Groningen: N. V. P. Noordhoff).

STEGGERDA, MORRIS
1941 *Maya Indians of Yucatan,* Carnegie Institution of Washington Publication no. 531 (Washington, D.C.).

STEGGLE, NORMAN
1977 "Water Travel and Trade in Mesoamerica" (M.A. Thesis, Brigham Young University).

STEPHENS, JOHN L.
1843 *Incidents of Travel in Yucatan,* 2 vols. (New York: Harper & Bros.; rpt. 1963 Dover Publications).

STERNSTEIN, L.
1965 " 'Krung Kao': The Old Capital of Ayutthaya," *Journal of the Siam Society* 53:85–121.
1966 "Research Note: Contemplating a Hierarchy of Centers in Thailand," *Pacific Viewpoint* 7:229–35.

STEVENS, RAYFRED L.
1964 "The Soils of Middle America and Their Relation to Indian Peoples and Cultures," in *Handbook of Middle American Indians,* vol. 1, *Natural Environment and Early Cultures,* ed. R. C. West (Austin: University of Texas Press).

STEWARD JULIAN H.
1949 "Cultural Causality and Law: A Trial Formulation of the Development of Early Civilization," *American Anthropologist* 51:1–27.
1970 "Cultural Evolution in South America," in *The Social Anthropology of Latin American: Essays in Honor of Ralph Leon Beals,* ed. W. Goldschmidt and H. Hoijer (Los Angeles: UCLA Latin American Center).

STUART, GEORGE E.

1975 "The Riddle of the Glyphs," *National Geographic* 148:768–91.

SURVEY DEPARTMENT OF CEYLON

1949 *Land Use Map,* Quarter Inch to the Mile Series, Sheet 1 (Colombo: Survey Department).

SWAIN, FREDERICH M.

1977 "Bottom Sediments of Lakes Nicaragua and Managua," in *Investigations of the Ichthyofauna of Nicaraguan Lakes,* ed. T. B. Thorson (Lincoln: University of Nebraska Press, in press).

SWEETING, MARJORIE M.

1964 "The Karstlands of Jamaica," *Geographic Journal* 124:184–99.

1969 *Boletín Hidrológico,* no. 38, vols. 1–3.

1972 *Karst Landforms* (London: Macmillan & Co.).

TENNENT, J. E.

1859 *Ceylon: An Account of the Island, Physical, Historical, and Topographical* (London: Longman, Green, Longman, and Roberts).

TERBORGH, JOHN

1974 "The Preservation of Natural Diversity: The Protection of Extinction-Prone Species," *BioScience* 24:715–22.

TERRA, G. J. A.

1954 "Mixed-Garden Horticulture in Java," *Journal of Tropical Geography* 3:33–43.

1958 "Farm Systems in South-East Asia," *Netherlands Journal of Agricultural Science* 6:157–81.

THOMAS, CYRUS

1882 *A Study of the Manuscript Troano,* Contributions to American Ethnology vol. 5 (Washington, D.C.: U.S. Geographical and Geological Survey of the Rocky Mountain Region, Dept. of the Interior).

THOMAS, D. H.

1973 "An Empirical Test of Steward's Model of Great Basin Settlement Patterns," *American Antiquity* 38:155–76.

THOMAS, PRENTICE M., JR.

1974 "Prehistoric Settlement at Becan: A Preliminary Report," in *Preliminary Reports on Archaeological Investigations: The Rio Bec Area, Campeche, Mexico,* comp. R. E. W. Adams, Middle American Research Institute Publication 31 (New Orleans: Tulane University).

THOMPSON, EDWARD H.

1897 *The Chultuns of Labna, Yucatan,* Memoirs of the Peabody Museum of Archaeology and Ethnology, vol. 1, no. 3 (Cambridge, Mass.: Harvard University).

THOMPSON, J. ERIC S.

1931 *Archaeological Investigations in the Southern Cayo District, British Honduras,* Field Museum of Natural History Publication 301, Anthropological Series vol. 17, no. 3 (Chicago).

1939 *Excavations at San José, British Honduras,* Carnegie Institution of Washington Publication 506 (Washington, D.C.).

1954 *The Rise and Fall of Maya Civilization* (Norman: University of Oklahoma Press).

1959 "The Role of Caves in Maya Culture," *Amerikanistische Miszellen* (Mitteilungen aus dem Museum fur Volkerkunde in Hamburg) 25:122–29.

1964 "Trade Relations Between the Maya Highlands and Lowlands," *Estudios de Cultura Maya* 4:13–49.

1965 "Archaeological Synthesis of the Southern Maya Lowlands," in *Handbook of Middle American Indians,* vol. 2, *Archaeology of Southern Mesoamerica, Part 1,* ed. G. R. Willey (Austin: University of Texas Press).
1966 *The Rise and Fall of Maya Civilization,* 2d ed. (Norman: University of Oklahoma Press).
1970 *Maya History and Religion* (Norman: University of Oklahoma Press).
1971 "Estimates of Maya Population: Deranging Factors," *American Antiquity* 36:214–16.
1974 " 'Canals' of the Rio Candelaria Basin, Campeche, Mexico," in *Mesoamerican Archaeology: New Approaches,* ed. N. Hammond (Austin: University of Texas Press).

THOROLD, C. A.
1972 *Diseases of Cocoa* (London: Oxford University Press).

TOURTELLOT, GAIR, AND JEREMY A. SABLOFF
1972 "Exchange Systems Among the Ancient Maya," *American Antiquity* 37:125–35.

TOZZER, ALFRED M.
1941 *Landa's Relación de Las Cosas de Yucatan,* Papers of the Peabody Museum of Archaeology and Ethnology, vol. 18 (Cambridge, Mass.: Harvard University).

TREWARTHA, GLENN T.
1961 *The Earth's Problem Climates* (Madison: University of Wisconsin Press).

TROLL, C., AND K. H. PAFFEN
1963 Karte 5, Jahreszeitenklimate der Erde, in *Weltkarten zur Klimakunde,* by H. E. Landsberg, H. H. Lippmann, K. H. Paffen, and C. Troll (Berlin: Springer-Verlag).

TSUKADA, MATSUO
1966 "The Pollen Sequence," in *The History of Laguna de Petenxil: A Small Lake in Northern Guatemala,* by U. M. Cowgill et al., Memoirs of the Connecticut Academy of Arts and Sciences, vol. 17.

TSUKADA, MATSUO, AND EDWARDS S. DEEVEY
1967 "Pollen Analyses from Four Lakes in the Southern Maya Area of Guatemala and El Salvador," in *Quaternary Paleoecology,* ed. E. J. Cushing and H. E. Wright, Jr. (New Haven: Yale University Press).

TURNER, B. L., II
1974a "Prehistoric Intensive Agriculture in the Mayan Lowlands," *Science* 185:118–24.
1974b "Prehistoric Intensive Agriculture in the Mayan Lowlands: New Evidence from the Río Bec Region" (Ph.D. diss., University of Wisconsin–Madison).
1976a "Ancient Agricultural Land Use in the Central Maya Lowlands," paper presented at the Forty-second International Congress of Americanists, Paris.
1976b "Prehistoric Population Density in the Maya Lowlands: New Evidence for Old Approaches," *Geographical Review* 66:73–82.
1978 "Prehispanic Terracing in the Central Maya Lowlands: Problems of Agricultural Intensification," in *Mesoamerican Archaeology and Ethnology,* ed. N. Hammond and G. R. Willey (Austin: University of Texas Press, in press).

TURNER, B. L., II, AND WILLIAM E. DOOLITTLE
1978 "The Concept and Measure of Agricultural Intensity," *The Professional Geographer* (in press).

TURNER, B. L., II, ROBERT Q. HANHAM, AND ANTHONY V. PORTARARO
1977 "Population Pressure and Agricultural Intensity," *Annals of the Association of American Geographers* 67:384–96.

TURNER, R. M., AND F. M. WISEMAN
in press *Detection of Short-term Changes in Vegetation Coverage by the Use of ERTS Imagery* (Greenbelt, Md.: NASA Miscellaneous Publications).

UNAM
1970 Carta de climas (Mexico City: Universidad Nacional Autónoma de Mexico).

URRUTIA R., VICTOR M.
1967 "Corn Production and Soil Fertility Changes Under Shifting Cultivation in Uaxactun, Guatemala" (M.S. thesis, University of Florida, Gainesville).

VAUGHAN, HAGUE
1976 "Prehistoric Disturbance in the Area of Flores, Peten, Guatemala," paper presented at the 1976 Annual Meeting of the Ecological Society of America, New Orleans.

VERBEEK, R. D. M.
1891 *Oudheden van Java: Lijst der Voornaamste Overblijfselen uit den Hindoetijd op Java met eene Oudheidkundige Kaart,* Verhandelingen van het Bataviaansch Genootschap 46 (Batavia).

VERSEY, HOWARD
1972 "Goundwater Sources for Public Supply: Northern British Honduras" (mimeo).

VILLACORTA CALDERÓN, J. ANTONIO, AND
CARLOS A. VILLACORTA CALDERÓN
1930 *Codices Mayas* (Guatemala: Tipografía Nacional).

VISHNU-MITTRE
1977 "Changing Economy in Ancient India," in *The Earliest Agriculture,* ed. C. E. Reed (The Hague: Mouton).

VOGT, EVON Z.
1964 "Summary and Appraisal," in *Desarrollo cultural de los Mayas,* by E. Z. Vogt and A. Ruz Lhuillier (Mexico City: Universidad Nacional Autonoma).

VOORHIES, BARBARA
1972 "Settlement Patterns in Two Regions of the Southern Maya Lowlands," *American Antiquity* 37:115–26.
1973 "Possible Social Factors in the Exchange System of the Prehispanic Maya," *American Antiquity* 38:486–89.
1974 "Paleoecology of Early Coastal Settlements, Chiapas, Mexico," paper presented at the Forty-first International Congress of Americanists, Mexico City.
1976 *The Chantuto People: An Archaic Period Society of the Chiapas Littoral, Mexico,* Papers of the New World Archaeological Foundation, no. 41 (Provo: Brigham Young University).

VUILLEUMIER, BERYL SIMPSON
1971 "Pleistocene Changes in the Fauna and Flora of South America," *Science* 173:771–80.

WADDELL, ERIC
1972 *The Mound Builders* (Seattle: University of Washington Press).

WADDELL, HAKON
1938 "Physical-Geological Features of Peten, Guatemala," in *The Inscriptions of Peten,* by S. G. Morely, Carnegie Institution of Washington Publication no. 437, vol. 4 (Washington, D.C.).

WAGNER, HELMUT O.
1968 "Subsistence Potential and Population Density of the Maya on the Yucatan Peninsula and Causes for the Decline in Population in the Fifteenth Century," in *Verhandlungen des XXXVIII Internationalen Amerikanisten Kongresses,* 1968, vol. 1 (Munich: Kommissionverlag Klaus Renner).

WAGNER, P. L.

1964 "Natural Vegetation of Middle America," in *Handbook of Middle American Indians,* vol. 1, *Natural Environment and Early Cultures,* ed. R. C. West (Austin: University of Texas Press).

WALTER, H., AND H. LEITH

1967 *Klimadiagramm-Weltatlas* (Jena: Gustav Fischer).

WASHBURN, A. L.

1956 "Classification of Patterned Groups and Review of Suggested Origins," *Bulletin of the Geological Society of America* 67:823–66.

WEBB, MALCOLM C.

1973 "The Peten Maya Deline Viewed in the Perspective of State Formation," in *The Classic Maya Collapse,* ed. T. P. Culbert (Albuquerque: University of New Mexico Press, School of American Research Advanced Seminar Series).

WEBB, T., III

1974 "Corresponding Patterns of Pollen and Vegetation in Lower Michigan: A Comparison of Quantitative Data," *Ecology* 55:17–28.

WEBB, T., III, AND R. A. BRYSON

1972 "Late and Post-Glacial Climatic Change in the Northern Midwest, U.S.A.," *Quaternary Research* 2:70–115.

WEBBER, M. I.

1974 "Food Web Complexity and Stability in a Model Ecosystem," in *Ecological Stability,* ed. M. B. Usher and M. H. Williamson (New York: Halsted Press).

WEBSTER, DAVID L.

1976 *Defensive Earthworks of Becan, Campeche, Mexico: Implications for Maya Warfare,* Middle American Research Institute Publication 41 (New Orleans: Tulane University).

1977 "Warfare and the Evolution of Maya Civilization," in *The Origins of Maya Civilization,* ed. R. E. W. Adams (Albuquerque: University of New Mexico Press, School of American Research Advanced Seminar Series).

WEST, ROBERT C.

1957 *The Pacific Lowlands of Colombia,* Louisiana State University Studies, no. 8 (Baton Rouge: Louisiana State University Press).

1964 *Natural Environment and Early Cultures* (ed.), vol. 1, *Handbook of Middle American Indians* (Austin: University of Texas Press).

WHEATLEY, PAUL

1963 "What the Greatness of a City Is Said to Be: Reflections on Sjoberg's Preindustrial City," *Pacific Viewpoint* 4:163–88.

1971 *The Pivot of the Four Quarters: A Preliminary Enquiry into the Origins and Character of the Ancient Chinese City* (Edinburgh: Edinburgh University Press).

WILKEN, GENE C.

1971 "Food-Producing Systems Available to the Ancient Maya," *American Antiquity* 36:432–48.

WILLEY, GORDON R., AND WILLIAM R. BULLARD

1965 "Prehistoric Settlement Patterns in the Mayan Lowlands," in *Archaeology of Southern Mesoamerica, Part 1,* ed. G. R. Willey, vol. 2, *Handbook of Middle American Indians* (Austin: Univeristy of Texas Press).

WILLEY, G. R., W. R. BULLARD, JR., J. B. GLASS, AND J. C. GIFFORD

1965 *Prehistoric Maya Settlements in the Belize Valley,* Papers of the Peabody Museum of Archaeology and Ethnology, vol. 54 (Cambridge, Mass.: Harvard University).

WILLEY, GORDON R., AND DEMITRI B. SHIMKIN
1973 "The Maya Collapse: A Summary View," in *The Classic Maya Collapse,* ed. T. P. Culbert (Albuquerque: University of New Mexico Press, School of American Research Advanced Seminar Series).

WILLEY, G. R., A. L. SMITH, G. TOURTELLOT III, AND I. GRAHAM
1975 "Introduction: The Site and Its Setting," in *Excavations at Seibal,* ed. G. R. Willey, Memoirs of the Peabody Museum of Archaeology and Ethnology, vol. 13, no. 1 (Cambridge, Mass.: Harvard University).

WILLIAMS, PAUL W.
1969 "The Geomorphic Effects of Ground Water," in *Water, Earth, and Man,* ed. R. J. Chorley (London: Methuen & Co.).

WILSON, E. M.
in press "Physical Geography of the Yucatan Peninsula," in *Yucatan: A World Apart,* ed. E. H. Moseley (University, Ala.: University of Alabama Press).

WING, E. S.
1974 "Factors Influencing Exploitation of Marine Resources," in *The Sea in the Pre-Columbian World,* ed. E. P. Benson (Washington, D.C.: Dumbarton Oaks Research Library).
1975 "Animal Remains from Lubaantun," in *Lubaantun: A Classic Maya Realm,* by N. Hammond, Peabody Museum Monographs, no. 2 (Cambridge, Mass.: Harvard University).

WISDOM, C.
1940 *The Chorti Indians of Guatemala* (Chicago: University of Chicago Press).

WISEMAN, FREDERICK M.
1973 "The Artificial Rain Forest," paper presented at the Thirty-eighth Annual Meeting of the Society for American Archaeology, San Francisco.
1974 "Paleoecology and the Prehistoric Maya" (M.S. thesis, University of Arizona).
1976 "The Maximal Habitat Model of Mayan Agriculture," paper presented at the Forty-first Annual Meeting of the Society for American Archaeology, St. Louis.
n.d. Ph.D. dissertation, University of Arizona, in preparation.

WISSEMAN, J.
1977 "Markets and Trade in Pre-Majapahit Java," in *Trade in Early Southeast Asia,* ed. K. Hutterer, Michigan Studies of South and Southeast Asia (Ann Arbor: University of Michigan).

WITTFOGEL, KARL A.
1956 "The Hydraulic Civilizations," in *Man's Role in Changing the Face of the Earth,* ed. William L. Thomas, Jr. (Chicago: University of Chicago Press).
1957 *Oriental Despotism: A Comparative Study of Total Power* (New Haven: Yale University Press).

WOLF, ERIC R.
1966 *Peasants* (Englewood Cliffs, N.J.: Prentice-Hall).

WRIGHT, A. C. S.
1962 "Some Terrace Systems of the Western Hemisphere and Pacific Islands," *Pacific Viewpoint* 3:97–101.

WRIGHT, A. C. S., D. H. ROMNEY, R. H. ARBUCKLE, AND V. E. VIAL
1959 *Land in British Honduras: Report of the British Honduras Land Use Survey Team,* Colonial Research Publication 24 (London: Her Majesty's Stationery Office).

ZIDE, A. K., AND N. H. ZIDE
1972 "Semantic Reconstructions in Proto-Munda Cultural Vocabulary," paper presented at the Second All-India Conference of Linguists, New Delhi.

ZIPF, GEORGE K.
1949 *Human Behavior and the Principle of Least Effort* (Reading, Mass.: Addison-Wesley).

Index

Italicized page numbers refer to illustrations.